The author with his son Richard on the Sallalli Ranch with the
volcano Ampato in the background.

Detail from a watercolour painting by Evaristo Callo Anco

Also by the Author

The Veterinary Detectives:
More Sherlock Holmes than James Herriot
(BOOK GUILD, 2015)

The Veterinary Detectives

A Vet in Peru

Roger Windsor

The Book Guild Ltd

First published in Great Britain in 2018 by
The Book Guild Ltd
9 Priory Business Park
Wistow Road, Kibworth
Leicestershire, LE8 0RX
Freephone: 0800 999 2982
www.bookguild.co.uk
Email: info@bookguild.co.uk
Twitter: @bookguild

Typeset in Times

Printed and bound in Great Britain by CPI Group (UK) Ltd, Croydon, CR0 4YY

ISBN 978 1912362 462

British Library Cataloguing in Publication Data.
A catalogue record for this book is available from the British Library.

This book is dedicated with affection and respect to
Luis Lozada Casapia

Without whose vision, drive and hard work
LABVETSUR would never have existed
and to

Aurora Salazar Calcina   Roxana Bustinza de Vergeray   Reynaldo Roberts Billig

Who ensured that LABVETSUR was a success
and to the memory of
Keith Haskell, CMG, CVO,
1939 to 2014

Who, as British Ambassador to Perú, helped to save LABRENOR
My colleagues and my friends

Contents

Introduction

This, the second volume of my 'sortabiography', tells of my stay in Perú, setting up a veterinary diagnostic laboratory and clinical services in the southern departments of the country and my efforts to resuscitate the British laboratory set up years before in the Department of Cajamarca. For the convenience of the reader, conversations are written in English, although most of them were actually in Spanish. Spanish words are given in italics, and the first time it is used the translation is given; there is a glossary of terms at the end. I make no apologies for giving some measurements in imperial and others in metric units: I have chosen what seemed the more appropriate for the context.

Professor George Boddie, my old teacher of veterinary medicine, regularly mumbled that 'Chronology is the key to successful narrative.' However, I have disregarded his advice; for these books, sticking to a time line would have been very confusing to the reader, and so the chapters are grouped by topics rather than time. I also regularly intersperse anecdotes from an earlier part of my life, where they are appropriate.

This book would not and could not have been written without the help of Aurora Salazar de Fernandez, my former secretary and dear friend. To this day she does not realise the part she played in the success of LABVETSUR. She was really my second-in-command: she understood exactly what we were trying to achieve and how I wanted to do it. It could not have been written without her help as she tracked down former colleagues; she checked most chapters and many statements, and pointed out where I was likely to unintentionally offend.

I am indebted to many people for ensuring the accuracy of the narrative; none more so than Ingeniero Luis Lozada Casapia who was of great assistance with FONGALSUR background and dairy farming in southern Perú. Reynaldo and Evelyn Roberts, Dr Enrique Lopez, Dr John Claxton, Dra Lita Araujo de Pino, Dra Milagro Terán, Dr Fernando Fernàndez Fernàndez, Sr Fernando Alverado Paredes, Dr Héctor Begazo Sucla, Srta Claudia Choque, and Sra Roxana Bustinza de Vergeray all played their part in ensuring the accuracy of the narrative. However, the errors are mine alone.

Sadly some of the major players have died: Keith Haskell, John Taylor, and Marcos Chavary in particular: Dougie Russell and sisters Marjorie Michell and Claire Bedoya are no longer with us. I am grateful to Toni Haskell and Joan Taylor for checking my facts and to Toni for providing the photo of Keith. Pam Russell added to the story of the Majes project. I finally was able to trace David Perkin to his new home in Cornwall.

Miss Fany North of the Peruvian Embassy in London was most helpful putting me in contact with various official bodies

As with the first volume I am indebted to my wife, Maxine, for correcting facts, spelling and grammar and for removing the bits she did not like. My dear friends Iain and Fiona MacLaren, and Frank and Mary Barrie again read chunks of the text to ensure that it was readable and intelligible to non-vets. My son Richard has made many of the photographs suitable for publication.

My sincere thanks go to all of them.

1

Off to Perú

"What do you want me to do?" I was sitting in the office of the 'Brighton Queen', who was the administrator in charge of the South American desk at the Department of Overseas Development, in Eland House. This is a department/ministry of government that is forever changing its name: when I first applied to work in Kenya it was called a department of the Colonial Office, and when they offered me the job it had changed to the Department of Technical Co-operation of the Foreign and Commonwealth Office; it then became the Overseas Development Administration and today it is a ministry in its own right with a cabinet minister at its head – the Department for International Development, but all the Brits who worked for it called it ODA.

> *God works in a mysterious way,*
> *Yet not so strange as ODA.*

(Anon)

I had left Botswana with three teenaged children at public schools in England, with no job, but with possibilities of three: one setting up a veterinary investigation service for Ethiopia, the chair in veterinary pathology in the Lusaka Veterinary School, Zambia, for which I had been interviewed by the dean of the school in the transit lounge of Lusaka Airport where he had made me a tentative offer of the post, and the third was to set up a diagnostic laboratory for southern Perú, in Arequipa. The school fees for the three children in those days were £10,000 a term and so my wife, Maxine, and I had agreed that I would accept the first one to give me a firm offer. I thought that it would be Zambia, when Professor Lee phoned me to say that the Zambian Government would be writing to me in the next few days to offer me the professorship. A week later he phoned again to say that, as a mark of respect to President Machel of Mozambique, whose plane had been shot down over South Africa when he was returning from the heads of government meeting in Lusaka, the Zambian Government had decided to stop the recruitment of all international personnel for a period of three months. My disappointment was short-lived as I soon received a letter from the ODA confirming my appointment for the Arequipa job, subject to approval by the Peruvian Government. We were on tenterhooks waiting for Peruvian approval, because if we could get to Lima before the end of term, the British Government would pay the school fees for the winter term, and so now I was sitting in the offices of ODA trying to find out what was expected of me.

"You cannot really expect me to set up a laboratory from scratch with a budget of £30,000."

"Well, you go out there and just see what you can do, and if all goes well we may be able to find you a little more." It was a hopeless task, trying to set up a laboratory from scratch with £30,000. I tried to explain to the administrators that I had just equipped a new laboratory in Botswana and my budget for that was one million dollars (about £700,000 in those days) and we already possessed all the equipment from the old laboratory!

"Do you want the job or not? Because that is all we are going to give you; Perú is not high on our list of priorities."

"I do want the job and I want to make a success of the laboratory, but I do not know what we will be able to do with so little equipment."

"You must appreciate that this is a bit of an experiment on our part, which is why we are chary about investing too much at the start."

"Experiment!?"

"Yes, this is the first time that we will be financing a project outside the control of the local government. You will be working for, and responsible to, FONGALSUR (*Fondo de Fomento para el Desarrollo de la Ganaderia Lechera de Arequipa* – Fund for the Development of Dairy Farming in Southern Perú), the local farmers' co-operative, which represents about 10,000 farmers, mostly dairy farmers in Arequipa, Moquegua and Tacna, the three coastal provinces in your area. Our aid contract is with them; this has all been negotiated through the Peruvian Government and they will be providing a veterinary member of staff for the laboratory. The second major change for us is that your laboratory will charge for its services and be expected to make a profit!"

I was somewhat taken aback because I had never worked in a laboratory that charged for its services, let alone one that was expected to make a profit. However, this would be an interesting and new challenge. I did not realise how much of a challenge it would be.

I was then asked how I would set about my task, to which I replied: "The first thing to find out is what FONGALSUR want from their laboratory, the next will be to find out what the vets and the farmers want in the way of services. Before setting up anything it will be essential to find out how livestock are kept and what other services are available to the farmers. Once we know what will be expected of the laboratory, then we must determine what facilities the co-operative will let us have and then we will need to equip the laboratory the best we can on the budget, to carry out the work that is needed to be done. It will be some time before anything happens and the laboratory starts work."

This seemed to satisfy the administrators and they then turned to practical and personal questions, and I asked how soon I could start and received the warming reply that FONGALSUR wanted me out there as soon as possible. This was wonderful news because I wanted ODA to pay the school fees. When we had arrived in Britain without a job, my wife Maxine and I had visited the children's schools to explain our financial situation: we were gratified that the head teachers were happy with the progress of our three children and they had told us that they would do everything possible to keep them in the schools.

It was a race against time, but we finally made it and were on the plane for Lima at the start of December, with the children's flights booked for a week after us: they had to go a circuitous route as there were no direct flights available. They had to fly from London to Miami, from there to Mexico City and then to Lima, as the KLM flights from Amsterdam were all fully booked. We arrived in Lima to a very different reception from the one I had experienced in Argentina. The ambassador's driver was there to meet us with the official Bentley and we were whisked away to Nelly's Guest House which was just a few blocks away from the embassy. The driver waited while I had a wash and brush up: we had spent the night on the plane, and I needed to be presentable to meet my new boss.

John Shakespeare was charm personified; a small, spruce man with grey hair and sparkling eyes who was nearing the end of his career. I was given a very warm welcome and informed how important my job was going to be.

"This project is by way of an experiment: the government of this country is too fickle to deal with on any long-term development and so I have persuaded London to allow us to deal directly with the farming community and later this morning you will meet Ingeniero Luis Lozada Casapia, who through the force of his personality and his desire to succeed, has talked me into supporting your project. He said to me that if Britain gives aid directly to the Peruvian Government it would be like taking money from poor people in a rich country and giving it to rich people in a poor country, as this government is so corrupt. It is therefore important to him, to me and probably to you that this project succeeds. My reputation in Whitehall depends upon your success: your project could pave the way to more successful projects by the British Government in Latin America."

There was little doubt in my mind that I would have a very active supporter in the ambassador. He talked to me of the country and of his interest in all the wonderful people and civilisations that made up the patchwork of Perú's history. I later found out that Mr Shakespeare spent as much time as he could visiting the many different archaeological sites that Perú had to offer, including those of the Chavin, the Chimu and the Inca. It was such a pity that he left so soon after the project started.

I should explain the naming system in Perú, which is very different to the British. Each child has two surnames, thus Ingeniero Luis Lozada Casapia; his first family name is Lozada, his father's name, and Casapia is his second family name, the surname of his mother. Were I Peruvian, my name would be Roger Windsor Brown and Maxine before marriage would have been called Maxine Apergis Andrew. On marriage the woman drops her mother's surname and takes that of her husband, so Maxine would now be called Maxine Apergis de Windsor.

Those first days in Lima went by in a haze; there were meetings with various members of the embassy staff, commencing with John Taylor, a second secretary in the embassy with specific responsibility for the project; he was about my age, small and dark-haired with a cheery smile and a 'can-do' disposition and he and his wife Joan were to become good friends and also indispensible in getting the children to and from school. If only all the embassy staff had been so helpful. Official visits were made to the Minister of Agriculture, the Permanent Secretary of Agriculture, the Director of Veterinary Services, and I was taken to other organisations associated with agriculture, whose names I only remember as initials – CIPA, INIA; all meetings had to be conducted in my halting Spanish. Despite our week with Sr Chavez, a Chilean teacher at the language school in Old Street in the City of London, I was still six years rusty. In a break between visits John took me for an excellent lunch in a traditional restaurant near the embassy where the walls were lined with classical Spanish tiles and we quaffed large quantities of a light white wine as we ate delicious shellfish concoctions.

We decided to go to the ballet before the children arrived and booked to see *Swan Lake* in Lima opera house in the old part of the city. It was the first time I had seen ballet danced to a gramophone orchestra but the dancing was very good. There was a curfew in place in Lima, which was an attempt to prevent the activities of the *Sendero Luminoso* (Shining Path) terrorists who wanted to return Perú to a pre-colonial society. At the time they were blowing up power lines and destroying buildings; they had not started killing people, which came later. The *toque de queda* (curfew) did not come into force until 1:00am, although it was later brought forward to 11:00pm (before it was cancelled) and it went through until 6:00am.

We had been warned about thieves in Peruvian cities and how pickpockets and jewellery thieves were everywhere on the streets; yet on my first venture into the market area I lost my watch, despite it having a continuous steel band strap. I was looking at a stall that sold newspapers when I felt this sharp pain in my left wrist: the thief had undone the clasp without my noticing it and with a quick flick had broken the union and had the watch in his pocket. I looked down and there was this little old man in a neat grey suit. "He went that way, Señor," pointing down the street; I looked, there was no one hurrying away, but when I looked back, the little man had made his escape. A different welcome to South America.

The children arrived… just. They flew to Miami in the States where they had to collect their luggage and check in again. From Miami they flew to Mexico City where again they had to collect their luggage and check in yet again, and then on to Lima. Richard as the firstborn took charge: Claire had to look after the passports, as she was the most reliable and Guy was put in charge of the luggage; Richard handled the check-in. A great advantage of the children flying long distances together was the effect that it had on their relationship: the three of them together against a large, noisy, bureaucratic world. And they enjoyed getting away from British winter weather. They were able to have a day or two of rest before we set off on the long drive to Arequipa.

My entry into the Peruvian agricultural community was greatly eased by David Perkin, a specialist in livestock husbandry, who had many years of experience in South America; he made sure that I met all the right people and knew to whom I should go when the problems started. He also knew his way round Lima and where to find the best restaurants and cafés; despite Perú producing excellent coffee beans there were few restaurants or hotels where one could get a decent cup of coffee to drink. For the past few years David, who was now based in Lima, had been working in Cajamarca, the capital of the department of the same name in the north of the country. He informed me that, at his request, an additional duty had been added to my terms of reference. An earlier British project had established a veterinary laboratory in the city which had had a very chequered past, with many staffing problems. Despite this the laboratory had managed to survive without outside assistance for several years. My job would be to give it a new management system which would help it prosper. I would have to visit Cajamarca four times a year, which meant that, as it was almost 2,000 miles away from Arequipa, I would be able to see a great deal of the country. I inwardly blessed David for this additional task.

I was entitled to purchase a duty-free car and David took me to the Nissan works so that I could order and pay for a Nissan Sunny. I could have purchased a car from Europe but the delay would have been months, and spares were not easy to obtain for European-made cars. At the time Nissan and Volkswagen were the only companies assembling cars in Perú. The Nissan office was most efficient and assured me that I would have my car within three months. This was the first time in my life that I had been able to buy a car without having to borrow money. The cost of the car without tax was $5,000 or in Peruvian money intis 100,000 (at the time the inti was twenty to the dollar). When we left six years later there were more than a million intis to the dollar: the intis we had paid for the car would not then pay for a gallon of petrol!

David had decided that we should drive to Arequipa, a journey of almost 1,000 miles along the Pan-American Highway including a night in Nazca, and he had hired a car large enough to take the Windsor family and all our luggage. David would lead the way in his car with his partner Marion and Andrew and Charlie, his two sons by a previous marriage who had come out from school in England for the Christmas holidays. The two legs of the journey were very uneven, Nazca being about 400 miles from Lima, but there was nowhere else to stay until Camaná, which was only 150 miles from Arequipa. We would leave on Saturday morning, take the journey slowly until I was used to the road conditions, including driving on the wrong side in a car that I did not know.

The following day was frantic. Instead of having a quiet, peaceful day in which to rest before setting off on the long journey, Ing Luis Lozada, who was always called Lucho although his Christian name is Luis, had arranged a 'media' day where he could show me off to the Lima press before we returned to Arequipa. Lucho was a small, stocky, solidly built man with black curly hair but blue eyes, which was the reason he was often called '*El Gato*' (the cat). Normally he was of a quiet temperament and sunny disposition, but he could get very cross if provoked. He collected me, and at 8:00am, he and I were sitting in the recording studio of Canal 7, an important television network in Perú, and I was being asked how I was going to help the country. I tried to answer in my creaking Spanish; luckily Lucho was able to answer but I was unable to understand what he said as he spoke so rapidly. However, the studio managers seemed pleased and so the tone was set for the rest of the day as we drove from newspaper office to TV or radio recording studio with barely a second to get my breath. We did stop for lunch in a *picantería* where I was introduced to *cebiche mixto*, one of the great dishes that Perú has given the world. *Cebiche* is normally made from white fish, *linguado* (Pacific sole) or *corvina* (Pacific cod), to which are added *gambas* (prawns), *conchitas* (queen scallops) or *machas* (pink tongue-shaped clams) for the *mixto*. The raw seafood is marinated in juice from fresh limes, to which is added chilli, garlic and other spices including large quantities of fresh coriander. The liquid is known as *leche de tigre* (tiger's milk) and effectively cooks the fish which is served with *camote* (sweet potato) and sections of *choclo* (sliced maize cob). Washed down with a good Peruvian beer it is truly one of the great dishes of the world. We then returned to the fray and by the time I had completed my tenth interview for the day I was shattered, but my new boss was extremely pleased with our day's work: the name of FONGALSUR would be on all the airwaves and in all the newspapers the following day.

We had had a most enjoyable stay at Nelly's Guest House: Nelly and her husband were both British and she ran the guest house to supplement their income. She liked to take care of her guests so we were very well fed. Also resident were a young British couple from the embassy – the Martinez;

the husband was from a Gibraltar family but he was born and educated in Britain. The guest house was on the first floor of a block of flats in the Avenida Arequipa area of central Lima, a short walk from the embassy. We were made very welcome and when we said goodbye we were presented with a splendid wooden salad bowl as a reminder of our stay.

Can you describe a city in a paragraph? In two words? – 'Past glories'. When the Spaniards ruled, it was a city of wealth, grandeur and beauty, but today Lima is a city of great contrasts: it was once described as 'The pearl of the Pacific' but in the mid 1980s it was more of a scuffed pebble. The old city should have been a tourist paradise but it was dirty, everything was in need of restoration and the place was alive with thieves. Many of the buildings were *casonas* (mansions) of traditional Spanish design with carved wooden balconies protruding into the street, wonderful examples of a bygone age.

La casona de Torre Tagle – Old City

Some of the old suburbs had been magnificent with streets modelled on nineteenth-century Paris, and buildings with much stone and wrought-iron decoration, sadly all in need of a coat of paint and everything covered in graffiti.

From the old city, Avenida Arequipa, the main thoroughfare of the capital, lined with trees and flowering shrubs, runs west for the five miles to Miraflores, and was the area of the embassies, art galleries, fine commercial buildings and vegetation. Miraflores ('look at the flowers') at the coastal end of Avenida Arequipa was the home of the rich, and an excellent commercial centre. Despite the Peruvians growing coffee, the cafés of Miraflores were the only place in the city where you could get a decent cup of the beverage. Many of the best restaurants in Lima were to be found here and some of the best shops. The apartment blocks and the houses along the clifftops were among the most expensive places to live. The contrast between La Victoria and Miraflores could not be more extreme: drab streets lined with stalls; it was not a place to visit. Much of Lima was brown; brown, dusty streets, brown buildings with no vegetation to relieve the monotony. To the north and south of the original city were the numerous *pueblos jóvenes* (young towns) into which the Andean peoples were constantly moving in search of a better life and these were among the largest suburbs of the city – Villa el Salvador had developed into a city of its own with a population of more than a million. To the west was the Pacific Ocean and to the east the Andes. The reason for the existence of Lima is the River Rimac and the natural port of Callao, and it was from here that the viceroy ruled Spain's colonial empire. It was from Lima that the *conquistadores* (soldiers) and priests colonised South America (except Brazil) and so it was little wonder that the old city had once been grand.

The embassy was on the sixth and seventh floors of a block of business premises on Avenida Arequipa. I could never understand why, in a country with rampant terrorism, the British Government should stick its embassy up in the sky; to actually get into the embassy meant passing through strict security but there was little check on who went into the building. However, it commanded great views of the city and one could look down on the American Ambassador's residence, sensibly set on terra firma across the Avenida; it was a source of amusement and pride to John Shakespeare that the ambassadors to Perú formed an 'Oxbridge Club' with the ambassadors from Britain, the United States, India, West Germany and several other countries, being graduates of either Oxford or Cambridge universities.

David took me to the car-hire firm to collect the car for our journey and I was greatly dismayed. He had hired for me a Volkswagen Combi, a bigger car than I had ever driven and with no bonnet in front. It would be a steep learning curve: had I known what I was letting myself in for, I would have flown! Early on the Saturday morning David arrived at Nelly's to lead us out of town and on to the Pan-American Highway, that great trunk road that runs from Alaska to Tierra del Fuego in southern Chile with only a break in the Darien Gap in Columbia. The stretch that runs through Perú was the worst part of the whole Pan-Americana.

Lima has many fine highways in and out of the city and as mentioned above is ringed with shanty towns or *pueblos jóvenes* as they are called. The development of a *pueblo jóven* is amazing: a group of Indian people from the mountains decide that they are going to move into a city and it is accomplished overnight. An area of desert is selected and the Plaza de Armas, the centre of all Peruvian towns, is demarcated and the Peruvian flag is flown. Administrative offices are also demarcated, plots for church and a school are also laid out. The new citizens then erect temporary living quarters from sticks and plastic sheets and by daybreak there is a new *pueblo jóven* up and running, with no water, no electricity, no sanitation, just sand, sticks, shacks, the Peruvian flag and a name. Once established, the municipal authorities do nothing about it but add the name to the list of satellite towns. The people have come to work, but there is no work for them and so they swell the numbers of itinerant market and street traders (*ambulantes*). Despite the hardships, the people triumph; running water is brought, sewer pipes are installed and finally they have electricity. The committee controlling the new town is very strict in how the town develops, what long-term structures may be built; the people have to find the money to pay their share when the new sewage system is installed. A new town is born. A more imaginative government would have developed schemes to keep the people in their mountain homes. It was in these *pueblos jóvenes* that the terrorists recruited their members. It had not taken me long to realise what was the major problem of Perú: the massive class distinction between the white Spanish settlers who lived at the coast and the coloured Indian people who lived in the Andes, never mind those Indians who live in the massive jungle on the far side of the Andes – they live in different worlds.

Within a quarter of an hour we had joined the highway to the south and were passing through all these new towns. Around Lima the coastal plain was very wide but I was to find before the day was out that in places the Andes came right to the sea which meant that there were no places for human habitation at all. We were on our way, but immediately the first problem arose: there was something wrong with the steering and the faster we went the less responsive were the wheels. I had to resign myself to driving at fifty miles an hour until I could get it fixed. When we stopped for lunch

I told David of the problem and we decided to change plans and stop the night in Ica where we could get the car fixed, thus adding a hundred miles to the journey on Sunday. The remainder of the journey to Ica was interesting if slow. The countryside was a complete desert: unlike the Kalahari, from which we had just come, where there was a covering of vegetation, grass, bushes and trees, here there was nothing, just mile after mile of more or less flat terrain of varying shades of brown, interspersed with small hills; in some places the rock was covered with a thicker or thinner layer of sand and there were cones of rock of various heights, some towering above the surrounding land while others were no more than fifty feet in height. I later found out these were in fact the cores of old volcanoes, which being of harder rock than the remainder of the volcano, had not been eroded by the wind.

On arrival at Ica we sought out the *Turistas* Hotel and booked rooms for the night. Thanks to the increasing terrorist problem, (the *Sendero Luminoso* were taking advantage of the worsening economic situation in the country), there was no problem about finding accommodation. David and I left the families at the pool and went off to sort out the car. There was something wrong with the geometry of the steering and the front wheels were not properly aligned. This was rapidly sorted out and we were able to join the rest of the party in the pool. However, I was still distrustful of driving a car with no bonnet!

With an extra hundred miles to go we decided to set off at 6:30 in the morning and have breakfast in Nazca. This we did and made good speed to Nazca where we stopped in a pleasant café and ate *huevos revueltos con jamón* (scrambled egg with ham) and toast with *mermelada* which bore no relationship to good British marmalade. So far the road had been good and straight with some dual carriageway which was a bonus as there was a large number of lorries delivering produce for the approaching Christmas. So far so good, the countryside was not very different from what we had seen the day before, when I noticed that we were on a very long, straight incline towards a mountain that barred our progress. Two thirds of the way up this mountain I noticed a small black circle towards which we were driving – a tunnel that was still a good five miles away. Peruvian road-makers have a different approach to their British counterparts and this was definitely not a British tunnel, it was just a hole bored into the mountain; no lights, no internal finishings, just a hole. I felt like Alice falling down the rabbit hole as the road had a slight decline once we entered the tunnel, and we came out into... wonderland. As we drove out of the tunnel I saw that we were driving along the ridge of a hill, no more than thirty feet wide, and the land sloped away getting steeper and steeper with a drop of at least 1,000 feet on both sides. Were that not all, the road consisted of little more than a series of hairpin bends for as far as the eye could see, descending down to sea level, and packed with lorries going slowly in both directions. The journey had definitely begun and I did not look forward to steering my Combi round all those bends. For the next 200 miles driving was a nightmare without any straight, flat road to negotiate: in Botswana the roads were all flat and straight. To make matters worse I was driving on the wrong side of the road. And it got even more frightening as at times we were driving along a road and to one side there was a sheer drop of 2,000 feet or more, straight into the Pacific Ocean. We were going south and so I was driving on the side of the road closest to the sea, and I was terrified. For the next hundred miles or so I think that the car rarely exceeded twenty-five miles per hour.

For miles the road ran along the crest of the foothills of the Andes and every time there was a river to cross, the road had to descend to sea level, which meant another ten to fifteen hairpin bends as we descended followed by another ten to fifteen as we climbed up again. I was petrified. I had never driven on such a road and what made it worse was that I had no faith in the car I was driving. The surface did not help: there were potholes everywhere and from place to place the whole surface had gone. What made things even worse was that I was clutching the wheel for dear life and I could not relax my concentration for a millisecond. Things could not get worse... and then they got worse... we were driving along the Pacific coast and several bays ahead I could see that the Andes were completely perpendicular down to the sea and two thirds of the way down there was a tiny little blip in the wall, where the road had been cut into what I thought was the rock. We finally arrived at *Cerro de Arena* (Hill of Sand); the hill was actually made of sandstone and as the sand was eroded from the top it was pouring down the hillside and despite a retaining wall about three-foot high, it just flowed across the wall, across the road and down into the sea in a ceaseless stream. I could not believe my eyes and I thought that my last hour had come. By now my speed was down to fifteen miles an hour. Despite having been cooped up in the car for hours, the children were very well behaved; I think they understood the battle I was having.

We survived and somehow we arrived in Camaná where we met up with the Perkins: I needed the cold Coke and the ham sandwich. However the worst was now over as we turned inland and started the long climb to Arequipa, but night was coming on and I was concerned at driving these dreadful roads in the dark. Richard jumped ship and joined the Perkin boys, sacrificing comfort for speed. What describes the Peruvian Pan-American Highway best of all was a massive boulder at the head of yet another hairpin bend and painted on it in huge letters was '*PERÚ MERECE MEJORES CARRETERAS*' ('Perú deserves better roads').

It was half past eight when we finally arrived in Arequipa and then we had to find the hotel. There were only two bridges across the Rio Chili in the town centre, the Puente Bolognesi and the Puente Grau, and our hotel was in the Avenida Bolognesi, obviously near the bridge of the same name. But this was Perú and of course Avenida Bolognesi came off the Puente Grau. In desperation we hired a taxi to take us to the *Posada del Puente* (the Resting Place by the Bridge) only to find that we had been there twice before but there was no hotel to be seen: the buildings were all below road level on the steep bank leading down to the river and there was no sign at the entrance where you descend the steps. But we had arrived in one piece. The hotel staff unloaded the Combi while I had a shower and we sat down to dinner and a well-earned beer at 10:00pm. The delightful staff had stayed to cook dinner for us, to welcome us to Arequipa. Bed.

The whole drive became worthwhile at breakfast the next morning, which we took outdoors, sitting at tables arranged along the riverbank. The majestic river raced down the mountainside towards the Pacific Ocean and towering over it was the volcano Misti with its snow-capped peak against a blue, blue sky with the sun shining (Plate 1). This was to be our home for the next six years.

2

Arequipa – FONGALSUR and the Story Really Starts

We were still eating breakfast at 11:00 when Lucho came to see how we were settling in. He was amused to hear of my travails with the vehicle on the long road journey and pointed out that the Pan-Americana was one of the better roads in the country. He told me that the FONGALSUR board would meet that afternoon and that he would be delighted if I felt able to join them. Of course, I agreed; David was also invited and since he knew where the offices were, he would bring me. Until 4pm we were free to sit in the glorious sunshine, watch the river, the snow-capped volcanoes, relax and chat.

Arequipa is considered to be one of the most beautiful cities in South America: it is certainly the most beautiful that I have seen. It nestles into an Andean valley, 12° south of the equator and at an altitude of 8,000 feet and so although in the tropics, the climate is temperate, hardly ever rising above 75°F, and the evenings are cool but neither air conditioning nor heating are required. The city is surrounded by mountains with three snow-capped volcanoes dominating the landscape. It is a colonial city with many wonderful eighteenth-century *casonas*, a delightful cathedral, elegant public buildings and a plethora of beautiful churches; all are built from *sillar*, a variety of white volcanic rock which, like soapstone, is soft when cut from the ground, but hardens on exposure to air. This makes it very suitable for carving and the Spanish builders in the seventeenth and eighteenth centuries had constructed the city on the classic grid pattern. The old buildings all have exquisite facades, a tribute to the stonemasons' skill. As in all Peruvian towns and cities, the Plaza de Armas is at its heart (Plate 2). The cathedral occupies one side of the plaza and has a strange connexion with London in that the cathedral clock was built by E. J. Dent and Co, the firm that built the clock for Big Ben. On the opposite side stand the Municipal Chambers, while in one corner is the most beautiful building in the city, *la Iglesia de la Compañía*, the Church of the Jesuit Order, with its incredibly ornate entrance. Like many Catholic churches the building interior is very dark, which makes it difficult to see the fantastic carvings and the gold leaf on the altar. The remainder of the buildings in the plaza are also difficult to see, obscured by the colonnade that shades the pavement. The centre of the plaza has a beautifully laid-out garden and immediately opposite the *Municipalidad* stand the flagstaffs at which an important ceremony is carried out every Sunday morning: the town band plays and the *alcalde* (the mayor) says not a few words after which the national flag is raised followed by the flag of Arequipa. We knew that the project had been adopted by the city when Lucho and I were asked to raise the flags during this ceremony (Plate 3).

Arequipa is known in Perú as the 'white city', not for the stone used for its construction but for the people: for many years the city was ruled by seven families, all of pure Spanish descent. The same families still have some control of the city to this day, although their power is waning. Radiating from the plaza the streets contain the houses of the great families and merchants. Built on the grand scale these houses are of traditional Spanish design with the great front door often twelve-foot high or more, set in an exquisitely carved portico leading into a courtyard, many of which have an elegant fountain adding to the beauty; rooms open off the courtyard.

Each central city block is one hundred metres square and close by the city centre is the Santa Catalina Monastery, which occupies an entire block and is in effect a town within a town. The construction, which commenced in the sixteenth century, is one of the oldest built by Europeans on the American continent and while much of the original monastery is open to the public there is still a closed order of nuns living within the walls. Although called a monastery it is in fact a convent, into which bored husbands looking for a change put their wives; once inside, they remained there until death. The daughters of important families unable or unwilling to make a good marriage were also incarcerated there, and it provided a home for those women who had a vocation for service. The walls, twenty-foot high and almost as thick at the base, have but one opening and inside there are streets of small houses, a church and communal buildings. The nuns were a completely closed order and how an Irish nun ended up in a closed Arequipeño convent I do not know. An American visitor to our house was able to have a one-to-one meeting with this nun and said it was like the scene from an American prison movie as they sat in separate rooms and communicated through a barred window; however, the nun was able to receive the present for which she had asked, namely a bottle of Bailey's Irish Cream.

The beautiful Rio Chili runs through the city and there are meadows along its banks: it is a wonderful sight to see in the middle of the city, cattle grazing along the riverbanks. Along the east bank of the river runs the splendid dual carriageway, Avenida Marina, linking the two major bridges, the Puente Bolognesi and the Puente Grau. There are statues of local dignitaries and heroes along the central reservation. Many years later I am still captivated by the beauty of the city.

The Rio Chili runs through the centre of the city only two blocks from the plaza and, apart from the two main bridges crossing the river, there is a third, a little way from the town centre, which was built for the railway by the great French engineer Eiffel, and like his tower is constructed from cast iron. It was built for the railway but today it is no longer strong enough for trains and is used by motor vehicles.

David drove me through the city centre and out to the north along a wide highway, Avenida Parra, and onto Avenida Alfonso Ugarte with increasing signs of commercial activity as we went; we turned right into the compound of FONGALSUR, an area of about one hundred metres square with a single-storey building occupying most of the right side and obviously of multiple use – offices, a showroom, stores for farm equipment, chemicals and animal feed. On the left side was a small square building and all the rest was down to grass but there were no animals grazing.

David parked the car and we entered through the first door, to be greeted by Milagros, the secretary to the *gerente* (managing director or chief executive officer) Dr Aldo Meza, himself a veterinary surgeon, and we were both most warmly welcomed. He was a small, slightly-built man with a round face and curly black hair that was beginning to recede; as I got to know him, I found him to be open and approachable and he always had a smile on his face. His was very much a 'can-do' approach. There was little time for a chat because we were expected in the boardroom, where we were met by a beaming Lucho, and I was introduced to a bewildering succession of middle-aged or old men some of whom I never set eyes on again, while others were to become a regular feature in my life. Black coffee was dispensed (luckily it was Nescafé) and the speeches of welcome began during which I learnt that the building on the far side of the field, which was to be my base, had been originally built as a milk testing laboratory but had never actually been used for anything.

When asked what I planned to do, I threw the question back to them; what did they want me to do? Even with my poor command of the Spanish language, it became obvious that no one had any idea of what they wanted from their laboratory. Perú had only ever had one functioning public veterinary laboratory which was the one in Cajamarca that the British had set up; it was therefore not surprising that the farmers had no idea what a veterinary laboratory could achieve. And in my halting Spanish, I expanded on the talk that I had given the Brighton Queen. First and foremost I needed to know what the farmers did, how they kept their animals, what were their problems, and what help they required. I would spend at least a month visiting farms and once we had seen the problems I could work out what sort of services we would need to offer. Once we knew what we were going to do then we could plan the equipment and reagents we would need and could afford. It was possible that the laboratory building would need to be modified. If that was not enough, I had to work out a price list for our services and perhaps the most important of all, I had to find a regular source of work that would ensure that the laboratory could cover its costs. Where were we going to find trained laboratory technicians in a country which had none?

With regular inputs from David, I managed to get my thoughts and ideas over to the expectant farmers. Lucho was pleased and I could see that I had an ally in Dr Meza who was most supportive during the meeting, and it was obvious that he and his second in command, Dr José Diaz del Olmo, would do everything to help. The FONGALSUR lawyer Dr Chávez made it very clear to me that I could expect his help with the all-embracing bureaucratic legal system that operates in Perú.

The meeting was over, the party could begin. I had my first introduction to pisco sour, the quintessential Peruvian drink. The basis of the drink is pisco, a rough, clear distillate of wine; this is mixed with lime juice, sugar, egg white and ice in a blender and served with a drop of Angostura bitters on top of the froth. I soon learnt the technique of swirling the glass to clear the froth and what a delicious, apparently innocuous drink it is, combining the freshness of the lime, the smoothness of the egg and the zip of the pisco. This was a drinks party and not a cocktail party and so the only food offered were pink and yellow wafer biscuits. We toasted the success of the project, of the British Government for supplying this *wonderful expert* who would be the answer to all their prayers, and then to Mr Shakespeare, the ambassador, who had made it all possible. And then it was my turn to toast FONGALSUR and its president, who had had the vision to request the British Government for a project, and the *ganaderos* (cattlemen) who comprised the board of the co-operative. By the time the toasts were finished I was barely sober. Luckily I had David to drive me back to the hotel. We had arranged to meet Drs Meza and Diaz del Olmo at eight thirty the next morning when the work would begin (Plate 4).

What a delight they were: I was to find that most Peruvian men are charm personified and delightful to deal with. Even the rogues and crooks could charm. Dr Diaz del Olmo came from a veterinary family and was a good six inches taller than Dr Meza; he was slim and had a long, narrow face. He, too, had receding hair; he was quiet and unassuming but had a sound knowledge of veterinary medicine and the dairy industry. For an hour or more we sat and talked about livestock production in Arequipa. I thought that I was used to working in deserts, having just left the Kalahari, but there it rained; in coastal Perú it never rained and so where there was no irrigation, there was no vegetation. Over the years several irrigation schemes had been developed and some of these had almost a thousand small farmers and a new one was being developed at the time: The Majes Project.

This project had planned to construct two massive dams high up above the Colca Valley: the Majes river had been dammed to form the Condoroma Dam, which could hold up to 4.2 million cubic metres of water. The River Apurimac flowed into the Amazon and then into the Atlantic Ocean; the plan was to change the course of the river to flow into the Angostura Dam with a capacity also of 4.2 million cubic metres. The water would be taken down the Pacific side of the Andes. The water captured had to be transported 230kms by existing rivers, and by tunnel and canal, to the Majes and Siguas plains.

The outflow of the Angostura Dam was to be taken by tunnel to join the Colca river and the water was then conveyed by canal, 88kms of tunnel and natural river to the Majes and Siguas plains, the area of land designated to be cultivated. The canal system is capable of carrying water at a rate of thirty-five cubic metres per second. This was the largest irrigation project ever undertaken in the country with 60,000 hectares of farmland, four urban conurbations and twenty-two villages to be built; it was estimated that the total population of the irrigation would eventually reach 200,000. It was calculated that the cost of bringing the water to Majes was $864 million, or almost $15,000 per hectare. Linked to this project was a hydroelectric scheme to produce 850 megawatts of electricity. To the present day the second phase has not been undertaken: there is no Angostura Dam and no hydroelectric scheme. Instead the money was diverted to constructing a hydroelectric power scheme on the Rio Chili, a much less secure source of water. Corruption?

A massive compacted earthwall was constructed to hold the water in the Condoroma Dam; at either end the wall was embedded into the mountains. When they started to fill the dam the pressure of the water moved the foundations in the mountains and the mountains began to shift: the engineers had got it wrong. It is often said that the Andes are God's rubble heap; when he finished creating Earth there was a huge pile of rocks left over and so he dumped these in South America. The Andes are not solid rocks but rock piles. Millions of tons of concrete were poured into the hills to consolidate them before they could continue to fill the dam.

The first tranche of land had been allocated and the farmers were already in production. Application for the second round of farms was just about to start. The development of an irrigation is not a simple matter in Perú. The Andes are a young mountain range and still growing. As the tectonic plates in the earth's crust collide, the Andean mountain range gets higher as the rocks are forced out of the sea. Because all the land had been under the sea it contains a great deal of salt, and since there has been no plant growth there is no vegetable matter in the soil. Until these two problems are overcome then the soil cannot be used to grow vegetables or fruit. The salt is removed from the soil by repeated washing with mountain water. The first growth of plants has to be able to put vegetable matter and protein into the soil; this is achieved by planting alfalfa, or lucerne to use its English name. This is a leguminous crop related to clover, which provides excellent nutrition for cattle, while at the same time 'fixing' nitrogen from the air and turning it into protein in the soil. The roots put fibre into the soil which greatly enhances its capacity to retain water. It takes several years of this husbandry to convert the desert sand into productive soil. During this period cattle can graze the alfalfa and turn it into milk and at the same time their dung helps put vegetable material into the soil. Alfalfa grows extremely well in the Arequipeño climate and a good farmer can produce ten or eleven crops a year (in a good year in Britain we can produce two!). As a result, there were almost 10,000 smallholding dairy farmers in Arequipa, with more in the departments of Moquegua and Tacna.

It is amazing the amount of new knowledge you need to acquire when working in a new country, but David, Aldo and José, as they soon became, were good teachers and were keen to inform me about the livestock industry in southern Perú. It was at this first meeting that I learnt about the political problems that beset the country under the woeful presidency of Alan Garcia; I was about to receive a tirade. It took me several weeks to fully understand what was going on in the country, but in order to stimulate agricultural development, farmers and the cronies of Garcia were given access to the Dollar MUC (monetary unit of commerce) for the importation of farming necessities. They could purchase US dollars from the government for about half the true cost but only use them to import agricultural necessities. FONGALSUR had taken advantage of this policy and a team had gone to New Zealand and purchased 25,000 sheep mostly of the Corriedale breed but with a few Suffolk and Hampshire animals as well. The ship was well on its way and was due to dock in the port of Matarani any day. Aldo thought that this would be a good way for me to meet the vets working in the area as they would all be visiting the quarantines where the sheep would be held. It was then time to go and see my new laboratory and it was very promising.

The building was single storey and L-shaped. You entered into a good airy reception area that could comfortably accommodate two receptionists/secretaries. To the right opened a corridor and the first door on the right gave into what was to become the library and my office. The next door along was the lavatory (only one) and finally a space that could easily be converted into a cloakroom/locker room for the staff. Also from reception there was a door into the laboratory itself, a single large space at least fifteen feet high, with concrete benches running the length of the walls with sinks placed at regular intervals. This area would need to be sub-divided but thought would be required to determine how. The internal angle of the L was an open fenced yard with large double iron doors opposite the building. This would make an ideal post-mortem room. It was all very promising.

There was no point in speculating what specific work would need to be done until we had talked to the farmers, but we would require a bacteriology unit for the examination of tissue samples from post-mortem examinations and samples sent in; also, an area where faeces could be examined for worm eggs, intestinal contents for worms, and skin scrapings for external parasites. We would definitely need to examine blood samples, and so we would require a teaching microscope plus one other. It made sense to use the far end of the laboratory as the 'dirty' end for washing up, media making and sterilising equipment and media. It made good sense to separate this manual section from the scientific section of the laboratory.

A Land Rover had been ordered for the project and the costs did not have to come out of my equipment budget, but until that arrived I would be dependent on FONGALSUR for transport; Lucho gave me the use of a company vehicle – a locally assembled Brazilian Volkswagen Beetle, which meant that after work Maxine and I could go looking for a house and take the children down to the coast. José organised a plan to visit the various irrigations to meet the farmers and Aldo agreed that he should be my guide and chauffeur; this plan was overtaken by events and never really put into action, although I did manage to visit the majority of the irrigation schemes that were within a reasonable distance. Firstly I had to do another round of visits with Lucho, where I was introduced to the great and the good of the city: the *alcalde,* the *prefect* (the president's representative in the department), the Archbishop of Arequipa, the army commander, the departmental Minister of Agriculture and all the agricultural organisations providing services to the farmers; we finished by visiting Sr Reynaldo (Reggie) Roberts, soon to be honorary British Consul in Arequipa. Reggie was of British stock, his grandfather coming from Liverpool, although his mother was German. The present consul, Charles Ricketts, was ill and not expected to recover. In fact he did recover and lived into his nineties. Reggie and his family were to become good friends and he and his American wife Evelyn introduced us to many members of the British community in the city. There was no doubt that for Lucho, having a British project was a great propaganda success for FONGALSUR.

David had been of inestimable value to me having introduced me to Arequipa and FONGALSUR but his job was now done and so he, Marion and the boys set off on the long road back to Lima so that they could be there in time for Christmas.

The sheep arrived from New Zealand in excellent condition and were put into trucks and driven to the Ministry of Agriculture quarantine in San Camilo where they were to be housed for twenty-one days; unfortunately, the ministry had only purchased enough food for three days and so the chaos commenced. The ministry decided that they could not buy more food because that would upset their budget; I suggested that all they needed to do was to charge the farmers more for the quarantine, but this would not do because the money they received could not be used to offset the increased costs. It was beginning to look as if Peruvian bureaucracy was even worse than that in Britain. The farmers in many cases had already arranged the transport to collect the sheep after three weeks, not three days! And then the sheep started to die. I was asked to carry out the post-mortem examinations; for some reason I had brought a post-mortem gown and boots with me, but I had no instruments. However, FONGALSUR had a German travelling post-mortem set in a beautiful cedar wood case and they were able to supply me with buckets, disinfectant, rubber gloves, plastic boxes, bags and bacterial swabs; they also provided me with an insulated cool bag to store the samples and I purchased a white trilby for the occasion. Lucho arranged with the various broadcasting stations for an announcement to be made over the radio and TV that their new British expert would be holding a workshop on sheep management and would also teach the art of necropsy.

There were about twenty vets there when I arrived, most had been sent by their farm managers. This was a real eye-opener to me; vets were very much at the bottom of the agricultural pecking order. There were no veterinary practices such as we know in Britain and the larger farms employed a vet to work under the direction of the farm manager. These vets worked from 8am to 4pm Monday to Friday and then returned home daily to Arequipa, usually by bus. This was definitely something that would need to be changed; for a laboratory to be successful it requires field vets to supply the material. I decided to start off with the necropsies. I put on the boots, stripped to the waist and donned my gown, rubber gloves and the trilby, and found a 44-gallon drum to use as a table (there is always something on a farm that can be used as a table). A couple of buckets were filled with water, into one of which I poured some disinfectant and commenced the cutting up. There was some muttering among the onlookers, especially from the older ones, that it was not the job of a vet to cut up dead bodies; that was for labourers, not professionals. I realised that there was a big job ahead for me to break down the reticence about getting their hands dirty. I pointed out that it was a great idea to have help with removing the skin, or in the case of cattle, camelids and horses to have assistance with the heavy weight, but unless *you* handled the tissues you could never be sure that they were healthy. There were some raised eyebrows at that suggestion and I knew that it would be an uphill battle to convince some people.

Things improved once we started looking at the organs and it became obvious what was the cause of the problem: 'shipping fever'. The purple discoloration of the muscles indicated that there was a generalised congestion of the tissues of the body and this was most pronounced in the lungs where there were signs of pneumonia. It seemed strange that animals that had been travelling for many days on board a ship should develop this condition as soon as they stopped travelling. There was a rational explanation in that the animals had been fed on hay made from grass while on board ship and there had been a too-rapid transition to fresh alfalfa on arrival in the quarantine: 'shipping fever' should really be called 'change fever'!

I gave a demonstration on how to take samples from the various organs and most importantly how to label them and to get them into cool storage as soon as possible. I explained that the laboratory would not be functioning for at least three months, while we made changes to the building, ordered the equipment and recruited some staff. In the meantime they were free to contact me at any time if they wanted, to discuss clinical cases, or any problem where they felt that I might be able to assist. It was a strange place for a discussion about their requirements for a veterinary laboratory, with me standing under the shade of a tree leaning on a 44-gallon drum, while an assortment of men from thirty to sixty years of age stood around in a semicircle sporting various types of headgear, from the formal trilby or cloth cap, to the south American straw *sombrero*, an American baseball cap and even an English boater with a striped ribbon. A very valuable discussion ensued. I explained that I knew nothing about livestock production in Arequipa and that I would need to be guided by them.

There was no doubt that the only important animal in the irrigations was the dairy cow; until the present consignment of sheep had arrived there were almost no sheep at all in the department. This might be a very useful importation because it would introduce some new and valuable bloodlines, and offspring could be sold to the sheep farms up in the hills (at the time we were at 5,000ft above sea level). There were a few specialist pig farmers

23

in the various irrigations but no commercial poultry keepers. Many cattle farmers kept a few chickens on the farm to supply eggs and the odd fowl. I asked about veterinary services for the llamas and alpacas of the people in the high Andes but it seemed that there were none. Guinea pigs were an important source of food for the Andean people but only the research workers in the agricultural universities were doing anything about their health and productivity.

From the species we turned to diseases in the dairy cows and there was general agreement that lameness, that major scourge of British dairy cows, was not a problem but that the most important problems were infertility and mastitis. It seemed that we would need to provide specialist microbiological techniques and one fact caught my attention: brucellosis was a definite problem. This is a bacterial disease of cattle which can infect man resulting in 'undulant fever'; the name is most appropriate as when a person becomes infected their temperature goes up and down like a yo-yo and they can hold on to the infection for weeks. Luckily today there is a specific drug which in humans is very effective in killing the bacterium in the body. In cattle there is very little to be seen; however, affected cows abort between five and eight months of pregnancy. Although they rarely throw off the infection they almost never abort more than once; however, they continue to excrete the organism in the placenta, uterine fluids and milk, and so spread the disease to the heifers. Since the organism can be present in the milk it is a source of infection to the cowman and his family who often drink raw (unpasteurised) milk. I might have found the solution to financing the laboratory.

It is very difficult for a laboratory to pay its way without having a regular, guaranteed throughput of samples. A *Brucella abortus* eradication scheme could solve the problem for us. In Britain, brucellosis in cattle had been eradicated by regular testing of milk samples, with blood testing of those herds which showed positive to the milk test, and slaughtering all animals that were positive to this blood test. To ensure all animals are included it is essential to test the milk three times a year. With 10,000 dairy farms in the region this should give us a throughput of 30,000 tests per year, or 600 per week. If I could find a way of ensuring that all farmers had to take part, then the laboratory finances would be on a sound footing. Details of how we carried out the milk test will be given in a later chapter.

We adjourned to the *picantería* in the irrigation for lunch and the discussions continued. We ate *rocoto relleno*, a classic Arequipeño dish (the name means stuffed peppers). *Rocoto* is a large, globular, very hot type of chilli pepper; the inside is removed and it is stuffed (*relleno*) with a mixture of minced beef, onions and spices, a wedge of potato covers the aperture and a slice of cheese is placed on top; it is then cooked in an oven, the melted cheese soaks into the potato and down the sides of the pepper. A dish fit for a king and certainly for a vet who has spent the whole morning trying to teach in poor, if improving, Spanish. Traditionally, it is washed down with beer and followed by fresh fruit. The *picantería* was little more than a shack, constructed of wood with a thatched roof; tables with formica tops and plastic chairs were the simple furnishings. The food was delicious.

Problems of calves was the main topic over lunch and to my amazement, neonatal diarrhoea, such a problem in Britain, was almost unheard of. This reinforced a lesson earlier learnt, that management plays a massive role in animal disease, for unlike Britain, calves are not kept in houses but outdoors in individual hutches, and they run free and mix during the day. The yard and the hutches are on sand, which is everywhere; the faeces soak into the sand and pathogens are killed by the daily dose of sun: this part of Perú has 300-plus days of sunshine a year and on most days there is not a cloud in the sky. The dry sand is also the reason that there is no lameness problem in the cows; the hooves are always dry as they are never standing in mud or faeces and overgrowth of horn is not a problem as it is worn down by the 'sandpaper' on which they walk. The dry atmosphere and the absence of crowding into confined spaces means that pneumonia and other respiratory diseases are not a problem. The major problem with calves was nutritional and this affected the heifers and cows as well. Basically the animals were not given enough to eat. Animals were not free to graze in the alfalfa paddocks but were chained to a peg knocked into the ground. I was later to see the herds of ten to twelve animals in a sea of grazing with each animal surrounded by a circle of bare sand and stubs of plants. If the *ganadero* forgot to move his animals then they starved. Alfalfa being a leguminous plant is rich in protein but low in energy and so it needs to be supplemented by food rich in carbohydrate such as maize or barley: these were expensive in the country because there were no great savannas or plains where cereals could be grown on a large scale. Again this was the opposite of conditions in Britain where protein is expensive and energy is cheap. Although molasses was reasonably cheap the *ganaderos* did not like using it because, if they were not careful, they ran into problems of diarrhoea or other digestive disturbances.

The game was on! I felt that I had started my job; I had met some vets and I was beginning to find out about the problems of the industry and how it was run. It was early days but I was beginning to get a feel about what sort of services we would need to offer. As I drove back to Arequipa with José we discussed the possibility of setting up a *Brucella* eradication scheme.

"I had been planning to take you to meet Ing Luis García Calderón, *el Superintendente de Campo de* Leche Gloria, as he will be vital to the success of your plans," said José.

"Why?" I asked.

"Leche Gloria purchases almost all the milk produced in southern Perú – Arequipa, Moquegua and Tacna – and they put it into tins and sell it as evaporated milk. They have almost a monopoly, which FONGALSUR has been trying to break. There is a small plant in Arequipa called LAIVE that produces cheese, and Lucho's brother, Enrique, is opening a milk processing plant called PROLACSUR in the new Majes irrigation, where they will produce Tetrapak milk and other milk products such as yoghurt.

"But I had better explain: fifty years or so ago, Carnation Milk, a company from the USA, and the Nestlé company from Switzerland, came to Perú and divided the milk industry between them; Carnation took the south and Nestlé took Cajamarca in the north. In those days Cajamarca had a much higher production of milk than Arequipa, and Nestlé produced the baby milk, dried milk and tinned condensed milk. Over the years the number of irrigations in the south has expanded dramatically and now Gloria is much bigger than Nestlé. Two or three years ago Nestlé bought Carnation and the Peruvian Government decided that they had to sell one of the companies to prevent the whole of the country's milk production being in the hands of one organisation. Nestlé decided to sell Gloria and keep the Cajamarca operation because, although now smaller, it had the high-value products. And so Gloria is now owned by the Rodríguez family who are big industrialists in the south."

"What a fascinating story," I said. "I wonder if Nestlé made the right decision."

"Maybe not," said José. "Perhaps they thought that a Peruvian company would fail and they could take it back, but Gloria is a very well-run company, right next door to FONGALSUR; in fact your laboratory is closer to them than to us. They do everything themselves. The tinplate is shipped down on barges from Chimbote in the north and it comes by lorry from the port of Matarani; in the factory it is converted into the tins to hold the milk. They even have a department that not only maintains the machinery but it also makes parts for their machines. The raw milk is pasteurised, mixed with milk powder, which is normally imported from New Zealand or Australia or wherever it is the cheapest, put into tins and sterilised and then sealed. I will ask Ing García Calderón to show you round the whole plant. You must sell him on the idea that it would be good for the health of the staff of their plants, and they have nine milk collection plants throughout the whole of the south, if we could help to eradicate a human pathogen. They could insist that their suppliers take part in the scheme."

"When can we go and visit Ing García Calderón?"

"Why not tomorrow? I will arrange the visit."

On arrival at the hotel that afternoon Maxine presented me with a great list of houses that were for rent, mostly in the smart suburbs of Cayma or Yanahuara but some across the river. The children piled into the back of the Beetle. They were having the time of their lives; nobody bothered what time they got up, and they found out that they could get breakfast any time that they liked and all they had to do was to ask the waiters and it soon dawned that they could get what they wanted to eat at any time. The waiters were not used to children from Europe who were polite and treated them as equals. There is a much greater sense of class distinction in Perú than in Britain and our children with their experience of different cultures had learnt not to judge people by their position in society but by what they were and how they behaved. They had soon made friends with the younger members of staff. They all spoke some Spanish from their time in Argentina and Guy and Claire were learning Spanish at school. Language was no barrier.

The first house we visited was in Cayma and was a delightful little cottage with a small garden and only two bedrooms: not enough for us. We asked the cost of the rent: it was $1,000 per month. This could be nasty. We looked at several houses in Cayma and no matter the size, condition or furnishing, the rent was $1,000 per month. We crossed the river to Selva Alegre (Happy Forest) and saw this wonderful house built in *sillar* with six bedrooms and a ballroom with the most glorious chandeliers; the garden was massive with an orchard of mature fruit trees (citrus, peach and quince) and the rent was... $1,000 per month. I think that the rent was based more on the tenants than on the house itself. This house was much too grand and not really homely enough for us. We had had our experience of country-house living when we rented the east wing of Heydon Hall, a Tudor manor house in Norfolk, when

I was working in the Norwich Veterinary Investigation Centre. Over the next few evenings we looked at several more houses but none of them fired our imagination nor felt comfortable. Lucho mentioned that he had a cousin whose marriage was breaking up and that the wife who was an Argentine had a house for rent in Calle Lima in Yanahuara. From the Puente Grau, the Avenida Ejército continues up the hill and the Avenida Bolognesi runs along the bank of the river. These two roads form the boundary of Yanahuara.

We arranged to meet Kuki Lozada at the house after work. Avenida Lima was the second turning off Ave Ejército and the house was invisible from the road as there was a high brick wall with double doors as the only entrance (Plate 5). The maid answered the bell and let us into the grounds and house. The front garden was small but neatly planted with some mature shrubs (Plate 6). The house itself was a modern building with a flat roof with much wood and glass in its construction. The front door opened into a large hall extending the full height of the building with a single great wrought-iron chandelier. An open-plan staircase led to a mezzanine floor with a large wood-panelled room containing built-in bookshelves at either end, a comfortable three-piece suite, and hidden lighting. A perfect family room to house the first television set that the Windsors had ever owned (Plate 7). Next to this room was an in-house conservatory with a glass roof, containing many Amazonian jungle plants. The staircase led on up to the first floor where there were two suites, each consisting of two good-sized rooms, one a bedroom and one a living room together with a large bathroom. Each of these suites was currently being rented to a student…

"But they can be evicted at very short notice," hurriedly interjected Kuki.

With very little effort they could be converted into four individual bedrooms with a bathroom at either end of the passage. Below the staircase on the ground floor there were a few steps which led into a large room, which seemed to have been a children's playroom as the walls were plastered with pictures cut from colour magazines; all the rooms upstairs were similarly plastered with these pictures. Beyond the playroom was the garage.

At the foot of the stairs there was a door into the master bedroom suite, with a huge bedroom containing a large double bed and one wall that had cupboards along its length. A dressing room with more fitted cupboards, and a beautifully equipped bathroom completed the suite. There were French windows occupying one whole wall, which opened onto a covered patio (Plate 8) and the garden, which had been carved out of the hill. At the far end of this small garden there was a wall about twenty feet high, at the top of which were our neighbours; a small *chosa* housing a family of *campesinos*. Again Kuki hurriedly pointed out that these Indians living in their shack were our best insurance against thieves, as any crime would immediately be laid at their door.

Below this wall was a kidney-shaped swimming pool that ran almost the width of the garden, which was neat if not imaginative. From one of the upper bedrooms there was a staircase (fire escape) down to the garden and guarding the staircase was the largest moonflower tree (*Datura stramonium*) I have ever seen smothered with large white bell-shaped blossoms, which in the early evening gave off their wonderful heady perfume (Plate 9). In Britain this plant is advertised in the gardening catalogues as angels' trumpets. Facing this staircase were the staff quarters, a small flat with all the essential services. Returning to the hall there was an archway leading to a large reception room, formally appointed with sofas and chairs, but looking as if it was never used. Another archway led into the small dining room with an oval table, eight chairs and a sideboard. We were then shown the kitchen, a sort of peninsula from the main house and a pure delight (Plate 10). By the entrance was a large dining table which led to the work area proper with a huge American cooker that required a large transformer so that it could be used on 220 volts. I commented to Kuki that the construction seemed strange, with pillars of brick and concrete at regular intervals with inset panels of wood and glass. She explained that Arequipa was in an earthquake zone and so the house was constructed to withstand massive shocks as all the pillars were made of reinforced concrete with steel rods in the centre. The panels were designed to fall out in the event of a severe quake. From the kitchen was another exit to the garden. Sitting at the table I could see the great snow-capped volcano Chachani, whereas from the other side of the table you could see two more volcanoes, the conical-shaped Misti and Pichu Pichu (an Indian man) which was reputed to look like an Indian lying on his back. It is said that 'while the Indian sleeps, Arequipa is safe' (Plate 11).

We had found the house that would suit us very well and what was the rent? $1,000 per month! I told Kuki that we would need to convert the two suites into four bedrooms and we would need to redecorate two of the bedrooms and the anteroom to the garage because the walls had been totally papered with pictures cut from glossy magazines. She was happy for us to do so providing that we paid. The whole family were happy with the house and so we decided to take it, but then the problems began. The house was larger than my rank warranted. No problem I said – I will pay the difference in rent. That was not allowed. There was much toing and froing with the staff in the administrative section of the embassy, who had been against the project from the start. Finally, with the aid of John Taylor and the ambassador, the administrator capitulated and agreed that since all houses were the same rent it did not matter which house I chose to live in.

My meeting with Leche Gloria could not have gone better. We were met by *el Superintendente de Campo*, Ing García Calderón, who gave José and me a tour round the plant before we adjourned to his office where we were given excellent coffee and the inevitable pink and yellow wafer biscuits.

"And what can Leche Gloria do to assist you? We want to help because we are certain that if you are successful then the production of milk will go up and the quality will improve." He spoke perfect English.

"For any laboratory to be financially successful it has to have a regular supply of work," I said, "and the best way to ensure this is to run an eradication scheme in which all the farmers have to enrol. From my discussions, it is obvious that for the dairy industry in southern Perú that scheme is brucellosis."

"We have always been concerned about the risk of brucellosis for our staff," said Ing García Calderón.

"The scheme I envisage will be based on using the milk ring test to identify infected herds. Local vets will then visit the farm and take blood samples from all mature animals, including the bulls. Infected animals will be slaughtered. In this way it will be possible to eradicate the infection from a herd. If Leche Gloria offer an increase in the price that they pay for milk from 'accredited' herds, then the farmers will be less averse to paying for the testing."

"It will be in Gloria's interest to have clean milk because it would present no threat to their staff who handle it," said José.

We tossed around ideas about collecting the samples and it soon became clear that it would not be possible for the plants to do it themselves, as it would be too time-consuming and so slow down the work. We would therefore have to factor into our pricing the costs of taking a team to the plant, including the costs of overnight accommodation in Tacna, Moquegua, Mollendo and Pampacolca. It might also be necessary to set up a temporary laboratory in the plant and carry out the test on the spot. The details would have to be worked out later, once we had the materials and staff to carry out the work.

"And how do you propose to charge the farmers for this work?" asked Ing García Calderón with a twinkle in the eye and a grin on his face. He obviously knew the answer when he posed the question. Ever since I had been informed that the laboratory had to make a profit, this problem had been at the forefront of my thoughts. How could we set up an invoicing system, get the invoices to the farmers in areas where there was no postal system, and, more importantly, get them to pay? The next few minutes resolved the whole problem in a perfect way as Ing García Calderón dropped his bombshell.

"If you can tailor your computer system so that it synchronises with our accounting procedures, we can not only get your invoices to the farmers, but we can take off what they owe you from what we have to pay them and each month we will give you a cheque."

At a stroke he had reduced the thirty thousand invoices a year to twelve. This would save us a vast amount of labour, paper and problems of collecting small amounts of money from people, some more than a hundred miles away. Here José joined in:

"We could duplicate the system that FONGALSUR has with Leche Gloria. Once you have your computer up and running we will ask Ing Elio Cruz to write a programme for your invoicing that is compatible with the system used by Leche Gloria; he is always working with them."

"Brilliant," I said. "And would it be possible to include all our diagnostic charging such as post-mortem examinations or checking faeces samples for worm eggs, with the monthly *Brucella* charges?"

"I do not see why not, providing that we can have a compatible computer system. It will be necessary for our lawyers to draw up a *convenio*, and it will also be necessary for the farmers' associations to agree with the discounts, but I do not see there being any problem."

"By doing this," I said, "Leche Gloria will have gone a long way to ensuring that the laboratory is a success. It is very hard for a farmer to put his hand in his pocket to pay for the examination of a dead animal, when he has already got the loss of the animal itself. Taking the money from his milk cheque will be a passive way for him to pay for laboratory services; he will never have had the money and so he does not have to take money from his pocket. The facility you are offering us will go a long way to ensuring our success." In my excitement I was repeating myself. "I do not know how I can thank you enough."

"A successful laboratory will benefit everyone, farmers, consumers, vets, and at the end of the day, Leche Gloria. But what you do not know is that you have a significant well-wisher. Sr Jorge Rodriguez, the owner of Leche Gloria, is a great admirer of all things British. He was given a British Council scholarship to study engineering in an English university, I do not know which, but he now believes that the British way of doing things is best, and things made in Britain are always good. I personally want your project to succeed and will always be available to help you if I can, but in addition I have a boss instructing me that I have to help you!"

Ing García Calderón suggested that when I visited the irrigations where there was a Leche Gloria plant then I should take the opportunity to call in and introduce myself to the staff and tell them what we would be doing. Our business concluded, we had a chat about personal matters, where I had been and what I had done: we left on very amicable terms and I was told that the door was always open should I need any help.

I could barely contain myself: this had been one of the most successful mornings in my entire professional life; the project had received a massive boost and at one stroke I had solved my two biggest problems in setting up the laboratory: I had found a regular source of work for the laboratory and we had an easy way of charging 10,000 customers. Christmas had definitely come.

In fact it was rushing towards us: we had brought out presents with us for the children. It was the first time that the Windsor family were to pass a Christmas season in a hotel and Maxine did her best to give our rooms a festive look (Plate 12). We had discovered that there was an Anglican church in Vallecito, a suburb not far from the town centre, and that there would be a service of communion at 8am on Christmas Day.

The hotel had been visited by a variety of Arequipeños with youngish children of British heritage: they were mostly of Richard's age and no great friendships ensued, but by the end of the school holiday they had commenced making friends among the local people. Luckily they had all brought plenty of books with them and they found the new city strange and interesting. There were many cinemas to try; we had purchased a television and video recorder because we thought that there might be few cinemas and that they would only show Spanish language films, but we could not have been more wrong. There were a dozen or more cinemas and they all showed American films, not dubbed but with subtitles for the local people.

I remember little of the festivities themselves but do remember we attended the service on Christmas Day at the Church of Christ the Redeemer and were made very welcome by the vicar of the church, Alan Winstanley, and his wife Vivien and the rest of the small congregation. We learnt that the man who had been vicar of the Anglican church in Salta when we lived there, was now the Anglican Archbishop of South America, based in Chile. There were many people in Arequipa with British roots, but they were mostly Catholic in their religion. There were three things that had attracted the British to southern Perú: building the railways, shipping guano, and the alpaca fibre industry; later there was a fourth reason, building the Majes Dam and the irrigation scheme, which was in the hands of a consortium of South African, Canadian and British companies. The congregation that Christmas Day was about 50% Peruvian while almost all the British people were missionaries in various parts of southern Perú; one family came from Cusco, where the husband's job was to chair the committee that was translating the Bible into Quechua. The service was quite moving, but as it was very happy-clappy, we had great difficulty in stopping the children from falling about each time a young American missionary shouted out "Halleluiah" or "Praise the Lord" when the spirit moved him. After the service we adjourned upstairs for coffee: it was my first meeting with a vicar who lived above his work. The church was in Selva Alegre, a fine, modern suburb of Arequipa and was in effect a two-storey house where the ground floor was devoted to the church itself while the first floor was where the family lived. One is frequently confronted by coincidences and the Church of Christ the Redeemer was no exception: it had been set up by the South American Missionary Society and financed by All Saints Parish Church in Woodford Green, Essex, England, where I had been at school and where my parents then lived.

Two incidents that Christmas have stuck in my memory, the first being the trip to Mollendo for the children to see the sea. We climbed into the FONGALSUR Beetle and drove the 100kms to the old port of Mollendo. No sooner had we entered the town than we were stopped by the police, for what reason I never ascertained, but we all feigned complete ignorance of the Spanish language and I waved my British passport at the officer. Finally they gave up and in desperation indicated to us that we should drive on. The second incident was the New Year's Eve dinner in the hotel. We had invited Lucho and his delightful wife Roxana to join us. Our younger son Guy, then aged thirteen, took a shine to Roxana and kept inviting her to dance with him, and she gracefully accepted every time and he had a wonderful evening. We saw in the year 1987 in some style.

3

What's in a Name?

The festivities were over and although the children had not yet returned to England, it was time to make a big move forward to put together a team, prepare lists of equipment, media and reagents, and draw up and cost the changes required to turn the building into a laboratory. With me, the first priority is the staff; with good staff, you can turn out first-class work in poor facilities as we had seen in the old buildings in Gaborone. Never mind how good the facilities, you cannot produce good work with poor staff. It was time to meet my counterpart, the ministry vet, who would carry out all the official duties required by the Ministry of Agriculture. José took me to meet Dr Jorge Carrasco, a delightful little man with a large black moustache, who spoke like a machine gun and was totally unintelligible; he was much older than me and heading for retirement. His 'laboratory' consisted of a monocular microscope, an analytical balance, a few test tubes and a few bacterial stains. It never ceases to amaze me how governments can expect people to carry out scientific work in a converted office with a minimum of equipment; the equipment that Dr Carrasco possessed could not have cost more than £500, and I had been complaining about a budget of £30,000. With José interpreting we were able to agree that Dr Carrasco would stay put until the changes in the building had been completed, when he would bring all the equipment (!) he had to the new laboratory, and most importantly of all he would bring his official rubber stamps and ink pad. Thoughtfully, he had photocopied the inventory of his equipment. He gave me the impression that he would not stay long working with me as he had been forced into running the laboratory and that he would be back to his office as soon as he could escape.

I had no need to advertise for staff. Just a few days into the new year after a trip with José to meet the *ganaderos* on the old irrigation of La Joya (The Jewel), I was sitting in my office, which now contained a desk, two chairs, a bookcase and a filing cabinet, trying to puzzle out how we could staff the laboratory with no money to pay them, when there came a gentle tap on the door, and in walked an attractive young woman in her late twenties.

"Sit down," I said. "And what can I do for you?"

"I understand that you are looking for staff to work in your laboratory. I have a degree in biology from the University of San Agustin, here in Arequipa, and I should like to work here as a technician." The word had got out quickly. Sra Roxana Bustinza de Vergeray had a delightfully open personality, and was married with three young children. She was happy to admit limitations to her knowledge and experience. This was a trait that I came to cherish among the Peruvians; they knew their own worth but also, they were not ashamed to admit their shortcomings. How different from Africa! I explained to Roxana that at present we had no funds with which to employ staff but I suggested that we went over and had a chat with Dr Meza about the possibility of FONGALSUR employing people till we got off the ground.

Aldo was happy to see us and we sat down in his office and I outlined the problem. This would be no problem as the FONGALSUR board had already agreed that they would give contracts for one year to a vet, a laboratory technician, a manual worker and a secretary and if I was happy to employ Roxana, then he would organise a contract for her for a year, by which time the laboratory should be well established and she could be transferred to the project. I suggested to Aldo that Roxana be employed immediately as she could be of great assistance in the preparation of equipment lists and help with the design and layout of the laboratory, and this was agreed. Roxana was to prove competent, industrious and efficient and she was an excellent role model for the younger members of staff who followed; the first member of the laboratory staff was to prove the very best.

FONGALSUR was able to give us some equipment including a monocular microscope, various items of glassware, including of all things McMaster slides for counting worm eggs in animal faeces, and some reagents and stains including those necessary to carry out a Gram's stain. The whole bacterial world is divided into those bacteria that are Gram positive and those that are Gram negative, depending upon the ability of the bacterial cell wall to retain the stain. FONGALSUR also gave us some Giemsa stain which is essential for examining blood smears; and so Roxana was able to make a start on getting to grips with the work of a veterinary diagnostic laboratory.

Our first task was to redesign the laboratory so that the builders could get working. The laboratory ran from north to south and the central concrete workbenches with their built-in sinks would have to remain as the cost of removal and replacement would be high. The southern end of the laboratory would be walled off to make a separate washing-up, preparation and sterilisation unit, thereby separating the clean from the dirty. However, we not only had to design the laboratory for the immediate work to be done, but also to take into account the work that we could do once the budget had been expanded to purchase the more expensive equipment. A modern dairy industry requires tests for determining pregnancy from milk samples, counting the cells in milk to determine udder health, and chemical and physical tests to determine the quality of the milk. Talks with the farmers and vets had indicated that milk quality and infertility were among their major concerns. However, we would need to commence with the basic tests for which we had sufficient money to purchase the necessary equipment. The bacteriology would need to be carried out on the west side of the laboratory nearest to the post-mortem room. The walls on both sides of the laboratory building were glass from waist height to the ceiling which meant that the space was very well lit. We needed to get samples from the PM room into the laboratory for further examination and so in addition to the separating wall there was need for a hatch into the lab. That hatch would have to be immediately next to the door into the washing-up room, and so it became clear that we should use the whole of the western side of the laboratory for all the incoming specimens, and so along that wall would be workbenches interspersed with 'dirty' refrigerators and freezers. The concrete benches facing them would then be dedicated to bacteriology, and so we had already divided the laboratory into a "clean" half and a 'dirty'. Dirty samples are those that are potentially carrying infection such as faeces, milk, a foetus, organs from a dead animal or skin scrapings; clean samples are those that are not thought to carry infection: blood, serum, and animal feeding stuffs.

On the clean side we would need to have a refrigerator in which to store media, reagents, and volatile chemicals, and a freezer for biochemical and serological test reagents and long-term storage of sera. At the top on the eastern side of the laboratory there would be space to carry out tests required by the Ministry of Agriculture. A place was needed to carry out other serological tests (where we would measure the level of antibody against different disease agents), haematology (where you examine blood for anaemia or increases in white cells), and biochemistry (where you measure the levels of different constituents of the blood such as calcium, or glucose). The floor plan shows how we finally worked out where the different work was to be carried out. Instead of having a simple wall between the laboratory and the preparation room, we put two small rooms and a passage, that in the centre would become the microscopy room with a curtain that could darken it for when we were using phase contrast or fluorescence microscopy.

LABVETSUR FLOOR PLAN

Rooms – Numbers, Equipment - Letters

1 Reception/Office
2 Main Laboratory
3 Microscopy Cubicle
4 High Security Cubicle
5 Washing Up and Preparation Room
6 Office of Project Manager
7 Toilet
8 Locker Room
9 Post Mortem Room

A Desk
B Tiled Work Bench
C Sink
D Desk for Official Documents
E Deep Freezer – specimens (dirty)
F Deep Freezer - reagents (clean)
G Sample Reception Bench
H Bacteriology Section
I Parasitology Section
J Hatch to PM Room + Bench
K Media Preparation Bench
L Autoclave
M Equipment Washing
N Lockers
O Hand Basin
P Foot Bath
Q Steel Cabinet for equipment
R Steel Cabinet for receptacles
S Post mortem Table
T Bookcase
Z Computer

To the left would be a security room where we could work with high-risk material such as brains for rabies diagnosis. We were not to be allowed to undertake rabies examinations, since that was the prerogative of the Ministry of Health. But we might still have to remove brains if only to send to the ministry. The passage/room to the right would have the hatch to the post-mortem room and in there all the necropsy specimens would be processed.

To convert the yard to a post-mortem room was a simple matter, if not cheap: there would need to be a high roof to keep out the sun and the rain on those few days when there was precipitation. We would need stainless steel tables and steel locking cupboards in which to keep the equipment for carrying out the work: knives, scissors, saws, scalpels, forceps, buckets. Also required was equipment for taking the samples: stainless steel trays, jars, bottles, plastic bags, swabs, chemicals and reagents, which would also need to be stored in the cupboard. There would have to be a water tap and hoses together with basins for hand washing and foot baths for boots. Luckily none of this would come from my equipment budget as it would all be paid for by FONGALSUR. Inside the building there would be developed an area in which to hang plastic gowns and rubber gloves and a place to keep the rubber boots.

It required no discussion for Roxana and me to decide that we would go for the modern systems where possible and so we would use plastic disposable Petri dishes for bacterial culture instead of the original glass dishes that could be used many times. The plastic plates came with the inbuilt guarantee from the company that they were sterile, whereas glass plates had to be sterilised each time they were used. Over the previous decade there had been an incredible leap forward in 'kits' for the identification of bacteria. When I first started out in Kenya we had to prepare all the different media for every single biochemical test and each of the different sugars used had to have its own batch of media. The commercial strip for the identification of a bacterium carried individual small wells each containing its own freeze-dried sterile medium. To carry out the test, one or more colonies of the bacterium from the agar plate were mixed with sterile saline and with all aseptic precautions each well was inoculated: the saline would reconstitute the freeze-dried medium; the strip was returned to its containers and put into the incubator for twenty-four hours after which the results could be read. The purists decried the modern inventions but my view was that they were much cheaper in the long run and again the manufacturer guaranteed the purity and quality of its testing system. I thought back to those Kabete days when we had problems with bacteria that were unable to use lactose, but which suddenly developed the ability to use it very well. After a day or two of strange results I went to the media room to investigate, to find that they had run out of lactose and rather than bother us, they had used glucose instead! Kits were all but idiot-proof.

Roxana had heard of these systems, but they were not available in Perú. Perhaps when other institutions heard about what we were doing they would follow our lead and such materials would then be imported on a commercial basis into the country. When we were equipping the National Veterinary Laboratory in Gaborone we had received exceptional service from Ron Sykes of Vectrol Ltd and so it was to Ron that I turned to organise the purchase of the equipment that we needed. Again he did not let us down and we received excellent service and very good prices. As he was always telling us, he was a one-man band with small overheads and willing to quote cheap prices on which he made only a very small margin. His prices were so good that it got him into trouble with the Inland Revenue; they could not believe that he had made so little money on such a huge turnover. As a result, he was 'turned over'. We were able to help by writing letters confirming the prices that we had paid. The bureaucrats in London raised no objections to my placing orders directly with Vectrol, providing that they had seen them and agreed to the purchases.

I was sitting in the reception area of the laboratory when another attractive young woman came stumbling in her high-heeled shoes down the grass path. Beautifully turned out in a smart business suit, with not a hair out of place and with a radiant smile on her face, she asked

"Could I please speak to Dr Windsor?"

"I am Dr Windsor, please sit down and tell me what I can do for you."

And so began a life-long friendship. The young lady before me spoke perfect English with just the hint of an American accent and this was amazing as she had never been outside Perú. Aurora Salazar Calcina sat down and told me all about herself: she was born in Arequipa, the only child of elderly parents. When her father retired he set up in business as a tailor. She attended a state school where she received just two hours of English tuition per week. In her last weeks at high school she started English classes at the Instituto Cultural Perú Nortamericana and completed their English course. After that she took an executive secretarial course for two years and three months and when she successfully completed that, she was offered a job with ICPNA for four years where she was able to practise and perfect her English as she had to deal with American, British and Australian teachers. She was currently employed by Southern Copper Corporation, an American mining company that ran a huge mine in the department of Tacna at Toquepala. The mine was miles from anywhere up in the mountains and as a young lady she wanted to see some of the lights of the big city.

"Would it be all right if I gave you some dictation and you went up to the FONGALSUR office and typed it out?"

"I thought that you might ask that," Aurora said, "and so I have brought my dictation pad and some pencils." And with that she opened her voluminous bag and drew out the required items.

"You will have to learn a large number of new technical terms," I said, "but do not be frightened to stop me, and ask me to spell any words you do not know; or if you do not know what a word means, please ask and I will try to explain. I am not particularly interested in speed today, because everything is new to you, including my voice, and so I want accuracy rather than speed. And please, please relax as I want you to be successful almost as much as you do!" In the few minutes in my office she had impressed me greatly and I really was hoping that she would do well; however, much as I had taken to Aurora, it was more important that the laboratory had a good secretary.

The majority of her work would be typing reports on laboratory examinations and so I sat back and dictated a fictitious laboratory report; Aurora was perfectly happy with the different parts of the body but she had never heard of *Streptococcus agalactiae* or *Escherischia coli* and so I spent some time explaining about bacteria and how they all differ. When the dictation was completed we walked up to FONGALSUR and Milagros went and found a typewriter of a make and type that Aurora had used and while she typed out the report, I went into Aldo's office for a chat.

"I have found just the secretary for the lab and if she makes fewer than ten mistakes then she has the job, providing that you approve."

"Is she a pretty girl?" came Aldo's laconic reply.

"Yes, very," I replied, "but she also appears intelligent and bright and I am certain she will turn out to be a great asset for the laboratory."

There was a discreet knock on the door: it was Aurora who had completed the typing of the report, which she handed to me. Aldo's eye lit up. The report was perfect, without a single typing error, and beautifully laid out.

"Is it all right?" she said. "Without too many mistakes?"

"It's perfect and neatly laid out. Aldo," I said, "can you find a post for this young lady in the laboratory?"

"That should present no problem. Miss Salazar, how did you know there was a job in LABVETSUR? Surely the news has not percolated all the way to Toquepala?"

"Indeed not, a very close friend of mine who used to work in the office here has remained in contact with Dr Diaz del Olmo; he told her, she told me and here I am!"

And so Aurora joined us: we had to wait for a couple of months while she sorted out her affairs in Tacna. The laboratory now had two Peruvian members together with a ministry vet once we got started. Aurora and Roxana were the first two members of staff to be appointed and they were with me until I left six years later and I could not have had two more diligent, delightful, able or efficient people to work with. Aurora was able and willing to turn her hand to anything, and she became the confidante and teacher of many of the people who joined us. She had the ability to organise without seeming bossy and basically she oiled the wheels of the laboratory and ensured that all went smoothly. Despite having seen her only twice in the past twenty years my friendship with Aurora is as good as it ever was and over the years she has been so kind in sorting out problems for artists wanting to come to Britain. But I am jumping the gun.

Roxana and I soon had the details for the plan for the changes to the laboratory sorted out and the equipment lists were on their way to the Brighton Queen. We soon had the construction workers, joiners, glazers, plumbers, and electricians all plying their trades in the laboratory and it was a real hive of activity. The first equipment to arrive was a couple of locally purchased computers and a printer and so Roxana and I were able to start working on a price list for our services. It was then that I made the most astute decision of my entire professional life: I decided that our prices would be based on the price of milk. Because of the rampant inflation in Perú caused by Alan García's disastrous economic policies it was obvious that prices for our services would go up every month. FONGALSUR had established a *Comité de Administración* (board of control) for the laboratory and they would need to approve any increases. The committee consisted of Ing Luis Lozada as chairman, with the vice-chairman being the representative of the Ministry of Agriculture, and the treasurer was also a representative of FONGALSUR; the secretary was the representative of INIAA, a government agricultural advisory and research service. AUTODEMA, which was the body that controlled the Majes Project, the latest and largest irrigation in the department, had a representative, and the veterinary profession had a seat on the board, normally the president of the *Colegio Medico Veterinario*; the honorary British Consul completed the team. It can be seen that the board comprised a group of senior and important people and getting them together to take rapid decisions would not be easy. This was my stroke of genius: we would not charge in cash terms but our prices would be based on the price of a litre of milk. The milk price was controlled by the government and each month they adjusted it ever higher. As the government increased the price of milk in intis, the national currency, so our prices would rise automatically, without having to trouble the laboratory board. Provided that the government allowed the milk price to rise in line with inflation then the laboratory's income should keep pace. All went well with this system until 1989 when the economy hit the bottom and milk prices were held stable; this almost brought the laboratory to bankruptcy and we had to go to the board to increase our prices and salaries, the only time that we had to do so.

A second idea that had almost as much impact as linking our prices to the price of milk, was to have a sliding scale for the *Brucella* milk ring test, depending upon the amount of milk the farmer produced. A farmer who sent in:

1-2 *porongos* per day paid the equivalent of 1 litre of milk
2-5 *porongos* – 2 litres
6-10 *porongos* – 5 litres
11-20 *porongos* – 10 litres
More than 20 *porongos* – 20 litres

The small farmers paid very little for the work and the larger wealthy farmers subsidised the costs. Lucho thought that this would be acceptable to all farmers and as he and his brothers were among the biggest producers in the region it seemed that most farmers would accept our prices. In the six years that I worked in Perú we never received a single complaint about this subsidy, nor indeed about any of our charges. I honestly believed that they were delighted that after many years they were receiving a proper veterinary laboratory service.

"Before we can complete this price list, we need to give the laboratory a name," I said to Roxana. I had been trying to find a suitable name and had come up with nothing that was usable. "We are a regional laboratory for the whole of southern Perú; veterinary is a bit of a mouthful for Peruvians, animal health is easier to say and so why not call ourselves Regional Animal Health Laboratory for southern Perú?" (*Laboratorio Regional de Sanidad Animal del sur del Perú*) Roxana was not impressed!

"You will have to cut that down because it is much too long," she said. "How about LABSANAMSUR?"

"That sounds like a *chifa* [a Chinese restaurant]," I said. "It is too long, let's go back to vet, and call us LABVETSUR." Roxana, and Aldo who had just popped in, agreed that there was something catchy about that name and so we looked no further.

"Now that we have a name we need a logo," I said. "We have to convey the concept of science with the idea of Arequipa and the fact that we are an international project. Having been in Arequipa for all of a couple of months, there is no doubt in my mind that the volcano Misti dominates the city and you people, and I am sure that wherever I go, whenever I think of Arequipa, I will see that majestic snow-capped mountain."

"Could I ask my husband to produce some drawings for us along those lines?" asked Roxana. "My husband, Rodolfo, is an engineer and a good draughtsman, I am certain he will be able to do something for us."

A few days later Roxana produced a piece of paper with the perfect logo as we all agreed. I showed it to Lucho who was more than happy that we should use it. The microscope, which represents science, within an equilateral triangle that indicates the volcano, is enclosed within a circle of words in which two, FONGALSUR and GOBIERNO BRITANICO, are in bold type and a slightly larger font than the other names. That logo adorns all LABVETSUR documents to this day; it is simple but very effective.

We were discussing working hours and I was told that it was normal to work on Saturday mornings; it has always been my belief that veterinary laboratories should be open on Saturdays, as animals do not stop becoming sick because it is the weekend. I always considered Saturday working as unpaid overtime and as a sweetener I suggested that staff should be able to have a half day off in return, or to work two Saturdays and have a whole day so that they could have a long weekend. It was agreed that I should put our suggested working hours to the board: we would work Mondays to Fridays from 8.30am to 5pm with an hour for lunch, staggered so that the laboratory could remain open, and on Saturdays, half the staff would work from 8.30am to 1pm. Overtime would not be paid but the staff would be given time off in lieu of payment.

I was discussing these arrangements with José Diaz del Olmo one Saturday morning; it was the usual weather, not a cloud in the blue, blue sky. We were outside his office taking in the sun, and I was leaning against the wall of his office, when I felt it start to sway. I could not understand what was happening as the movement got worse and worse. Suddenly the doors to the building opened and the people started filing out. This was normal drill for an earthquake, but it was the first one that I had experienced of this magnitude. It went on and on and the hills around appeared to be on fire as what seemed to be smoke was filling the air; it was not smoke but dust. The Andes is an immature mountain range, mostly composed of rubble from the seabed; as the tectonic plates move the earth's crust, the force is ever upwards and it breaks up into rock fragments of varying sizes. When an earthquake occurs then the rubble is disturbed and minor or major landslides occur; then the rocks roll down the hill under the force of gravity. José was most concerned because the following day he and I were scheduled to depart for the south to visit the provincial capitals of Tacna and Moquegua and meet various dignitaries in the Ministry of Agriculture and the FONGALES; I also hoped to visit a few farms during the journey.

"This is a big earthquake," said José, "and being Sunday tomorrow, there will be no attempt made to clear the rubble from the roads, which will make the journey fairly tedious because we shall have to weave our way round the rocks and this could add an hour or more to the journey."

This was the 1987 earthquake with its epicentre in Arica, a coastal town in Chile about 160 miles away; it had a value of 7.8 on the Richter scale, and much of the old town was destroyed. It was the first and worst earthquake that occurred during our stay in the country and I was later to learn that Arequipa was in a serious earthquake area. The reason for this is that two of the earth's tectonic plates, the Nazca and the South American, meet under the Pacific Ocean to the west of Perú. The Nazca plate was moving under the South American and this was responsible for the increasing height of the Andes, the volcanoes and the earthquakes. I was later to learn that the ground below the city was constantly on the move and because of this regular readjustment underground the city rarely experienced serious earthquakes. The strength of the earthquake is not the only factor determining the damage. Some years later (July 1991) there was an earthquake of only 4.7 on the Richter scale in Maca, an Andean town in the Colca Valley about 150 miles from the city, and this seemingly innocuous earthquake killed more than ninety people and destroyed the whole town, leaving only the church still standing and that badly damaged. The reason for the devastation was that beneath the town was a large underground lake and the earthquake started a tsunami with the water oscillating back and forth in the confined space, and this powerful movement shook the buildings until they fell down.

As José predicted, the journey to Tacna was protracted as he was never able to get up speed, and for much of the journey the road was strewn with rubble of all sizes, from small stones up to boulders more than a metre in diameter. On several occasions, we had to stop and clear a path among the rubble. We were booked into the *Turistas* Hotel in the centre of this attractive small city, and it proved to be comfortable and pleasant, a far cry from many of the *Turistas* Hotels of that era.

Monday morning was spent calling upon the various dignitaries in the city to explain what our project was doing and how we planned to assist their department. My Spanish was coming on in leaps and bounds under its regular daily use and I now felt more comfortable talking to people about what we were planning to do. After lunch we visited FONGALTACNA and received a very warm welcome. This was a much smaller operation than FONGALSUR but the headquarters, which was just out of town, was a very much more solid building than its Arequipa counterpart. Knowing of my interest in meeting the farmers, the co-operative had invited a group to come and talk to me, and we had a most profitable afternoon discussing diseases, management problems and general problems with the economy of farming. As in Arequipa, the Tacna farmers were up in arms about the Dollar MUC which was allowing Leche Gloria to import milk powder from New Zealand and Australia for two-thirds of the price that they were paying Peruvian farmers for their fresh milk. This in turn allowed Leche Gloria to put more milk powder into their evaporated milk. I had difficulty in seeing the logic of importing milk powder to mix with fresh milk and then putting it into a tin. The problem for farmers in Tacna would be to get their samples to Arequipa in a condition in which they could be examined. Buses and taxis were the answer and FONGALTACNA undertook to hold discussions with local companies to establish a system whereby samples would be sent expeditiously to the laboratory. After formal farewells, we were on the road back to Moquegua and a night in a second decent *Turistas* Hotel.

Moquegua is a pleasant little city and its officials were equally pleasant and genuinely thankful for the help being extended to them by the British Government. The major source of revenue for the Department came not from agriculture, nor from mineral extraction, but from the copper smelters of Southern Copper in the port of Ilo. Another important product from Moquegua was the spirit pisco, which was made by the distillation of rough wine produced from the locally grown grapes. Moquegua was famous for its Pisco Biondi, a delicious spirit which is drunk on its own; it is made from the *uvas de Italia* variety of grape which gives the spirit a strong raisiny flavour. The vines are grown in the valley in which sits the city, and driving along the highway both sides are lined by mile after mile of the vines and stands of avocado pear trees. FONGALMOQUEGUA was even smaller than its counterpart in Tacna but its staff were no less welcoming and offered us whatever facilities we needed for us to extend our service to their farmers. The return to Arequipa was faster and safer as the roads had been cleared of the rubble.

I had made contact with the main areas of my patch and only Puno and Cuzco, which were included in my area, remained unvisited; neither had large livestock populations as both were purely mountainous and their main animal populations were camelids with few cattle and even fewer sheep. Although it was important for an aid project to bring services and assistance to the poorest people in the community, my first priority was to ensure that the laboratory paid its way. For me, failing to assist the really poor people was the biggest deficiency in the aims of the project and I was determined that once the laboratory was on a sound financial footing, LABVETSUR would takes its services to the people in the high Andes.

4

Open at Last

With the arrival of our computers came Ing Elio Cruz, definitely a man of the Andes, small, stocky, dark-complexioned with a smile that lit up the hills. He was definitely a ladies' man with an eye for the girls and a great flirt. He was never too busy that he could not stop for a chat, or to pass on the latest gossip, but with the computers he was a whizz, and for LABVETSUR he was a godsend as he wrote all the programmes that the laboratory needed to unite our systems with those of Leche Gloria. Whenever we had a computer problem we sent for Elio (Plate 13).

We had produced our price list, which together with the staff salary scales had been approved by the board, who had accepted my recommendation that both salaries and prices should be linked to the price of milk. This would ensure that I did not need to go to the board for approval before we could raise either salaries or prices. The workmen were all busy making the necessary changes to the building. FONGALSUR had provided all the office equipment and some laboratory supplies; the scientific equipment had been ordered by ODA and was probably negotiating the Panama Canal on its way to Callao (the port of Lima).

Lucho was in his element organising the grand opening of LABVETSUR on May 13th 1987 in the presence of the Senator for Arequipa, Ing Jorge Lozada Stanbury (who happened to be his cousin), His Excellency John Shakespeare the British Ambassador, the Prefect Sr Raul Diaz Uré (equivalent to the Lord Lieutenant in Britain), the Archbishop of Arequipa Monseñor Vargas Ruiz de Somocurcio, the *alcalde*, Luis Cáceres Velasquez, all the military heads, ministry representatives from the different departments, the boards of the various FONGALES, and the head of each of the irrigations together with a host of business people and the entire British community of the city. The national press, TV and radio stations were all instructed to be there. There was a great kerfuffle when the town band found that they did not have the music for the British National Anthem and so the embassy sent the band parts by courier and Maxine had to take them to the band and supervise a rehearsal.

The great day dawned and as always it was glorious sunshine, the marquees had been erected, the bunting hung and several hundred seats had been put out. The sound system was checked and rechecked. Meanwhile in the offices of FONGALSUR the goodies for the reception after the inauguration were being prepared and the ice for the pisco was brought in from Leche Gloria. The band played and the stage party marched in and took their places on the dais. Lucho, who was master of ceremonies, asked the assembled spectators to rise for the National Anthems and the band made a good attempt at the British, followed by the much longer Peruvian and finally, the longest of all, that of Arequipa. The archbishop said a prayer and then Lucho invited the senator for Arequipa to welcome the ambassador and the other distinguished guests. I had the feeling that the Peruvians were vying to see who could speak for the longest, all of them going into eulogies about the role of the British Government in providing the material for the laboratory, and not least, their 'world-leading veterinary scientist' who was going to revolutionise veterinary medicine in the south of Perú if not the whole of South America! Finally the ambassador was invited to open the new laboratory, which he did in a short yet eloquent speech in Spanish. The ambassador, with Lucho, then cut the ribbon and broke a bottle of champagne on the wall, to show that the laboratory was, at last, open.

There were more words from Lucho who thanked the ambassador for coming to Arequipa, and for all his kindness in setting up the project, which was going to improve the lives of the poor people in the irrigations of the south. After which the archbishop said another prayer, the band struck up and the assembled throng all set off to inspect the premises. I was grateful that I was not senior enough to have to speak in such august company, because my Spanish was still far from good. Most of the equipment had still to arrive, but there was enough, and together with that from FONGALSUR and the ministry it was laid out on the mostly completed benches: the workmen were behind with their work so they would need to carry on working for another week or so to finish. But it all looked impressive enough as I showed the ambassador and the senator round the building and explained what the equipment was for. And then it was time for pisco sours and canapés as the party began.

The Peruvians throw great parties; they are always very generous hosts and FONGALSUR were no exception that day. In honour of the ambassador, genuine Scotch whisky was served (I suspect that it was mostly drunk by the board of FONGALSUR) together with the pisco sours and the 'champan'. The food was royal: *conchitas a la parmesana* served in the shell, *machas a la criolla* (a Peruvian clam like a small pink tongue, in a sauce made from onions, chilli, sweet peppers and coriander), also served in the shell; ham and cheese served on biscuits, meatballs and chicken on toothpicks. No Peruvian party would be complete without a selection of *dulces* (sweetmeats). To round off the entertainment the dance troupe Folklórico Octavio Polar entertained us to some Andean music and dancing. It was a time for mixing and letting people know what we were planning to do; without exception our guests wanted to see the laboratory succeed. In southern Perú there was not a single competent laboratory, not even in the medical world, and so there was the possibility of broadening our services and thereby increasing the income. After the ambassador had departed I thought it reasonable for Maxine and me to leave and return to our new home in Avenida Lima. Once the carpenters had finished in the laboratory they would move to our house to convert the two suites into four bedrooms, giving each of our children their own room and still allowing us to entertain visitors.

Maxine made a cup of tea and we sat in our lovely kitchen thinking how lucky we were to be in such a warm, friendly country with a glorious climate and with a fascinating challenge ahead. Our children were happy and balanced and were performing well in their schools. Despite my not being able to take an active part in theatre (my Spanish was not good enough), Perú had a strong tradition of music both traditional and classical, and Arequipa had its own symphony orchestra and music school, which would keep Maxine happy; we were in for an interesting few years. The only blot on the horizon was the *Sendero Luminoso*, the Maoist terrorist organisation whose leader, Abimael Guzmán, came from Arequipa; it was said that terrorist activities were not carried out in Arequipa for fear of retaliation against the family. The frightening aims of the organisation were to return Perú to pre-colonisation days, destroy all remnants of Spanish and Western civilisation and start again from year zero.

At the time of our arrival, the major target was Lima and there was a curfew in the city from midnight to six in the morning. The main activity seemed to be blowing up the power lines, which they were able to carry out with impunity. During the visit of the Pope, at the moment he was about to celebrate mass in Lima Cathedral, out went all the lights, and it had been a regular occurrence at New Year for the past few years that on the stroke of midnight they put out all the lights. Whatever steps the authorities took to protect the power lines coming into Lima, the *Sendero* were one step ahead.

As the years went by the *Sendero* moved their targets out into the country and their violence and viciousness increased until they were finally using tactics that even their supporters could not accept: children being given a gun and told to shoot an innocent nun, and the kangaroo courts handing down death sentences by stoning, burning or slitting throats. During our stay they extended their grip, thanks to the poverty caused by the woeful financial policies of the president, to most of the landlocked regions of central Perú. Apart from our inability to travel to various places, our lives and my work were not much affected by the terrorists.

Word had got round that LABVETSUR was looking for staff and we had numerous callers at the laboratory looking for work. As the construction work in the laboratory continued it became apparent that we would need to recruit a cleaner, and when Epifanio Aguilar Chire, the younger brother of a staff member of FONGALSUR, turned up, we thought that he fitted the bill, as he was bright and enthusiastic and I thought Roxana would be able to show him what to do. These days it is not politically correct to say that you believe in nepotism, but I am afraid that I do. If one member of a family is industrious and diligent, it has been my experience that siblings or cousins are likely to be the same. However, in a small team, I am not happy to employ a husband and wife because when one goes on holiday, so does the partner, and losing two members at once can make working difficult.

For the opening, Dr Carrasco had moved his equipment and himself to the laboratory. This was not without its problems as he spoke so fast and so indistinctly that I had difficulty following what he was trying to say. I once said to José:

"I can rarely understand more than two words out of three when he speaks."

To which José replied, "I am doing well if I can understand one!"

But he was a willing horse and he had brought with him his set of official ministry rubber stamps, without which we could not operate. I have made little mention of the 'official' difficulty we had in setting up the laboratory. Perú operates under the Napoleonic Code legal system which differs from the British: whereas in Britain all things are legal except those that are illegal, in Perú everything is illegal except that which is legal. Unless you have authority to do so you may not set up and operate a laboratory. I had been working with Dr Chávez, the FONGALSUR lawyer, and Dr Carrasco to obtain all the necessary permissions: to run a laboratory, to employ staff, to carry out testing, the list goes on, but there was so much goodwill towards us that even the bureaucrats seemed keen to help us. Lucho's publicity and propaganda had certainly paid off.

A few days after the official opening a small incident occurred in the laboratory that had a long-term beneficial effect. I had been looking up a disease unknown to me in a textbook. I went into the laboratory to have a further look at the organs in the PM tray and noticed that the floor was covered in wood shavings: I was pleased to see that the few staff that we had were all busy at the benches carrying out diagnostic work and so I went to the cupboard and took out a broom and a dustpan and commenced sweeping the floor. Roxana saw what I was doing and stopped her laboratory work and rushed over to me to take over the sweeping.

"No!" I said. "You are already busy doing diagnostic work and everyone else is similarly occupied except me. It is therefore sensible for me to do the sweeping since I am otherwise unoccupied."

They all saw the logic of this, even though it went against the grain for them to see a professional person carrying out a manual task. However, the idea took hold that there was nothing 'demeaning' for a vet to wash the bottles or a secretary to help out in the post-mortem room. This started the spirit of teamwork among the staff which continued throughout my whole time in the laboratory.

The next addition to our staff was rather special: Sr Fernando Alverado Paredes, FAP as he was called, was a tall, thin, intense young man who was studying biology at the University of San Agustin and who, before he could qualify, had to undertake a period of work experience in a laboratory. They were called *practicantes* and often to show that they had completed this period they had to produce a *tesis* or thesis. My feeling was that the universities, aware of their own inadequacies, forced the students to find a place to complete their training. It hit me that this was a golden opportunity for LABVETSUR, as we did not need to pay a salary to these students; we could increase our work without increasing our expenses. At the same time it would help the laboratory fulfil its training role, and as a result on many occasions there were more *practicantes* in the laboratory than paid staff. But the system worked well, and as the reputation of the laboratory increased we received more and more requests from young men and women wanting to be vets or laboratory workers. In order to restrict the numbers we set up a waiting list. A massive advantage of this system was that we were able to try out these young people to see if they would be useful as a member of staff; thereafter, with few exceptions, all people recruited to the staff were selected from our *practicantes*. FAP became the first *practicante* to be employed in LABVETSUR and became an excellent member of the team.

Although they were not paid a salary they were given honoraria for various things. When an overnight stay was required they received board and lodging and senior staff paid for the drinks. They often received a gratuity, which helped with the bills. We almost got into trouble with the authorities because of our *practicantes*: to avoid exploitation a company is not allowed to employ anyone for more than three months without giving them a contract of employment and paying a salary, and some of our students stayed for more than a year! The veterinary students, in particular, required much more time as they were obliged to undertake a research project and write a formal thesis in order to qualify for their final degree. We circumvented this problem by giving a contract for three months to each *practicante*, although they were assured that if they did well it would be renewed and if a post became available they would be in the running.

The end of the first month approached and with some trepidation I submitted the floppy disc to Leche Gloria; I need not have worried as Elio had done his work well, the two computer systems talked to each other, and ten days later our cheque arrived. Our first monthly report was produced and it made pretty dreary reading with no exciting cases and no interesting stories; however, the show was on the road and it was time to spread our wings.

We had purchased locally made glass bottles with screwcapped plastic lids which held 200ml of liquid and could be sterilised and reused on many occasions. A local carpenter had made twenty wooden boxes, each to hold forty of these bottles. A team had visited the local Leche Gloria milk reception plant and we had watched the arrival of the *porongos* at the plant. They were much smaller than the British churn and only held about thirty-five litres. The contents were poured into a large aluminium pan (*tina*) which could accept and weigh up to 150 litres. Once the contents had been weighed and the weight recorded the *tina* was emptied into a bulk holding vessel where the milk was cooled. When all the milk from one farmer was in the *tina* we would collect our sample and write the reference number of the farm on the bottle top. The team was assembled for that first visit: Dr Carrasco and I would take the samples while Roxana and Aurora would write and label the bottles.

The team had to be at the plant by 6.30 in the morning when the first milk lorries arrived. We chose the plant that served the *campiña* of Arequipa as that was the nearest. Dr Carrasco left his car at the laboratory and I collected the two young women from their homes, and we were all ready and waiting in the plant when the first lorry arrived. It was a disaster! The *porongos* came down the slide much faster than we had anticipated and by the time one bottle had been labelled, the *tina* had been emptied two or three times. The staff in the collecting plant could not wait for us but had to go full tilt to get the work done and the plant cleaned and sterilised for the next day. The milch cow for the laboratory had not got off to a very good start and it was back to the drawing board. It was Dr Carrasco who provided the solution. The bottles had to be numbered in advance, one to forty in each wooden box, and each box was to be given a letter. In the laboratory Aurora made up a form for each box with the numbers one to forty listed with a column to write in the identity of the farm. There was a column to record the daily production of the farm, and a column to record the results of the milk ring test so that it would be unnecessary to write out the farm identity again. With a few minor changes this is the system that worked well for the next six years. It is still in use today.

Our second visit to the collecting plant was a much more successful happening: we collected all the samples with no problems for us and no dislocation of the work of the plant. One bottle was required for each filling of the *tina* and so for many farms more than one bottle was required; the technical staff soon became adept at working out how many bottles would be required and as they acquired the skill, the forms were filled as the *porongos* came down the chute. I am certain that at the start a few of the samples were incorrectly identified, but within a matter of weeks the team had sorted out all the problems and by the end of the year we had collected almost 3,000 samples.

Back in the laboratory everything was ready to test the samples. The milk ring test is based upon the principle that cows infected with *Brucella abortus* produce antibodies against the organism, some of which are excreted in the milk. A small sample of the milk is mixed with an antigen of killed *Brucella abortus* organisms combined with a haematoxylin dye which gives the antigen a dark blue to purple colour. Milk and antigen are mixed to distribute the dye throughout the sample which is then incubated at 37°C for one hour, after which the milk is examined. If there are no antibodies then little happens and the sample remains a uniform blue/purple; occasionally the dye will migrate out of the cream leaving it white and the milk coloured. Should there be antibody in the milk then it will unite with the antigen to form a mesh, which being lighter than the milk floats up into the cream and so the cream becomes blue and the milk is white.

It is a simple test to carry out and easy to read the results. For the test you require tubes about six centimetres in length which hold only one millilitre of milk. We had purchased large numbers of these tubes, and racks to hold them. Life is much easier today as it is possible to buy pipettes that deliver an exact volume of liquid. These pipettes come with single-use, disposable delivery tips. In Perú, the tips were expensive and labour cheap, so we washed the tips, sterilised them and used them again and again. The milk bottle was well shaken and one millilitre was taken and dispensed into a tube, using a new tip for each sample. With a second pipette that dispensed exactly 30μ (30 thousandths of a ml) the antigen was added. Once all the antigen was dispensed then the racks were shaken to mix the sample so that it appeared a uniform blue and it was put into an incubator at 37°C and left for an hour. Occasionally we would obtain a doubtful result but for the most part the results were clear and conclusive.

International organisations suggest that the milk should be held overnight before testing. We found that the quality of the milk was so poor that if we waited, then the milk would go off or coagulate and so we carried out the test as soon as all the samples had been collected. In order to ensure that the milk of all cows in a herd was tested at least once a year, it was necessary to check the bulk milk three times a year at regular four-month intervals. Farmers with three consecutive negative tests became eligible for a herd blood test; a ministry veterinary surgeon visited the farm and bled all the animals on the farm including the bull, and we examined these samples for the presence of antibodies to the bacterium. If they were all negative, the farm was declared free from brucellosis and an official certificate was sent to the farm with a copy to Leche Gloria; thereafter the farmer was paid a bonus price for his milk.

With increasing work we required another laboratory technician and we had no *practicantes* sufficiently advanced to be employed and so we advertised in *El Pueblo*, a local newspaper. Lucho, Dr Carrasco and I made up the selection board. Srta Lita Araujo Lama was easily the best candidate and she accepted the job when it was offered. Many years later she spoke about the interview at which she had apparently been very nervous. I asked her if she spoke any English and when she said that she had studied the subject, I then talked to her in English and she froze; the poor girl was terrified, and seeing her panic, I resumed speaking in Spanish. Of all the scientific staff that I recruited throughout my career she was the brightest and best; her degree was in biochemistry and pharmacy from the University of Santa Maria in Arequipa, usually referred to as *La Catolica*, a private Catholic university with a good reputation; she quickly made her mark. I decided that she should be our first laboratory technician to receive training in Britain. Roxana was unwilling to travel so far from her children. Lita soon passed the English test required for entry for a postgraduate course. A colleague suggested that she should study for the masters degree in microbiology at the Royal Veterinary College in London, where she performed outstandingly well.

Before leaving for Britain she married Alejandro Pino Figuera and what a wedding it was. The service took place in the evening at the *parroquia* of Lambramani in the church San Juan de la Cruz and almost all the laboratory staff were there (Plates 15 & 16). The reception was held in her parents' home, but before it took place the newlyweds did the customary drive round the town.

The wedding of Lita and Alejandro

I had had a hard day and was sitting in the reception waiting for the happy couple to join us and was sipping an Arequepeña beer and I must have fallen asleep or daydreamed that I was back getting ready for my wedding. We did not want to be late and so left in good time to drive across London to Crouch End; my best man, Richard Crouch, drove me and we arrived about an hour before the ceremony was due. All churches have a pub nearby and so dressed in our morning coats we went in for a beer; the drinkers must have guessed we were going to a wedding.

| Stanley and | Liz Creegan, Patricia Apergis, R & M, |
| Cissie Windsor | Richard Crouch, Susan Apergis |

We were in our appointed places in good time when a radiant Maxine arrived on the arm of her proud father with his military moustache precisely clipped and his bow tie neatly tied. My parents viewed the proceedings with bittersweet feelings: they loved Maxine and were delighted that we were getting married, but not happy that we were immediately flying off to live in Kenya. A moving service followed and in what seemed like no time I was walking my young bride down the aisle. The reception at Heathcroft in Hampstead again went by in a flash but was marred by Maxine being given a glass of sweet champagne instead of *brut*, which brought on an attack of asthma.

Having donned our 'going-away' clothes, I was about to assist Maxine into the car when I was lifted off the ground by a mixed group of Bancroftians and vets, and held head-high while I was paraded round the garden. We said

Going away in style!

our farewells and went off to the Russell Hotel. To prepare ourselves for our life in Kenya, I had booked seats for the South African musical *Wait a Minim*, which was enormous fun. The vinyl record of the show was banned in Kenya until the show itself was banned in South Africa. After the show and a light snack we drove to Tom and Jenny Auber's flat in Swiss Cottage as they were hosting a party for all Bancroftian and vet friends and so it was a good opportunity to say goodbye as we would be away for two years. Little did I know what they had done to the car while we were at the party.

Our honeymoon was in Ottery St Mary in the hotel owned by my father's close friend Bela Ullman and his wife, Audrey. Our stay in the hotel was their wedding present to us. Bela was a Hungarian orphan who had been brought up in a Belgian orphanage. He became a merchant seaman and transferred to a British company at the start of the Second World War and captained ships on the trans-Atlantic convoys. At the end of the war he was granted British nationality by a grateful government. With his wife, Audrey, he began a travel agency with little more than a telephone, a typewriter and great energy. With the expanding economy of the fifties and the increasing freedom of travel, the business flourished and I often worked for Fourways Travel during the school holidays, and even took parties to and fro across the Channel and the North Sea. Both Bela and Audrey were without family, and just before I went to university, Bela asked me to come to his office. He suggested that I give up going to veterinary school and join him in Fourways.

"As you know, I have no children and Audrey and I have no family at all;

your father befriended me and we have been close for many years and so if you come and work for me now, the business will be yours."

I turned down a fortune because I had always wanted to be a vet: I have never regretted the decision. Within a couple of years he had sold Fourways to Global Travel and retired to the hotel in Ottery St Mary.

It was on the Kingston Bypass that I found out what had been done to the car: a mile or two from the hotel the car developed a fishy smell which got worse and worse and I had to stop to allow Maxine to get out of the car and vomit. I lifted the bonnet and found that the contents of a tin of salmon had been liberally smeared across the engine and was in the process of burning itself off. There was nothing to be done but drive on with the windows wide open. By Basingstoke the smell had dissipated and later I was beginning to think about the glass of champagne that awaited me in Devon, when a sharp dig of Maxine's elbow into my ribs brought me back to the present day.

The bride and groom had arrived; usually the post-ceremony trip is to the old schools of bride and groom, but not Lita; she and Alejandro visited the *Mirador* in Yanahuara, a well-known beauty spot adjacent to the elegant Yanahuara Church with its magnificent *sillar* facade. Being high on the hill, the *Mirador* has a wonderful view across the city and the Rio Chili. After a splendid dinner, there was dancing for the young but Maxine and I said our farewells, thanked our hosts and returned home.

Lita set off for England in October 1989, and spent a few months in Norwich perfecting her English. She then went to the Central Veterinary Laboratory in Weybridge for a six-month internship taking in the BTEC Certificate of Achievement at the North East Surrey College of Technology at the same time. Finally she went off to the Royal Veterinary College in London, where she graduated with the degree Master of Science in Veterinary Microbiology, with distinction. To this day there is the only one other person (my daughter Claire) I have ever heard of who was awarded such an honour. The director of the course, Professor John Smith, informed me that she was the best student he had ever had, and he offered her a place to study veterinary medicine in the Royal Veterinary College; but Lita wanted to return to Perú and Alejandro; she declined.

During her time in England, Alejandro wanted to visit Lita. I helped him apply for his visa: he was a pharmacist and had a good job in Arequipa, but when he arrived at immigration at Heathrow he was taken away for questioning and one of the questions he was asked was what would he do were he to be offered a job in Britain; with a young wife in the country for two years what was he to say? Of course, he replied that he would accept it, and that was that: the iron curtain descended, Alejandro was refused entry and made a prohibited immigrant. He had no such difficulty in entering Belgium. Alejandro was a man to grasp opportunities and while in Belgium he found that the University of Liège were offering free classes in pharmaceutical studies and he enrolled; this resulted in the university offering him finance to study for a masters degree in the subject. Lita had to travel to Belgium to see her husband. Later she and Alejandro left Perú to work in the United States. Many years later just after she had obtained her doctorate, Lita wrote to me:

'I have good memories of my time in LABVETSUR. We were a nice, small team. And, of course, thanks to you and the project I studied in England, which was the best experience of my life.'

It is such a pity that the British Government has drastically reduced the number of British staff they employ in international projects; it is so much cheaper to train people using the Internet and money is no longer spent in large amounts on bilateral aid because it is channelled through the European Union. Most aid students who study in Britain return home with fond memories of their stay, and so 'think British', which is to the benefit of our country.

Héctor Begazo Succla was the next to request a place with us: he was a delightful young man full of bright ideas and enthusiasm. His father was a successful farmer in the La Joya irrigation and Héctor was in the final year of the Ica Veterinary School course. No sooner had Héctor started work than he arrived at the laboratory in a brand new Toyota Hi-Lux truck. When asked about his good fortune he explained that his father had sold a hectare of new-crop onions and the profit had been sufficient to buy his son a truck – the benefit of being the first to market with a new-season crop.

The next man to join the team was Edilberto Apaza Ccapa who turned up one day looking for a job as a driver; there was something about the man that struck a chord with me, he seemed so decent. We employed him as a driver and he was a gem, not just as a driver, but as a resourceful person who was prepared to do anything on a field trip. The ODA had agreed to pay the salary for a driver to look after their investment in the Land Rover! In my final assessment of Edilberto for my successor, I described him as 'hard-working, conscientious, intelligent and enthusiastic... He is a man of many talents: electrician, painter, plumber, carpenter'. He was also infuriating in his lack of ambition: he resisted all attempts to train him in car repair or maintenance. He was content with his life, his family, his job and seemingly with the low salary that he received. He just got on with the job. He was to prove invaluable with the *Brucella* field testing as not only was he a safe, careful driver but also a useful extra pair of hands with the work, and he kept the Land Rover in immaculate condition, forever washing and polishing.

More and more young Peruvians were applying to be *practicantes* and hoped to progress to a job: there was Fany, Claudia Choque and dear Percy Zambrano Chire, perhaps not the world's greatest intellect, but a good, solid, practical man with a great sense of humour, who could be called upon to raise your spirits, however down you felt. Percy was from an Andino farming family and had studied veterinary medicine at the young Puno vet school. He came to us as a *practicante* to write his thesis on mastitis control. No task was too difficult for Percy and he could always be relied upon to assist; this coupled with his enthusiasm for work, together with his humour, made him a very popular figure. Already married, Percy needed to find a job as he was building a house and wanted to start a family. Soon after he was employed by us as a vet, all the staff were invited to his 'house' for a party. At that time the house was only a concrete floor and a couple of walls, but as always the weather was kind. There was delicious food, beer and wine and music on a portable record player to dance to and the party went with a swing. Peruvians love parties and they can always find an excuse for one; it was a valuable tool in team building, and Maxine and I always joined in.

One of the problems for the bacteriology section was obtaining sheep blood to make the blood agar for bacterial isolation. Sheep blood was not easy to come by in Arequipa and we often had to make do with cattle blood. Hearing of our plight, Percy's father donated an old ram to us, which solved our problems. The staff immediately christened the animal 'Percy' and he was a regular donor of blood until we were able to obtain a second pet sheep.

Once we had sorted out the problems of sample collection for brucellosis, it was time to take the team to the more distant locations, where it would be necessary to carry out the laboratory work in the Leche Gloria plant. The plants at Mollendo, Moquegua, Tacna and Pampacolca necessitated overnight stays and so the team of four, a vet, two lab technicians and Edilberto, would set off the evening before to arrive at the plant in time to set up the testing equipment which we carried. We then adjourned to the hotel where we were booked for the night, for a convivial evening although it was 'early bed' so that we were ready to start work at 6:30 in the morning. Despite the disruption to their work, the staff at the Leche Gloria plants were invariably helpful and friendly, which made our work that much easier. The further from the cities, the worse the quality of the milk, and I sometimes wondered if the farmers realised that they were producing food. Some of the items that came out of the *porongos* along with the milk had to be seen to be believed: items of clothing were not uncommon but the two strangest items were a plimsoll minus its lace and an old-fashioned alarm clock with the pair of bells sitting on the top. I was thankful that this milk was going to be sterilised before it went into the tins.

Most visits to the outlying plants were uneventful and the staff were keen to go. Pampacolca up in the Andes was the exception; a team had been investigating a disease problem on a farm in Aplao and Aurora and I took the opportunity to visit the Leche Gloria plant in Pampacolca so that we could find out if there was a hotel in which the team could stay, and where in the plant we could set up the laboratory. It is a very pleasant small Andean town 3000m above sea level and it had a small *Turistas* hotel. The embassy was furious with me for going to this terrorist stronghold and I was instructed not to go again. Despite this problem there was no shortage of volunteers to make the trip. Most visits to the plant were without concern, but on one, a column of *Sendero* entered the plant to find out who the visitors were; luckily Héctor Begazo was in charge and he explained what the work was all about. The leader took Héctor to one side and said to him that they were to do their work well and make sure that what they did was of benefit to the farmers, otherwise…

Everything was settling down, the laboratory now had a regular source of income that had been calculated to pay the basic running costs of the laboratory: salaries, utilities, consumables and stationery. As has been described, a sliding scale of charges had been accepted by my board and so the smallest producers paid the equivalent of one litre of milk for the test, while the biggest producers paid the equivalent of twenty litres for the same test. To my amazement nobody ever complained at the discrepancies in their bills.

Looking after the finances of the laboratory had not turned out to be the problem that I thought. FONGALSUR had their own finance department and a young lady was assigned to keep the books and do the accounts for the laboratory. Eventually Sra Elsa Morán was transferred to the staff of the laboratory but she continued to work in the offices of the co-operative as there was no space for her in LABVETSUR.

The main problem that beset us was rampant inflation, sometimes more than 10% per month! This was caused by the disastrous economic policies of the president, Alan García. Perú is nominally a democracy but in reality it is an elected dictatorship, with the president having seemingly uncontrolled power. This was seen in his attempts to nationalise all the banks at one go, when for a week all banks were closed and it was impossible to obtain money. The owner of the Banco de Credito was so incensed by this action that he gave the bank to the staff who immediately went on strike against the president and refused the government staff access to the premises. Calmer heads prevailed and the threat of nationalisation was withdrawn, the banks reopened and we were able to replenish our cash resources. His next mad attempt was to ban street traders from buying and selling dollars. The banks' charges for changing money were so high that most transactions occurred on the street. Alan García made street trading illegal and money changers were threatened with imprisonment. All that happened was that when we wanted to change dollars into intis, instead of carrying out the transaction in the open we approached the *cambista* in a car, he or she hopped in, and off we went either home or to the laboratory. After several weeks of this madness, García saw the error of his ways and street trading again became legal.

Unless you have lived through it, it is difficult to understand how people can survive; the laboratory almost did not. To give a simple example you could walk into a shop selling saucepans and see row upon row of them on the shelves. Should you ask to buy one, the almost inevitable reply was:

"I am sorry but we do not have any saucepans."

They had them but they did not want to sell! The reason for this was that the government controlled the price of everything, which could only be increased by a diktat at the end of each month: were the shopkeeper to sell the saucepans before the price was increased, he would lose money as it would cost him more to replace the item than what he received for it. This was a mad system that obviously could not continue for too long. Despite fixing our prices in litres of milk and despite the price of milk going up each month, it was never enough, and slowly the price of milk was failing to increase in line with inflation and so the finances of the laboratory were being destroyed.

The crunch came in the middle of our second year, when the laboratory was beginning to be known throughout the south of the country: I had insufficient money to pay the staff their wages. I brought them all into my office and explained the position to the best of my ability, and asked them what we should do. Without exception they all agreed to forgo their wages for that month. Over that really difficult period there were three months (not consecutive) when no wages were paid, and we were forced to go to the board to increase prices and salaries. As the economy of Perú improved, so did the finances of the laboratory and we were able to pay the unpaid wages as well as give them all their monthly increases for inflation. I believe that the staff accepted the situation because their boss was not a Peruvian: they knew I was honest and was not trying to cheat them and it was better for them to do without for a short period than bring about the financial collapse of their employer. This brought home to me the importance of being a team and how much every person meant to that team.

Perhaps the best example of the inflationary problems beset our, by then, honorary consul, Reynaldo (Reggie) Roberts, a prosperous Arequipa businessman who owned a company that imported and sold office machinery and supplies. Reggie had been to Lima and was driving home. Reggie drove fast and was aiming to do the journey overnight when the road would be quiet. He planned to stop just the once in San Juan, the halfway point just off the Pan-American Highway, to fill his tank for the second half of the journey. He set off with a full tank and a full wallet, debit and credit cards were not then in use in Perú and petrol stations would not accept cheques. While Reggie was travelling from Lima to San Juan, the president, Alan García, went on television to announce an increase in the price of petrol from 10 intis to 300 intis per gallon with immediate effect. Reggie stopped to fill his tank to find that he was not carrying enough cash to buy the petrol he needed at the new price. Luckily he had friends in the small coastal town who were able to lend him the money to get him home.

A constant problem was that there were never banknotes of large enough value: when we arrived in Perú the highest denomination note was 1,000 intis, but when we left six years later, the largest was 10,000,000! Another problem was changing money from sterling to intis; this could only be done in a bank and their charges were exorbitant. A money changer on the street was the solution but they would only take dollars. And so there was role reversal: when we lived in Argentina and I worked for the United Nations, I was paid in Argentina in dollars and we had to get dollars out of the country to pay for the school fees. Richard travelled with dollar bills in his shoes or sewn into his jacket. In Perú I worked for the British Government and was paid in sterling in London and so my mother-in-law converted sterling into dollar bills which she sewed into the lining of Richard's jacket for the journey. When we needed intis I would take a hundred-dollar bill and go and visit Cecilia outside the Banco Continental; we ended up always using Cecilia because she was straight with us (and she was quite attractive!). The banks were losing their fat commissions, complained to the President, and that was why Alan García made street money-changing illegal. Government by decree!

The national finances were in a disastrous state and it was said that Perú existed on the illegal dollars produced by the *narco-traficantes* (drug-dealers). I had a wonderful example of this in action during a trip to Cajamarca. I had gone to Cecilia to change some money before I left Arequipa, but when in Lima I realised that I had not changed enough. Andrew Moore, who had taken over as director of the British Council from John England, told me where in Miraflores I could find an honest money-changer and so I went off to change another $200. Before doing any business, as always, I asked the exchange rate.

"*Mil intis por dolar*," said the man.

One thousand intis for a dollar! I could not believe my ears, as the day before Cecilia had only given me 600, and on a daily basis it only went up by ten or twenty intis.

"*Que pasa?*" I asked and the man replied that the truck bringing the dollars to Lima from the jungle had broken down, and the government, desperate for dollars, had to resort to buying them on the street, which had caused the dramatic increase in price. By the time I returned from Cajamarca, the dollar lorry had arrived and the price had fallen back to 640 intis.

The routine work was beginning to develop in the laboratory as the farmers realised that sending samples to us produced economically beneficial results. As the work increased so it became apparent to me that we needed a trained laboratory technician to teach the technical staff, so that I could devote more of my time to teaching my Peruvian veterinary colleagues about the investigation of disease problems in the field. When the project was visited by the ODA adviser, Dr Archie Hunter, I put the suggestion to him that we needed extra British staff to ensure the project had the potential for long-term survival. I needed a chief technician who would assist Roxana and

Lita with maintaining the stores, train the junior staff, and also introduce new techniques. In order to set up veterinary practices in the irrigations a British veterinary surgeon was essential: I had neither the time nor the expertise for such a task. Dr Hunter was in complete agreement and the bureaucrats in London, realising that they had a successful project on their hands, readily gave assent to the two new posts.

John Claxton, a young vet with a distinguished academic record, was appointed as a field veterinary surgeon to set up the practices. Denis Gosden, a senior laboratory technician with years of experience, was offered the second post. I was delighted when Denis arrived to work as chief technician in the laboratory: Denis and I had worked at the Veterinary Research Laboratory in Kabete, Kenya, in the sixties. Denis had been a senior virology technician, involved in vaccine production as well as the virology diagnostic work. While he had not been a close friend, he and his wife, Val, had been part of our social life in Kabete. Unfortunately, Denis had worked too long with viruses and his general laboratory skills were rusty; he never mastered the Spanish language. I think his problems revolved round the health of his wife Val, who was never fit enough to come to Perú and the constant worry about her affected his performance. I could never trust him to get things done properly and so with great personal sorrow, I was unable to recommend the renewal of his contract. In some ways I was sad to see him depart as I do not like to fall out with old friends, but the work of the laboratory had to come first.

In the laboratory in Argentina the locals spoke in Spanish and the expatriates spoke in English, which resulted in mutual distrust, and so with the arrival of British colleagues I made it a rule that only Spanish would be spoken in the laboratory: I wanted one team not two. Denis did do some useful work in Arequipa and was popular with the local staff. His replacement, Alastair Greive, was younger, more dynamic and had greater knowledge of general laboratory work. This was his first time working in South America and he found it very hard working in a foreign language, although his language skills were much better than those of Denis. He was a much happier man once his wife had arrived.

Dr Carrasco had gone back to work as a field vet and I never saw him again. He was replaced by two ministry vets, Dr Carlos Quintana and Dr Omar Barrio de Mendoza, who were as different as chalk from cheese. Dr Quintana was the younger of the two by some fifteen years and was tall, heavily built with a large black moustache and black curly hair. He was full of his own importance and was the only Peruvian that I met who had an exaggerated idea of his own ability. On the other hand, Omar was small, sandy-haired but going grey and thinning in front; he was self-effacing to the point of diffidence; he was also totally reliable and his reports were succinct and to the point. The reports of Dr Quintana were full of long, florid and meaningless prose, and I wasted hours trying to teach him to write a report that the receiver would want to read. I have always believed that vets should be responsible for their own work and that, where possible, the man who carried out the post-mortem examination should be the one to write the report. However, I could never trust that the reports of Dr Quintana would not harm the laboratory and so I read every one before he was allowed to send them out. I developed a technique where I would read his report and then ask him to rewrite it, only half as long; sometimes this had to be repeated on two or more occasions each time reducing the length and floridity. I do not think that he ever realised that I was doing this for his benefit and not for mine.

When we started sending staff to other South American countries for in-house training, Dr Quintana was of the firm belief that he had the greatest 'right' to be sent for training as he was the 'Official Vet' and destined to be the head of the laboratory once they had got rid of me. He did not realise that there was no way that the *Comité de Administración* would appoint him to the post. Being happy to be shot of him for a few months we sent him off to Dr Stela Maciel, head of LIDIAV in Paraguay. However, he left his wife without any money and one evening Miriam came to our house to ask if I could lend her some. We invited her in and tried to calm her down as she was distraught with no money to buy food, and as she came from Puno she had no family to turn to. She was a small, attractive woman in her late twenties, but looking old before her time. I found out the reason: when I drove her home I went into the house to find that they had almost no furniture; the poor things were living in absolute penury but I never found out what caused their poverty. Admittedly, vets were not paid very well but LABVETSUR was paying Dr Quintana a supplement to his government salary and as far as I knew he was neither a drinker nor a gambler. It remained a mystery. Throughout Dr Quintana's stay in Paraguay, I ensured that the LABVETSUR supplement was paid directly to his wife and Maxine and I lent Miriam money to keep her going but I made sure that she signed a note each time we gave her money as I wanted to show Dr Quintana that we had tried to help while he was away.

Even in a foreign land, Dr Quintana could not do what he was asked and as a result he was seriously injured when handling cattle and ended up in hospital in Asunción. Once he was fit to travel he returned to Arequipa but although pronounced able to work he did not return to LABVETSUR. I made several visits to his home but was unable to persuade him to return. Eventually the *Comité de Administración* wrote to him, dispensing with his services; he made no attempt to come back to work. We were in Perú and Dr Quintana had friends in the union, consequently the Ministry of Agriculture took no disciplinary action at all; on the contrary, he was promoted to be head of animal health in the department. Lucho Lozada attempted to set up a meeting with various bodies to get the decision reversed and I had a long conversation on the telephone with Senator Lozada. It was great fun. The appointment of Carlos aroused a storm of opposition within the ministry and there were pamphlets circulated calling for Quintana to be assassinated! It got to such a state that Miriam Quintana came to my office and asked me to help her husband! She was in my office for over an hour and I had to show her all the letters that Carlos had written complaining about me. It was a most odd meeting. At least his promotion meant that he was off my hands. But we were a vet short and had no *practicantes* ready to be employed and so an advertisement was made in the local press and we were inundated with applications. A selection committee of Lucho, Omar, Aurora and me sifted through the applications and we each selected the six we thought best; four of the six were on all four lists, we interviewed those four, we all agreed that Dra Milagro Terán was the best candidate and she was offered the job, which she readily accepted. As I write, she remains on the staff of the laboratory.

A couple of years later we decided that we needed more vets from whom to select my replacement. ODA had agreed to fund two vets for a minimum period of three years and since we wanted the best, we decided that we should make a national search. Andrew Moore, the director of the British Council, agreed to underwrite the costs of the publicity and advertisements were placed in all the national and regional newspapers and Andrew arranged for a board to be set up to make the selection. John Claxton was now working in the La Joya irrigation; he, together with Lucho, helped me draw up a shortlist and six candidates were selected for interview. The board consisted of Andrew as chairman, his office manager and myself. All six were good candidates but two were outstanding and were offered British contracts. Dr Luis Olivera was the older of the two with a degree from San Marcos in Lima; he came from Huancayo in the Central Highlands of Perú and was married with a growing family. Dr Fernando Fernández Fernández, a graduate from Cajamarca, was much younger with a new wife and as yet no children and was working in Chiclayo in the north. Both agreed to accept the contract for three years and move their family to Arequipa. Dr Olivera did not comply with this requirement and regularly went off to Huancayo to visit his family. Both spoke reasonable English and were keen to undertake postgraduate training in Britain. The laboratory was rapidly running out of space and neither Denis Gosden, the chief technician, nor any of the vets had a private office, although FONGALSUR provided them with a sort of common room in which they would read or study. This could only be a short-term solution and I persuaded Lucho that we needed to put on a second storey to the building to provide office accommodation and a common room for all the staff. This was agreed by the FONGALSUR board and within a few weeks we had the 'shack on the roof', which provided office accommodation for vets and the chief technician and a common room for the staff.

The laboratory was also rapidly running out of space not only for staff but for the equipment that was arriving. Despite the economic problems of the country, the work was increasing and the laboratory was paying the majority of its local costs with a decreasing subsidy being required from FONGALSUR. ODA realised what we were doing, and had increased my equipment budget. There was insufficient bench space for all the equipment and work had to be carefully planned so that we were not forever putting one piece of equipment under the bench in order for it to be replaced by another. Although the electronic counter was too delicate to be humped about, all the other equipment required for cell counting in milk had to be removed from the bench if we wished to carry out haematology or biochemical tests on blood. It was time to begin planning for the expansion of the laboratory facilities.

The work was divided up among the vets and we had a daily rota for duty vet and duty technician who were responsible for all the samples that came in on their day, which included ensuring that a report was put out within forty-eight hours. As in all the laboratories where I have worked, there was the regular daily meeting for all vets and technical staff, at which every ongoing case was discussed. Over the years I found that this was one of the best ways of teaching young people how to present their cases. The atmosphere was always friendly, although on some occasions the discussions could become heated. Junior staff were encouraged to speak at these meetings and it was a great way to make them think about what they were doing. Shy or timid speakers were also given space and time to draw their conclusions and make their suggestions.

And the work continued to increase in volume and more and more *practicantes* were on our waiting list. Dra Rosa Perales de Vizcarra was working at the University of San Marcos in Lima when her husband obtained a job running the Nissan workshop for Alfredo Roberts (the brother of the British Consul) in Arequipa. How she managed to arrange it I do not know, but she persuaded the Limeño authorities to allow her to work in Arequipa but retain her job in Lima. Providing that she returned to Lima to give her course of lectures, she was permitted to work with us for the rest of the time.

We knew that we had been accepted when congressmen and senators started asking questions in Parliament and requesting that the Ministry of Agriculture set up a national chain of laboratories along the lines of LABVETSUR.

5

Living in Arequipa

Arequipa is undoubtedly the most beautiful city in which we have lived, with its Spanish grid system of roads, the elegant seventeenth-century *casonas* built of the white *sillar* stone blocks and their grand entrances; once inside there are open courtyards with fountains. In every part of the city there are churches built by the different orders of monks: Jesuits, Franciscans, Benedictines. The grandest building of them all and one of the oldest in post-Columban South America is the Santa Catalina Monastery, now mostly a tourist attraction, but still hosting a convent within its walls. The cathedral occupies one whole side of the Plaza de Armas and the towers smile down on the town hall, facing it across the plaza, in the centre of which is a well-curated garden with benches and a central fountain. The streets lead out from the corners of the plaza, running roughly north-south or east-west; those running west are only two blocks from the Rio Chili, which provides a cool heart to the city. The climate is idyllic: the city lies within the tropics but is 2,500 metres above sea level, and so is never too hot. The sky is blue for 300 days a year and when the sun shines the daytime temperature is in the mid-twenties; in winter, when cloudy, it can be chilly but our house had neither air-conditioning nor heating.

Perú as a country is divided into three distinct geographical zones: *costa*, the coastal desert, *sierra*, the Andes, often rising to over 6,000 metres, and *selva*, the Amazonian jungle. It is a huge country: the jungle province of Loreto is larger than France. Because of the Humboldt Current in the Pacific

Ocean bringing cold water from the Antarctic the air is unable to take water from the ocean and so the only rain in the country comes from the Atlantic Ocean, and has to cross the landmass of South America and the Andes before it can deposit rain on the western slopes of the Andes. And so in Arequipa city it rarely rained and then only in the summer, and on one Christmas Eve it actually snowed, just a light powdering, which soon disappeared. Living at 2,500 metres presented no real problems and we quickly adjusted to the lower level of oxygen in the atmosphere. Being accustomed to this altitude had its benefits when travelling higher in the Andes as we found that heights up to 4,000 metres were no real problem. When working at 4,000 metres I found that I was quickly out of breath, particularly when bending down to examine an animal.

The commercial and industrial heart of the city lies to the east of the river, the smart suburbs, Yanahuara, Cayma and Uchumayo, to the west. Yanahuara has no commercial area but it has its own graceful Plaza de Armas, with a beautiful old church and the *mirador*, which has a wonderful view across the river to the city. Apart from the streets around the central plaza, the place for shopping was in Cayma, a few blocks from our house, in which there were a great variety of stores including a supermarket which sold almost everything you wanted to eat or drink. However, there was a problem: when we moved into our house we did a huge shop to stock up the cupboard, including a case of twenty-four bottles of tonic water to go with my evening gin. When we presented the case to the girl on the checkout, she said,

"Where are the empty bottles?"

We explained that we had only just arrived in the country and that this was our first purchase of tonic. She was adamant.

"Without empty bottles, you cannot purchase full ones!"

No amount of discussion would change her decision. We left without tonic. By then we had met our local vicar, Alan Winstanley, not himself a gin drinker but his wife, Vivien, loved tonic and he gave us six empty tonic bottles which allowed us to buy full ones and so got us started. For several years towards the end of the woeful presidency of Alan García, shopping became more and more difficult. Not only did the president control the price of everything, but goods began to disappear from the shops as imports dried up. There were shortages of bread, rice, coffee, sugar, and, of course, petrol, but strangely there was never a shortage of beer. The shelves of the supermarket finally became bare.

The shortage of sugar did not affect us because the government had made a huge importation of sugar from Cuba, but when it arrived the sacks were left lying outside on the docks and when they came to be moved they were found to be covered with bird excrement. The government decided that the sugar could only be used as animal feed, the whole consignment was purchased by FONGALSUR and we were asked to examine the sugar for contamination. The excrement was brushed off the sack, which was then wiped with a cloth containing a phenolic disinfectant and the sack was opened and the contents examined for sterility. We were unable to find any bacteria or, more importantly, yeasts or fungi. We decided that the sugar was safe to eat and we carried out the ultimate test – the contents were divided among the laboratory staff for feeding trials. No adverse effects were seen and we were able to report to FONGALSUR that their sugar was wholesome and could be used for animal feeding. I purchased two sacks, and took one home; the second was sold in small amounts to the lab staff at cost price. As the shortages mounted we realised that the next item to disappear from the shops would be bread. I phoned Ron Sykes of Vectrol Ltd who was our buying agent in Britain, and the next consignment from him contained a sack of wholemeal flour which was called on the packing list 'animal feedstuffs'. Maxine turned her hand to making bread and she became a master baker...

Arequipa boasted a large thriving covered market set in a former prison, with a great number of stallholders, many selling from their *ciclo* – a barrow with a built-in cycle at the rear, enabling the owner to ride to and from work. One could buy many things in the market that were not available in the shops; these were mostly smuggled in from Chile. You could buy almost any variety of electronic goods, household appliances and personal toiletries that were available in Europe. There was so much contraband that the police had to be involved in the smuggling operation. The market was also a great place to buy fresh food, particularly fruit, vegetables and fish. There were new fruits to be tried: custard apples were the size of a large orange but the flesh inside was pink with large, shiny black seeds scattered throughout. It was good to see passion-fruit again, and their more common cousin, the grenadilla. Mangos in season were a delight, and a new experience was papaya Arequipeña, a fruit the size of a large pear, but similar to a small pawpaw. We bought prickly pears, the rather tasteless fruit of the cactus. There were many different varieties of avocado, the most impressive of which was the variety *huevos de toro*, (bull's testicles!) up to a foot long and weighing more than two pounds! However, its flesh was watery and less flavourful than its waxy cousins. In season, around Christmas, the Vitor melons arrived, which were small, spherical, rough, brown- or yellow-skinned, and to die for: they were the very best melons I have ever eaten and I have never been able to understand why they are unobtainable outside Arequipa. Olives were grown in a village along the Pan-American Highway and were displayed along the sides of the road in huge barrels, and we rarely went through the village without buying some. They were sold unpitted, and yet again I felt that the farmers missed a trick: a little more processing and they could have sold their product at a much higher price.

Back in the market they sold a small freshwater fish called *pejerrey* that could be used like a sprat, but Maxine found a recipe to convert them to rollmops, such delicacies being unheard of in Perú. Apart from the wonderful variety of shellfish on the Peruvian coast, there were some splendid fish in the Pacific Ocean, in particular *corvina* (a fish resembling cod) and *lenguado* (a flat fish which could pass for Dover sole). Beef was bought from the butcher's shop just around the corner and not from the market. Peruvian beef, unlike that from Argentina, had little to recommend it. Because there were no prairies or large-scale cereal production, there were no pastures or feed-lots in southern Perú and most dairy farmers could not be bothered to rear their male calves with the care needed to produce a good product, and so most of the beef sold in the city was from cast-off cows. Lamb came onto the market towards the end of our stay in the country when the offspring of the imported sheep became available. There was one quality pork butcher, of German origin, in the city; his shop was a short walk from our house. The butcher was also the farmer with a large pig farm in the Vitor irrigation. They made sausages, hams and salamis and all were of very high quality. Available chicken was mostly of the boiling fowl variety, as there were no commercial poultry farmers in the south. However, there were several rotisseries in the town and again one was within walking distance of home. These chickens were broilers flown in from Lima or brought in by road from Ica, the main poultry producing area in the country. Camelid meat was not available in the city, and had to be purchased up in the Andes. Until PROLACSUR, the dairy company in Majes, came into production, the fresh milk was undrinkable (but that was part of the reason for my presence in Perú). PROLACSUR produced high-quality UHT milk in the classic Tetrapak; they also produced yoghurt. Before that Maxine had to dilute the Leche Gloria evaporated milk for the morning cereal and the tea. I find evaporated and condensed milk to be almost undrinkable.

Arequipa restaurants were generally excellent with a good range of dishes invariably made from fresh ingredients. The Chinese restaurants or *chifas* as they were called produced tasty food, but it was completely different from that served in restaurants in Europe, and probably unrecognisable from that served in China. Excellent coffee was grown in Perú but that served in almost all restaurants and hotels was almost undrinkable: it tasted like 'Camp' coffee, but then it was made like 'Camp' coffee. The freshly ground beans were stewed to within an inch of their lives, until a thick concentrate was made. This was served cold in a small jug along with a larger jug of tepid water. Serving Nescafé would have been better.

I have mentioned that Perú has serious problems of race and class discrimination and both the embassy and Lucho emphasised how important it was that I should establish myself in Arequipa society: to this end I was given an entertainment allowance, a rare privilege among ODA project leaders. This was why Maxine and I threw cocktail parties, or more correctly Pisco-sour parties, for that was what was invariably served, and all the 'brass' and opinion formers were invited. Being foreign automatically put us in a certain social position, below the Arequipa aristocracy but up there with the big merchants and industrialists, and it was this second tier that we needed to get on our side, the people who would decide whether the laboratory was successful or not.

We gave the very first such party during a school holiday when John and Joan Taylor were visiting with the boys, Mark and Andrew, and our children were home from school. Maxine wanted us out of the house while she and Joan prepared for the party. As my car was not large enough, I drove the Land Rover; John, his two sons and my three children piled in, and off we went to the coast, where we explored the port of Matarani, and the delights of the gritty beach and freezing Pacific Ocean at Mejia. We had lunch in a wonderful *picantería*, where John and I had *frito mixto de mariscos*, washed down with a cold Arequipeña beer, while the young ones had hamburgers. We took our time on the return journey and arrived home to find a furious Maxine, who was concerned that we would not be ready in time to meet the guests:

"Joan and I have been working away all day preparing the canapés and you can't be bothered to get back in time for the children to get ready."

This was our first party and Maxine was concerned that all should go well; and of course it did. Her mood was not helped by the power cut that had already started; luckily the pisco sours had been made and the children were positioned at the gate as, with no electricity, there was no bell to alert the maid. The Windsor lads made excellent butlers as they met and escorted the guests to the house while the Taylor boys passed round the drinks and canapés. The guests arrived and met the embassy man and his wife, and the party went with a swing; between John and me we restricted the consumption of pisco by Richard, Guy, Andrew and Mark. It was amusing to see the tall Anglican vicar towering over a minute Catholic archbishop (Plate 17). Reggie Roberts, the honorary consul, was concerned because he felt it was his duty to host a party for a member of the embassy staff, particularly since he had only just been appointed to the position; however, he relaxed as I explained that John was responsible for running our project and that the whole family were staying with us.

The staff at the embassy definitely fell into two distinct groups, the good guys and the bad ones, and it amazed me how some had managed to gain employment in the diplomatic service. John Shakespeare, the ambassador, and John Taylor were definitely in the former group as were Sra Maureen Chesterton in charge of the passport section and all the Peruvian staff. The man who ran the admin section certainly fell into the second category as he was always trying to make life difficult for me: it was he who decided that our house was too big for my rank and who regularly slowed down the payment of expenses claims, and it was he who sent the electronic counter to Arequipa atop a load of sewer pipes: this story will be told in a later chapter. He also strongly disapproved of a 'project manager' being given a hospitality allowance. Others were just incompetent. Being considered part of the embassy, we were allowed diplomatic privileges and so we put in our order to join the embassy bulk purchase from Peter Justesen, the Danish emporium, and hence we were able to make good the deficiencies of the Arequipa shops. We were also allowed to join the order to Concha y Toro, the Chilean vineyard, where we paid £1.25 a bottle for their fizzy wine, and a pound for their top-of-the-range Casillero del Diablo red wine.

There was a large community of British origin, at the pinnacle of which was the Michell family who owned the prestigious Michell y Compania, which purchased and processed alpaca fibre; the founder, Frank W. Michell, had fought in the First World War and with his gratuity purchased a passage to Matarani, the major port in Arequipa Department, which had developed as a result of the trade in guano. According to his widow, Marjorie, he arrived with a dog, a bicycle and £50, and having cycled up the hill (100kms) to Arequipa, looked about for a way to make a living. Trading alpaca fibre gripped his interest and soon he had a truck that could get him up into the hills to buy from the *campesinos* and he sold the raw fibre to the Stafford Company, which exported alpaca fibre and shipped it off to Britain for processing; such were the origins of what was probably the major alpaca fibre firm in the world. When Michell arrived, Stafford owned the exporting company, and Frank Michell became partner in Stafford's business. He later married Marjorie, the oldest daughter, who had been born in England, while her two sisters Beryl and Claire were born in Perú; when we arrived all three were widows and all three took it upon themselves to introduce us into polite Arequipa society.

Marjorie lived in a large imposing house in Selva Alegre, a suburb of Arequipa just across the river from Yanahuara, where we lived, and her house was across the road from the factory. She had two sons, Michael and Tony, who were totally different. Tony, the extrovert and a bit of a gadfly with a weakness for drink, was nominally the financial director of the company, but it was brother Michael who was the boss and in the time we were in Arequipa he turned Michell's into a large industrial complex, moving the headquarters to Lima in the process. They acquired Pacifico, a company producing fine material for suits, as well as a company producing carpets and, in a real diversification, they obtained the Peruvian franchise for Coca-Cola. Michael was small and slim, always very smartly dressed, quiet and seemingly introverted: he was impossible to get to know. He regularly came to our parties with his beautiful wife, Pilar Olivares, who went into hospital for liposuction: she never came around from the anaesthetic and she remained in a coma for many years until her death.

Michi Searle was a great friend of Marjorie's; they had been friends from schooldays and were inseparable. Michi is the slang word for 'pussycat'; it is also used in Perú for 'bow tie'. Her real name was Mercedes. She was also a widow, with an accountant son who worked for the Michell Co. and moved with them when the headquarters moved to Lima.

Although Charles Ricketts was honorary British Consul when we arrived he was suffering from an illness from which he was not expected to recover. However, he did recover and lived well into his late nineties and was a frequent guest with his second wife at most consular functions. We had little contact with the family. His successor also came from an important Arequipa family, the Roberts. Reynaldo/Reggie's grandfather, William, emigrated from Liverpool in the 1890s and worked with Stafford and Cia., the company which exported alpaca wool. William Roberts married an Arequipeña and became the partner of Stafford, but in the 1920s he left to start his own customs agency in Mollendo. Reggie's father was born in Arequipa in the Calle Merced. Both of Reggie's grandmothers were Peruvian and there was quite a bit of Spanish blood and according to Evelyn, there was probably native Inca blood in their background. Reggie was tall and slim with dark sandy hair and a neatly trimmed military moustache; he was always dressed in suits of different shades of grey or a smartly cut blazer and gleaming shoes. Reggie was a quiet family man; his wife was from North Carolina and as a result, Arequipa and Charlotte became twinned in the 1960s and Evelyn served on the Sister Cities Committee. They had children more or less the same age as ours; their children went to Max Uhle, the German school, but they did not hit it off. Both the Windsors and the Roberts felt it was a shame that our children didn't become friends.

Reggie was a great boon to the project and I was always able to turn to him if we needed material for the laboratory or help with officious bureaucrats. The computer world was beginning to open up and Reggie's office supplies company provided us with all the essentials, even discs and printer ribbons for my Amstrad computer. He had two brothers and three sisters. One brother, Alfredo, as already mentioned, was a businessman in the city with the Nissan concession, and had a large showroom and workshops in the town; he looked after our car. We rarely met the third brother, Willie, who seemingly spent his life as a wildlife biologist. One sister trained as a nurse but had married well and although she lived in Arequipa we only met her on rare occasions; one sister lived in Lima and the third in the USA and we met neither.

Reggie's passion was old cars and in the yard behind his offices he kept his collection, the pride of which was a 1956 Cadillac which he used when taking the British Ambassador around town, but there were another ten or so including a Buick, a Chevrolet, a Mercury, an Austin Healey and several from before the Second World War. All were kept in perfect working condition by his drivers, and I suspect his brother.

Children of various ages belonging to these families were brought to the Posada del Puente or Avenida Lima to be introduced to our children, but apart from Richard dating a few upper-class girls, they did not click. However, Guy and Claire soon made their own friends, mostly from the so-called *mestizo* (mixed race) echelon of Arequipa society, but lovely, warm people. It was with Charlie and Fernando, Rocio, Marisol, and Victoria that they made friends, and with whom they grew up (Plate 18).

The Russells, Dougie and Pam, were very British and yet neither had ever set foot in England; although of British stock they were both born and had grown up in Argentina. Dougie moved to Arequipa to work as an engineer for the railways and was still working with them when we arrived. Pam had secretarial training and had been the secretary to the international consortium that had undertaken the massive Majes irrigation project. They lived in a lovely house in Sachaca, just outside the city, with a large garden which they both carefully tended. It was from them that we obtained some loganberry bushes and our rhubarb plant – a fruit completely unknown to the Peruvians, but both Maxine and I loved it.

Although there was a large number of families of British origin, the number of expatriates in the city was small. In the church there was Alan and Vivien Winstanley, and Alan's curate, Simon, and his wife, Clare; there were also several other Anglican missionary families living in Tacna and Cuzco of British or American origin. Roger Middlebrook and Glyn Smith worked for Inca Tops, the latter had three children similar in age to ours, two girls and a boy; he was separated from his wife and lived with a Peruvian woman. The older daughter, Debbie, was a delightful young lady with blonde hair and she caught Richard's attention and they went out together for a short while. The younger daughter, Annette, had red hair and a temperament to go with it: she was a bit of a hellraiser and was not liked by any of my children. Glyn and Guy hit it off for a while, but basically our children preferred their Peruvian friends (Plate 18).

Like our children, Maxine and I are not socially concerned but as it was important for the laboratory to succeed, we had to rub shoulders with the great and the good. Reggie Roberts suggested that I should join the Arequipa Club, which was reputed to have the best chef in Arequipa. The club was housed in a delightful *sillar* mansion in the centre of the city, not one of the old *casonas* but an early nineteenth-century building with a great deal of wrought iron, and Louis Quinze furniture. Of course the club did not allow women to become members but it had moved sufficiently with the times to allow wives of members to use the club at lunchtime unescorted. The bar was for the men only but ladies could sit in the main reception salon and order a drink from one of the many waiters. They were not allowed to pay as cash did not change hands in the club, but the charges were added to their husband's account. There was a small swimming pool, which again was only for men. At night, ladies had to be escorted in the spacious dining room which was very well used; in order to obtain a table one had to book well in advance. On the first floor there was a billiards room, library and reading rooms. There was a 'waiting list' to join, but because I was a foreigner and supported by the 'British' community I was not long on the waiting list. El Club Arequipa is a very arcane institution with the strangest membership policy that I have ever experienced. Once a member you are always a member, not just for life but for ever: there is a large and growing section of *socios defuntes* – literally, dead members. But it was the place to meet people, and the place to impress visitors to Arequipa. It was in the club that we celebrated Richard's eighteenth birthday (Plate 19) and our farewell party took place. We caused great consternation after a dinner to which we had taken the children and Claire's friend Jackie. We adjourned to the billiards room, which had three tables, but the Windsor family were the only occupants and all three tables were soon in use. After about fifteen minutes a waiter came into the room and asked if he could have a word with me and he took me outside and explained that the ladies were not allowed to play on the tables, but they were able to sit and watch the proceedings.

The New Year Ball, at which all the debutantes were presented, was the highlight of, and marked the end of, the 'Arequipa Season'. This was in the late eighties! And it caused Maxine great mirth: at 10:00pm these exquisitely dressed and beautifully coiffured young ladies processed down the elegant staircase escorted by their fathers and at the bottom they were presented to the president and committee of the club. Maxine had great difficulty in suppressing her mirth as these gorgeous young girls paraded themselves in front of a lot of lecherous old men. I was not allowed to enter Claire in the procession! But it was a good meeting place and a good place to meet the decision-makers in Arequipa. Not the least it kept a good table and a fine wine cellar.

Arequipa offered an extensive cultural life. Several countries had cultural associations in the city, the biggest and best known was the *Instituto Cultural Peruano-Norteamericano*, which regularly offered concerts, theatrical performances, and art and photographic exhibitions. The *Alliance Française*, and the *Instituto Goethe* both offered cultural events; the British Council was noticeable by its absence. By the end of our stay, we had remedied this deficiency by persuading the director in Lima to send artistes to Arequipa: the deal was that there should be no local costs to the council. Maxine was able to arrange free use of venues for concerts and we accommodated the artistes in our house. This was greatly to our benefit as we met so many delightful people, some of whom have remained friends down the years.

Once our luggage arrived and Maxine had her piano, which we put into the 'games room' behind the garage, then she was able to start making contacts in the music world. None of the British community had much to do with the arts world in Arequipa. Graciela de Bedoya, the wife of Eduardo Bedoya, an engineer who had studied on a British Council scholarship in Manchester, was called Gachi and she knew everybody (Plate 14); she ran the 'Cultural', as the *Instituto Cultural Peruana-Norteamericana* was called. This was the American equivalent in Perú of the British Council, and brought art, music and theatre to Arequipa. We learnt that there was a flourishing music scene in the city with not only a symphony orchestra but the Duncker Lavalle School of Music. It was not long before Maxine was enrolled on the staff of the latter and she enjoyed meeting the musicians and teaching the students. At the end of her first month she went into the school to find it deserted, not a soul to be seen. She waited and waited and finally the staff began to appear. It was payday and they had all gone off to the bank to collect their salaries. A distraught Peruvian colleague, ashamed of his country's treatment of an honoured visitor, took Maxine off to the bank; too late, all the money had gone. That of course was the reason why the staff had rushed to the bank. He took Maxine to his own bank and paid her her money. Maxine was worried that he might not get the money back but he assured her it would be all right.

INSTITUTO CULTURAL PERUANO NORTEAMERICANO

PRESENTA

RECITAL DE PIANO
MAXINE WINDSOR

JUEVES 11, 7:00 p.m.

Concert programme

Within weeks there was a steady stream of young musicians wanting lessons or instrumentalists wanting her to accompany them. Several recitals were given in the 'Cultural' where she played music by Bach, Mozart, Beethoven, Schumann, Liszt and Brahms. She was invited by John England, the head of the British Council, to give a concert in Lima. This city was a constant surprise, boasting a cricket club with its own grounds; the clubhouse was used on a Monday night for Scottish country dancing and hosted the annual Burns Supper. The *Teatro Británico* had a long history and was still used by embassy staff for performing their amateur theatricals. Here it was that Maxine played to a packed audience, giving a delightful concert of Schumann's 'Scenes from Childhood', a Beethoven sonata, and some Mozart variations among others.

The distinguished French cellist René Benedetti had been brought to Perú by the *Alliance Française* to play a series of concerts. Each venue had to provide the piano accompanist and a local pianist had been contracted. René arrived the day before the concert in Arequipa and his accompanist was given the music. He took one look at it and decided that he could not play it and so on the morning of the concert, the director of the *Alliance Française* phoned Maxine in great disarray and asked her to help out.

Because of her performing in Botswana with the cellist Ulrich Balke, she had a great knowledge of the cello repertoire and she agreed to accompany René providing she had a veto over what music she played. Most of the pieces she had performed before and after a few runs through, although not up to her high standards, she was able to cope. The highlight of the concert was an unaccompanied piece by Messaien, René's friend, which ended the first half. René was not the only one in tears. It should not have been the last item in the first half, but René was so overcome by the emotion that he needed a break.

When he visited Perú again, René asked Maxine to accompany him in the various cities in which he played and she was duly contracted by the *Alliance Française* to accompany him in Arequipa and Cuzco. In Cuzco they were met by the *Alliance Française* representative, Pierre, who was putting them up in his house. He took them there and showed them one bedroom with a double mattress on the floor, made up. Maxine asked where she was to sleep. Some rapid discussion in French between the two men followed. René had to explain that they were not sleeping together and she was eventually shown a room with no bed in it. A mattress was brought and some bedclothes. The bathroom had a hand basin in it which had no waste outlet pipe, so the first time she used it, she flooded the floor. A bucket was then provided and it was explained that they were only supposed to use the bath. They went to the concert hall to practise, and found an old man on the stage with an open upright piano, lent by Pierre, with its front off. He had only managed to tune the middle section of the piano and said the rest of it was untuneable. Maxine was asked to play only the notes in the middle! They practised, and then he tuned it again. During rehearsal René said he did not feel safe without a lock on his bedroom door, presumably from the numerous men in the house! Also during the rehearsal Maxine had her pages turned by one of these young men but his body odour was so powerful she decided for the performance to manage the pages herself.

During the concert, which was rapturously received by the audience who were more or less starved of classical music, the piano kept going further and further out of tune so Maxine had to cut any piano solo interludes as well as having to leave out all the very high and very low notes!

Maxine had a troubled night as there was no lock on the door and despite jamming a chair under the door knob she was constantly disturbed by noises in the corridor outside her room. Luckily she passed the night unmolested.

The following day it was decided to take the visitor to Perú to the market. Maxine was horrified to find that Pierre not only was toting a revolver but also insisted that René carry one, which he stuck in his waistband. While at the market René said he didn't like carrying it and got Maxine to put it in her shopping bag (which he did not offer to carry). A very tense time and she was very glad to get back to Avenida Lima and safety.

Hans Nelting was a German water engineer who was a fine amateur violinist while his wife, Dagi, played the cello; with Maxine, they played trios and became firm friends. Another family with German roots were the Emmel, Jorst and Mirtha. Jorst, who taught chemistry in the San Agustin University, was a competent pianist but decided that he would take lessons with the English teacher and so began a friendship between the families. Claire Bedoya, Marjorie's sister, introduced Maxine to the Ladies' Circle, which met once a week for afternoon tea and English conversation. Here Maxine met Sonia Hallenbeck, the Peruvian wife of an American engineer working for NASA on the large telescope in Arequipa. They had three sons, the oldest of whom, Charlie, became a good friend of Guy.

Thinking that we would be living out in the wilds, and so that we would not miss out on the latest films, we had purchased a television set and video recorder, the first time for the Windsor family. We found on our arrival that there were more than a dozen cinemas in Arequipa, one of which showed porn films. All screened American and British films, with Spanish subtitles; as a result, they showed the film with the soundtrack turned down so that it was barely audible; frequently it was so low that we had to speak to the manager to ask him to turn up the volume!

Power cuts were a regular feature of life and for many months electricity was rationed in the evening: one night our half of the city had no power between 5:00pm and 9:00pm, and the next day the light went out at 9:00pm and remained off until midnight. Even when we had power the voltage was often very variable and sometimes so low that we could use neither the video player nor the computer. We had to purchase a pair of voltage stabilizers at £500 apiece – one for the computer/printer and one for the video player/ television.

I have written that it rarely rained in Arequipa; not so in the summer of 1989, a year of *el Niño* when in February it rained day after day. After seven days of rain we had a torrential downpour on the Wednesday afternoon. Drainage ditches which had never had water in them filled and those that

85

regularly ran were a torrent. All this water poured down into the Rio Chili, already swollen by days of rain in the sierra. I did not see it; apparently a tidal wave swept down the river causing great upsurges when a drainage ditch emptied its wall of water into the river. The Rio Chili, which normally runs at ten to twelve cubic metres per second, was up to 300. The unfinished Puente Bajo Grau impeded the flow and the river could not carry away this solid wall of water fast enough. It burst its banks and drowned the Barrio Obrero which fronted the Avenida La Marina and at the same time completely destroyed the road, which ran along the side of the river for a kilometre or more. On the river side of the dual carriageway ran a retaining wall which had designs painted on it by the local college of art. Much of that wall went; in places the majority of the road was swept away into the river. All that remained was a channel six to ten metres deep where the road had been. Walls were removed from some houses and others completely collapsed.

Luckily, the disaster occurred in the afternoon. Had it not been so, the death toll would have been hundreds and not two; these were night workers sleeping on the first floor of their house: they were drowned. Trees were uprooted and swept down the river; boulders more than half a ton in weight were carried along like matchsticks and deposited on what had been Ave La Marina. Any car parked on the avenida disappeared, never to be seen again. Several of the statues were overturned and swept away. Houses were filled up to ceiling level with water which, when it drained away, left two metres of mud. Once the flood had subsided, council operations swung into action: bulldozers taking away the mud, people digging the mud from their houses and piling it outside their doors for the diggers to take away, mattresses and blankets were everywhere to be seen hanging on walls to dry, SEDAPAR (the company responsible for infrastructure) had people trying to repair water mains and sewers and despite the despair and loss, the people were all working cheerfully away.

We had thirty-six hours with no electricity, and from that Wednesday, Arequipa was without water and it took more than two weeks for it to be restored. On the day of the flood the Ministry of Agriculture was on strike and the little man who should have shut the gates when the flood started did not do so. As a result of his failure, rocks, mud, stones and sand entered the main canal that supplied the water plant and completely prevented the entrance of water. This canal to the purification centre had to be dug out by hand for several kilometres; it was too shallow and narrow for diggers to be used and that took more than two weeks. Sta Rita Ocoña and several other rivers burst their banks; there was a massive landslide which buried the entire village of Cosos near Aplao and Arequipa was proclaimed a disaster area. The British Government sent £10,000 to buy water purification equipment, blankets and tents.

We had more rain after the flood, but luckily not of the torrential kind, and the river was soon down to flowing at seventy to eighty cubic metres per second. On three nights in succession it rained from five to six in the evening and Avenida Alfonso Ugarte was like a river with water up to a foot deep in places. A week after the flood, I was halfway up the avenida on my way home from work when the Land Rover died. Using the starter I got the vehicle turned round and pointed down the hill and we rolled gently back to FONGALSUR. After half an hour it had still not dried out sufficiently to start and so Maxine had to come and collect me in the Nissan. Of course next morning the Land Rover started perfectly and first time! The staff of LABVETSUR were lucky: Gloria had a borehole of clean water and all the staff were able to take home jerry cans of clean drinking water. Edilberto drove the staff to their houses and so they survived the 'drought'. We were able to use the swimming pool for charging the toilet, but we were unable to shower and so a good wash was required (or a swim in the pool.) Drinking water I brought home from Leche Gloria, but we still boiled it and put it through our water filter.

No sooner had the water been restored, than the outbreak of cholera that had been simmering in the north (brought to Chimbote by sailors from South East Asia) was diagnosed in the city. The rich wives fled to Lima and expatriate staff were given the opportunity to leave town by the embassy. I thought the whole exercise was patent nonsense and none of our staff left. Cholera is a water-borne disease and just boiling all drinking water is sufficient to kill the bacterium, and in addition we filtered the water. Nobody that I knew of developed the disease and soon it had gone. I was delighted at how quickly the authorities eliminated the infection from the country.

Because of our health problems when living in Argentina, which we decided were mostly associated with the drinking water, we boiled and filtered all water that was for drinking. As a result we had few health problems in Arequipa. However, one morning Maxine said that she was not feeling well and thought she was suffering from flu. She spent a couple of days resting but made no progress and so I asked our doctor Pedro Emilio to come and see her: he asked for a urine culture and a blood test, and Percy (still a *practicante*) came round and took a blood sample and I took a urine sample to the lab. I was surprised when the following day we isolated a Streptococcus and more surprised when it was a group B and even more so when it turned out to be *Strep. agalactiae*! This is the classic cause of mastitis in cattle! However, there are several strains that cause upper respiratory tract and urinary tract infections in humans that are unrelated to the cattle strain. I had heard of a case when in Cambridge, where a farmer whose cows were infected with *Strep. agalactiae* had a wife who developed cystitis. Maxine had to take antibiotics for a couple of weeks before she finally threw off the infection. She was certainly laid low by this bug.

6

Different Management, Different Diseases

Some animal diseases are common to all continents and countries while others are specific to climate or management system. Tick-borne disease is prevalent throughout Africa but it is not seen in Perú. Having discussed disease problems with farmers and vets we carried out a few visits to the Arequipa abattoir to see what conditions were to be seen in the dead animals. Our visits proved rather disappointing as we found very few conditions to interest us; the one that really surprised the team was the occasional finding of liver flukes in the livers of cattle and sheep. In such a dry climate with no rivers in the irrigations it was amazing that the snails, which are the intermediate hosts of the liver fluke, could survive, as they require a watery environment. However, on many farms there are small areas that never dry out and it is here that the snail and fluke are able to complete their life cycles. Because the climate is very dry and it almost never rains, it was not surprising that there were few animals showing any signs of lung disease, and not surprisingly, feet conditions were rarely seen.

It soon became apparent that the common diseases were those caused by the farmer! The animals were tethered in the alfalfa fields and were often underfed. Because they were eating alfalfa their protein intake was usually adequate; it was their intake of energy/carbohydrate that was lacking. We tried to persuade the farmer that his animals were very valuable and food cheap, going so far as to use the analogy that they were driving a Rolls Royce or Mercedes Benz and fuelling it with cheap paraffin instead of quality fuel.

Abortions were a regular occurrence but we thought that this was mostly caused by underfeeding, although we knew that there was brucellosis present in every irrigation. By far the most common cause of loss to the farmer was mastitis, usually caused by an appalling technique at milking time. When we made cultures of the milk we isolated the common pathogens that I had seen elsewhere in the world. We also isolated many bacteria that I had not seen before.

Perhaps the strangest case that we had was a farm in the *campiña* that reported a large number of cows affected at the same time; from all samples submitted we isolated a yeast which we did not identify. A visit to the farm was indicated. We sat in the farmer's kitchen while I asked questions about feeding, management and breeding policies, and generally discussed the running of the farm. This farmer was unusual in that he had a milking machine rather than using hands. Within a few minutes of entering the parlour we knew the source of the problem. The farmer used an old hessian sack to clean the udders and printed on the sack in letters 6" high was the word '*AZUCAR*' – he was wiping the udders of his cows with sacks that had contained sugar; it was not surprising that he had a yeast problem: where there is sugar, there are yeasts. Like most farmers that I met in South America there was no appreciation that they were producing a food, and that it should be produced under the best possible hygienic conditions. The general attitude seemed to be that the milk was going to be sterilised and so it did not matter that it was liberally contaminated with bacteria. Something had to be done. The farmer was given detailed instructions about the cleaning of his cows' udders and was informed that if he was going to use cloths then he had to have one cloth for each cow and that it had to be boiled after every milking. Far better would be to use paper towels to wipe the dust off the udder. Unlike Europe or even Argentina, the conditions were so dry that the cows' udders rarely got dirty or muddy and so rarely required washing: all that was required was to wipe off the dust.

It became obvious to us that, without any doubt, mastitis was the major cause of low productivity, but with 10,000 dairy herds it was difficult to know where to begin. What was needed was to identify the good herds and the bad ones and to do this we needed an electronic cell counter. It is possible to count the cells in milk by using the microscope but it is a long and cumbersome process; with an electronic counter it is possible to count the cells in fifty or more samples in an hour. To my amazement, ODA agreed that we could buy one and within a few weeks it had been flown out. The admin section in the embassy contacted me to say that it had arrived and I asked them to get it to us as quickly as possible. Instead of sending it by air they decided that it would be cheaper by road. You can imagine my horror and dismay when a lorry driver arrived in the office to say that he had a parcel for us, and there, tied on top of a load of sewer pipes in an open lorry, was our delicate electronic equipment. We unpacked the parcel, set up the counter and made up the reagents, but to our disappointment it would not work and no amount of jiggering around with the machine enabled us to get any meaningful readings.

It is said that the Lord works in a mysterious way his wonders to perform: our saviour was an Anglican priest based in the Church of the Good Shepherd in Lima, and named, of all things, the Rev. Richard Cross. Richard's father was British and his mother was Peruvian. He had a degree in electronic engineering from Bristol University, and before answering the call, Richard had worked as an X-ray engineer. The embassy agreed to pay his fare to Arequipa and within a couple of hours he had realigned all the parts and the machine was up and running. The electronic particle counter is a fascinating machine which passes a fixed volume of liquid through a tiny nozzle, across which is passed an electric current. Every time a cell passes through the nozzle it breaks the current and this is counted; what is truly wonderful is that you can set the dimensions of the cells you want it to count. If you want it to count the small red blood cells you set the dimensions and the machine only counts those, not the much larger white blood cells. In our case we wanted it to count the cells that were shed from the udder, which were about the same size as white blood cells. The normal healthy mammary gland is constantly shedding cells into the milk but these are very few; however, if the gland is injured from excessive pressure by the milking machine, or infection, then many cells are excreted: in some cases of bovine mastitis up to two million cells per millilitre of milk can be found – pus rather than milk – quite a lot to count by looking down the microscope! It was cell counting that resulted in the dramatic reduction of chronic mastitis in the dairy herds of Britain. The wholesale purchasers of milk set up a system whereby every dairy herd in Britain had its milk examined on a monthly basis, later to be increased to fortnightly. Single results are not significant but over a period of time one can build up a picture of the udder health of the herd. Originally the British baseline was set at 500,000 cells per millilitre of milk and farmers who produced better quality milk were paid a premium. Over time the baseline has been reduced and today farmers producing milk with more than 500,000 cells per millilitre are penalised. I wondered what we would find when we checked the herds of Arequipa.

We soon found out. Before starting any system we had to try out the test with samples collected from the field. We visited a friendly farmer in the *campiña* and sampled all his cows on an individual basis. Before the milk can be tested it has to be 'fixed' to stabilise the cells' size and shape, and so a few drops of formalin are added to the milk. Formalin used to be used in the process of tanning hide to make leather and it does the same to even tiny cells. Fixed milk cannot be used for bacterial cultures because the process kills all the bacteria, so two samples had to be taken, one fresh and one fixed. We were dismayed to find that most of the animals had counts above 500,000 per millilitre and some were well over a million.

Before proceeding further, it was necessary to talk to the three milk purchasers – Leche Gloria and LAIVE based in Arequipa, and PROLACSUR based in Majes. Ing García Calderón was not too bothered about the cell count because they were not using fresh milk but both LAIVE and PROLACSUR were interested as LAIVE used the bulk of the milk for cheese production, and Majes were producing Tetrapak (long-life) milk as well as yoghurts. LAIVE, having fewer suppliers and their plant being less than a mile down the road, were the first to receive our attention. We went along early in the morning and by the same method that we sampled for brucellosis we collected our milk sample from the 150 herds; but on this occasion the milk was poured into two universal bottles, one containing a few drops of formalin to fix the milk, and one that had been sterilised so that we could identify the bacteria present in the milk.

The results of the cell counting were most disappointing. There was not one herd with a count below 500,000 per millilitre, very few with counts between 500,000 and 1 million, and the bulk of the herds had counts between 1 and 2 million cells per millilitre. The bacterial cultures were just as disappointing as we isolated almost every organism in the textbooks and some that were not there: staphylococci and streptococci which are the normal inhabitants of the bovine udder were there, but along with them were all the different bacteria commonly found in bovine faeces, and then a few more! What were we to do? Did we start with the worst-affected farms where the problems might be easier to solve, or the least-affected farms where we could probably make the most rapid improvement? We did neither, but asked Ing José Valledares, the manager of LAIVE, to nominate the farmers who he thought would be the most receptive to our recommendations, and we started with them.

The preliminary work had shown up a major problem: it was probable that every dairy herd in southern Perú was suffering from problems of sub-clinical mastitis associated with poor management and husbandry techniques. In my previous experience, mastitis was primarily associated with the use of the milking machine, but in Arequipa more than 90% of farmers milked by hand. Their technique was atrocious. Most had no milking parlour but hand-milked the cows where they grazed in the field; going from tethered cow to tethered cow. The only advantage of this, that I could see, was that the farmer could see when the cows had eaten all the accessible alfalfa. Udders were not cleaned, hands were not washed before milking commenced and certainly not between cows, and the farmers had no interest in the quality of the milk, only the quantity.

It was way beyond the resources of the project to try and teach 10,000 dairy farmers the basic rules of food hygiene. Leche Gloria were not really interested in improving milk quality because they sterilised what they received and put it into a tin. The two companies that produced unsterilised products, LAIVE and PROLACSUR, were small players in comparison with Leche Gloria, but would need to invest heavily in laboratory facilities including automatic electronic counting machines before they could offer to pay a premium for quality milk. We were unable to offer these companies this facility because we had restricted laboratory space and staff. The best we could do was to try and resolve the problems on a few farms and hope that there would be a 'trickle-down' to other farmers.

Why should a farmer want to spend money improving the quality of his milk if he were to receive the same price for his product as all the others? LABVETSUR could not start offering free visits and examinations without undermining the basic premise of the laboratory and so we fudged it! Since I was being paid by the British Government, I could offer a farmer my services without charge and we could offer the first few farmers the laboratory services for free as a form of advertising. We started the service without many expectations of success and we commenced the long uphill battle to improve the quality of milk production in southern Perú. This work caught Percy's imagination: perhaps it was the thought that it offered him a lifetime of employment sorting out all the herds, but I thought it more likely that

Percy felt he could be of use in helping them improve their production. The problems were so severe and the solutions so basic that a few simple changes often produced dramatic results. Percy had found his niche, and twenty-five years later he is still working away at it!

It seemed to me that the importation of the sheep from New Zealand had resulted in the importation of the bacterium *Clostridium oedematiens,* or at least a strain of the organism unknown to the animals in southern Perú. We witnessed a massive outbreak of deaths in adult cattle and most of the original outbreaks occurred on farms that had purchased some of these sheep. The first outbreak was the most dramatic: John Claxton phoned one Sunday morning to say that a farmer had three dead cows; if he brought them in, would I carry out post-mortem examinations that day?

"I will be there," I said, "and I will ask Edilberto to come and help us."

"I will ask Héctor to come up as well and so we should have sufficient people to get the work done."

The farmer arrived with his three dead Holstein cows and the long and laborious work began. There is no doubt in my mind that the work increases dramatically with the size of the animal. Removing the skin from a fully grown bovine is hard work but no sooner had we got the skin off it was obvious that we were dealing with a clostridial infection, as there were massive subcutaneous haemorrhages and wherever there was fat there was massive bloody oedema containing gas bubbles. It was obvious that the animal had died from an acute infection or a toxaemia caused by the infection. The internal organs were all showing signs of toxaemia and the intestines were dark purple in colour. We made smears from the various organs and using Gram's stain the examination under the microscope showed the tissues to be full of Gram Positive bacilli (dark blue rods). Bacterial cultures from the three animals confirmed that we were dealing with *Clostridium oedematiens,* a well-known cause of gas gangrene conditions in animals called malignant oedema.

We left the carcasses in the post-mortem room to be cleared away the following day, and we all set off for La Joya to see what was happening on the farm. The only change on the farm in the previous few months had been the purchase of a batch of imported sheep, which were kept together with the dairy cattle. Giving a massive dose of penicillin to any animal appearing to be off-colour was the immediate answer, with vaccination being the long-term solution. Our Sunday had been completely written off but at least we knew what the problem was and the farmer could do something to prevent more deaths. This was what LABVETSUR had been set up to do.

Little did we know that this was to be the harbinger of worse things to come, as we confirmed the presence of malignant oedema in the irrigations one by one. There was an amusing spin-off to this diagnosis: when I was attending a farmers' meeting in the Sta Rita irrigation, I received a message that a farmer, Sr Rojas in the Vitor irrigation, wanted to see me and would I call in on my way back to Arequipa? I had diagnosed the infection in Sr Rojas' herd the previous week and he knew what he had to do. Vitor was one of the older schemes and had been going for many years. Sr Rojas lived on his farm, in the farmhouse that he had built himself, with grapevines growing round the front door. I was welcomed like a prodigal son with a huge bear hug and he explained why he needed my presence:

"This afternoon we are going to open a vat of wine and I want you to be *el padrino* [the godfather]."

This was my first experience of being a godfather to anything other than a human, but not the last! Sr Rojas and a couple of his friends led me to the winery, a shed made of a wooden frame but with thatched roof and walls, but with a surprisingly strong-looking padlock on the solid wooden door. The door was opened and I entered, to be taken back 2,000 years: there were stoneware jars standing almost six-foot high around the walls of the shed. They were the type of jars that you see in pictures from the Bible; expanding from a narrow base, the walls of the jar widened out until a foot before the top, where the shoulders, about four-foot in diameter, led to a mouth about eight inches wide which was closed by a cork bung. I noticed that each jar had a number etched into the pottery of the neck, which varied from 1580 to 1595. In my ignorance I assumed that this was the date that the jar had been made; I later realised that it must have been the holding capacity of the jar in litres.

Various incantations were recited by the friends of Sr Rojas while I watched on. Then the vintner removed the bung at the top and inserted a piece of rubber tubing and he then sucked till the wine flowed through the tube and was caught in a jug. As the godfather I was the first to drink and luckily it was a very pleasant wine. Much rustic Peruvian wine is undrinkable – little better than vinegar! – but this was a light, fruity wine that, like an early Beaujolais, would be best drunk cold and soon.

After I had praised the first glass my companions began to indulge. Having to drive back to Arequipa, I restricted myself to the one glass, but two bottles were filled for me to take home. I was informed that, as the godfather, I was entitled to drink as much as I wished until the jar was finished. When I climbed into the Land Rover to commence the journey home the bonnet of the vehicle was liberally doused with the wine by the merry drinkers. Edilberto was never able to completely remove the red stains. Whenever I passed the irrigation for the next few months I would pop in and refill my wine bottles. It was surprisingly good.

The important spin-off from our Sunday of labours was an incinerator. On the Monday, the lads spent hours digging holes to bury the carcasses. With an ever-increasing workload it was necessary that we had a better system of carcass disposal than burial. I asked Lucho to write to the ambassador to inform him of the burials that were turning the FONGALSUR grounds into a graveyard, and to ask the British Government to provide an incinerator; the cost of even a small incinerator would take more than my entire budget. Because of the ground water situation we were unable to use the 'long-drop' method of disposal that I had used in Kenya and Argentina, in which a deep hole is dug into the ground and a platform with a lockable door controls the entry. Our neighbour Leche Gloria relied on wells on their land for the milk plant and we did not want to contaminate them. Lucho and in turn the ambassador obliged, and without demur, ODA agreed to provide us with an incinerator. The arrival of which is another story, some time and several chapters later in the book.

As the number of cases of malignant oedema increased there was a rising demand for a vaccine, and clostridial vaccines were unobtainable in Perú. One morning I was visited by the chairman of AUTODEMA, the organisation that controlled the new Majes irrigation, and a member of the laboratory board. He was a worried man because farmer after farmer was reporting deaths from the 'new' clostridial disease that was sweeping the south of Perú.

"Dr Windsor, you must get for us a vaccine," he implored. I agreed to do all that I could to help but pointed out that importing such vaccines would require an import licence from the Ministry of Agriculture, which could take months to obtain.

"You can import the vaccine in the diplomatic bag and no one will know…"

My first course of action was to discuss the matter with Lucho, whose immediate reaction was that this could be an additional source of income for the laboratory. It made sense for us to become a provider of drugs and vaccines since we would guarantee to the farmer the quality of the products we sold. I phoned John in the embassy to see what he thought of bringing the vaccine in via the project, despite the fact that they were for resale.

"You charge for carrying out laboratory tests and so there can be no problem about charging for the vaccines." Dear old John, he always took the practical approach and so I phoned Ron Sykes and within days a vaccine containing *Clostridium oedematiens, septicum* and *chauvoei* strains among others was on its way. There was a huge demand for the vaccine but our supplies were equal to it. Of course the story leaked out and I received a phone call from Lima requesting me to attend a meeting in the Ministry of Agriculture.

I flew down to Lima on the Thursday before the meeting next day and stayed with the Taylors. John and I discussed tactics for the following morning. John considered it better for me to go alone, with the knowledge that I had complete support from the embassy.

"Don't forget that in the agreement between the embassy and the Peruvian Government, the main object was that the laboratory had to be self-financing. You can drive home this point, and don't forget that all the products you import come in under that agreement."

I set off for the ministry the following morning and my first appointment was with the man in charge of licensing biological imports. He went into great detail about the requirements for imports and could not have been nicer or more helpful. We spent a couple of hours going through all the regulations and sorting out what we should have done in the past and had to do to sort things out.

I then went down to the Animal Health Department to talk to Dr José Diaz del Olmo, the brother of Dr José Diaz del Olmo of FONGALSUR; one is José-Luis and the other is José-Fernando! I told them that we had imported the vaccines at the request of the government body – AUTODEMA. We brought them in via the embassy because they were urgently required. We subsequently had applied to obtain an import permit; almost a year had passed and we had still not received permission. Dr Diaz del Olmo informed me that the ministry had decided that the vaccine had to be destroyed.

"Why?" I asked.

"Because there is no evidence that the disease occurs in Perú."

This was red rag to a bull, since I had made the diagnosis and all my colleagues in the laboratory had been involved with the work. The disease was running wild in the irrigations and they had the gall to tell me that it did not occur. I was furious, and unfortunately lost my temper. I pointed out that if I was wrong and they were right we would lose nothing by vaccinating animals as it was a killed vaccine. No infections would or could be spread. However, if I was right and they were wrong, many animals would die in the irrigations of southern Perú this summer. I blew my top, and told them in no uncertain terms what I thought of people who lived in a country in which 80,000 children had died of starvation in 1989, while they sat on their arses and passed judgement on things of which they knew nothing; while they sat pontificating, children in their country were dying. I was incandescent, but knew I had gone too far and so I stood up, made my farewells and left. Once out of the office I realised what I had done: you must not insult the local authorities and so I went upstairs to bid goodbye to the director, Dr Castillo, who was an old friend from my first days in Perú. I explained to him how I had lost my temper and how I was expecting to be asked to leave the country. While I was with him, Dr José Diaz del Olmo came in to see him, and informed me that they had changed their minds and that they would allow the use of the vaccine. I was not going to be deported!

I needed to be alone and went to a nearby café for a beer and a *cebiche*. After lunch, I went to the Faculty of Veterinary Medicine and there was nobody there – Friday afternoon in early summer. And so I then went to La Molina, the Faculty of Agriculture and again there was nobody there – Friday afternoon in summer. Was it any wonder, I said to myself, that the country is in such a mess when the people had so little loyalty to their work? I contrasted this with the attitude of the staff of LABVETSUR.

I gave up and went to a garden centre and bought some azaleas to take back to Arequipa and returned to the Taylors' house to tell John of my doings. Our authority to import and use the vaccine finally arrived.

We thought that we were seeing a different manifestation of the clostridium story when bullocks died on another farm in La Joya. Post-mortem examination showed massive oedema of the true stomach and upper small intestine together with subcutaneous oedema, but no signs of septicaemia. We were able to rule out clostridial infection but were unable to work out what had happened. The farm was visited as several more animals were going off their food. The famer informed us that he was feeding brewers' grains, which he obtained from the Arequipa brewery, to his bullocks but not to his cows. Moreover, he was not feeding them direct, but converting them to silage by storing them in a large tank sunk into the ground. Brewers' grains are a by-product of beer production and these spent grains are a good source of nutrition for livestock. I asked the farmer why he stored the grains in this way, and he replied:

"I have a contract with the brewery and must collect them each week; just after a batch of animals have gone to the abattoir, I have not the need for so much, but if I do not take them I lose the contract."

My mind flashed back to when I was working in the Cambridge laboratory and a dairy farmer in Essex was doing exactly the same thing, namely turning the brewers' grains into silage to preserve its life. Rats, attracted by the alcohol, had entered his silage pits to enjoy a feed and some had died there. Unfortunately the rats were infected with *Salmonella typhimurium* and they infected the cows; sixty-seven animals died before we could bring the outbreak under control.

I was certain that we had the solution to the problem, not *Salmonella* in this case but a fungal infection with the fungi producing toxins which killed the bullocks. Without a very sophisticated laboratory, which at the time Perú did not possess, demonstration of mycotoxins is well-nigh impossible and so we were unable to confirm our diagnosis. The farmer was advised to stop feeding the grains immediately and to empty the tank completely. I suggested that he should spread the grains on his land and use it as fertiliser: the sun would kill off any fungi. The farmer took our advice and the outbreak as if by magic ceased. He made an arrangement with a neighbour to take his surplus brewers' grains and we had another satisfied customer.

A second outbreak of mycotoxicosis occurred on Lucho's farm in Sta Rita, but on this occasion it was in-calf heifers that were affected. Lucho did not feed brewers' grains but he bought in high-quality hay made from grass which he stored in a shed. Unfortunately, the shed had a large broken window and the hay was stacked against it when there was a heavy downpour of rain, unheard of in coastal Perú. Nobody thought much about it, but the rain had affected all the bales stacked against that window and the moisture was enough to allow the fungi present in the hay to grow and produce their toxins. When the offending bales were fed to the heifers they became ill and died. Lesions similar to those in the bullocks from La Joya were seen and so a visit to Sta Rita ensued. While on the farm I heard about the unexpected shower and the penny dropped:

"Let's have a look at the hay," I said, and we went to the shed; one look at the hay and the problem was solved. I teased open the sides of the bales that had been against the broken window and the evidence was there – the powdery white tell-tale signs of fungal growth, whereas on the side away from the window the hay was still green and sweet-smelling. I recommended that all the bales that had been in contact with the window should be burnt. This was duly carried out and the problem was solved. Another satisfied customer, this time the boss!

When troubles come they seldom come alone and it was only a few weeks after we sorted out the problem in Lucho's dairy herd than we diagnosed TB in the herd of his brother Enrique who farmed in the same irrigation. The Lozada brothers each had a large dairy herd (up to 200 cows) and they wished to set an example to others by using the most modern techniques of management, and to be seen to be in the vanguard in terms of animal health. We were asked to carry out a tuberculin test on Enrique's farm and were very surprised to find at least half of the animals gave positive reactions to the test. The animals all looked fit, so I thought that the results were very suspicious and suggested that we take no action but repeat the test in three months. This was done and again more than half the animals gave a positive reaction, but they were not all the same animals as in the first test. We decided to slaughter a couple of the older animals that had been positive in both tests and Percy and I went along to the abattoir to examine the animals. There were no signs of TB in the carcasses. Then the penny dropped... the cows were infected with the human strain of TB. For some reason the human strain of TB is able to cause an immune reaction in the bovine while at the same time being unable to establish itself; it produces a reaction for only a short time. The infected animals react positively to the TB test and then become negative. By contrast, the bovine strain is capable of establishing itself in the human and causing disease. Older readers will remember having seen people with scars under the angle of the jaws. The bovine strain often established itself in the parotid lymph gland of humans; the glands had to be surgically removed. The infection entered the body when people drank infected milk and this is the reason why the pasteurisation of milk was introduced, to kill the bovine strain of

TB. The avian (bird) strains rarely infect man or cattle but they can and do infect pigs.

The next step was to find the source of the infection as it was obvious that a member of Enrique's staff was infected with the organism and had what the doctors call an 'open case' of the disease, in which they excrete the organism and are able to infect other humans and some animals. Enrique, his family, and all the farm workers were duly taken along to the local hospital for chest X-rays and the Mantoux Test (very similar to the bovine TB test except that only one strain of tuberculin is used; in the bovine test two strains are used – bovine and avian.) One of the farm workers was shown to have the disease; Enrique paid for him to receive a course of treatment and as soon as he returned to good health he was given duties where he did not come into contact with the animals.

Anthrax was not commonly seen in LABVETSUR but we had one case that reminded me very strongly of a case in which I was involved when I was newly qualified and working in general practice in Yorkshire. The manager of the Arequipa abattoir drove up to the laboratory with a plastic bag containing a large bovine spleen. He was concerned that the animal had some disease because the whole carcass was congested. Smears were made from the spleen and stained with a dye called polychrome methylene blue, and when they were examined down the microscope we saw the tell-tale blue bacteria with their pale pink capsules. We had a case of anthrax. The manager was instructed that he had to incinerate the whole carcass – horns, hooves, skin and all. This took me back to that afternoon surgery that I was taking in the practice in Malton, when a young man appeared at the door with a bucket that was dripping blood everywhere. He had come from the abattoir with the bucket in which there was an enormous spleen. We made smears using the same stain, and had shown that the animal was suffering from anthrax, which in Britain is a 'notifiable disease', which meant that we had to phone the local government veterinary officer (DVO). This would have caused the abattoir a great deal of trouble. The worker was instructed to take his bucket and spleen back to the abattoir and my colleague Colin Sutherland followed him with a can of Jeyes Fluid, a phenolic disinfectant, pouring some onto each drop of blood spilled. Colin returned with more smears taken in the abattoir and we were able to report to the DVO that we had diagnosed anthrax in a beast at the abattoir. This was the start of a large outbreak of anthrax that blew up throughout Britain.

The second case in Yorkshire I completely missed: sows were dying on a large pig farm. After examining a few sick animals which had a high fever and massive oedema round the throat, I recommended that the farmer take the two dead ones to the local veterinary investigation centre for them to carry out a post-mortem examination. The Thirsk VI Centre were not at all impressed when having opened up the carcasses they realised that the sows had died from anthrax, which they confirmed by making smears from the fluid around the throat. Pigs do not get a bacteraemia (the organism in the blood) as do most other mammals. The Ministry of Agriculture investigations showed that it was a boat-load of imported barley that was the source of the problem. The barley had become contaminated when it was transported in the hold of a ship that had previously carried raw hides from China; the hold had not been properly disinfected, the barley became contaminated and the outbreak ensued.

The sample submissions were not restricted to cattle, although they formed the bulk of our work: we also received samples from pigs, sheep, goats, camelids, chickens, rabbits, guinea pigs, horses, dogs and cats and even humans. The best restaurant in Arequipa was called *La Choperia* (*chop* is a slang word for local beer usually made from maize in Perú) and a *choperia* is a place where they sell beer. On the main road round the corner from the restaurant and owned by them was a pork butcher, *La Salchicheria Alemana* – The German Sausage Shop – which was owned by a family of German origin with the name Portugal! Their pig farm was in the Vitor irrigation and they kept almost one hundred sows. Sr Portugal was a worried man when Aurora showed him into my office.

"Please sit down," I said. "What can I do for you ?"

"We are probably the largest pig producers in southern Perú," he took a seat, "and for many years we have kept pigs with surprisingly few problems, until the last month or so." He was silent for a moment or two and as I said nothing he went on:

"Recently we have had difficulty in getting the sows in-pig and if we do succeed in getting them pregnant, some of them abort about a month before they are due to farrow; some have farrowed, producing weak pigs that die soon after birth; and I am rather worried."

"The first thing for you to do is to bring us some aborted piglets or dead pigs and we will see if they give us any indication of the cause of the problem."

Over the next few weeks we received several batches of aborted or dead pigs but were unable to make a diagnosis of the cause. I suspected that *Leptospira* species might be involved but the organisms are notoriously difficult to find in pathological material as they cannot survive for long in the dead animal or outside the body. It was obviously necessary to visit the farm; it was the school holidays, my sons were both at home and were happy to join me when we visited the farm. They were each given a plastic beaker and told to watch the sows carefully.

"If you see any sow urinate, try and catch some urine in the beaker," they were instructed. Between them they managed to get two good clean samples. We bled a dozen of the sows that had aborted or produced dead pigs and a further half dozen 'healthy' animals. The management of the pigs left a great deal to be desired; it was the old South American story: the owner did not live on the farm and was only an infrequent visitor. Consequently, standards were not maintained. Having looked at the farm and the losses, I was positive that *Leptospira* was the cause of the problems. There were no stray dogs to act as vectors but there was, as on all farms, something of a problem with rats. If we were lucky our samples might confirm the diagnosis. They did, and using specific antisera we were able to state that *L. pomona* was the problem. However, that came later.

Sr Portugal invited us to lunch at *El Gato Vitoreño* (The Vitor restaurant owned by 'El Gato', a Peruvian with blue eyes), considered to be the best *picantería* in the department. Fifty miles from the sea and they served the best seafood imaginable. They were so popular that they opened a branch in Arequipa, which we regularly visited. Their *frito mixto de mariscos* (fried shellfish platter) was to die for! We placed our orders and the beers arrived along with a saucer of sliced chillies. Guy pounced and was just about to eat a slice when Sr Portugal intervened rapidly.

"We do not eat the membrane or the seeds," he said, and demonstrated how they were removed before the appetiser was eaten. "These parts are much too hot and will burn your mouth."

Such words were a red rag to a bull for a fourteen-year-old lad and with a flourish, Guy popped the whole slice into his mouth and chewed. His face was a picture as it grimaced and contorted and his eyes ran with tears. But he said nothing and chewed until he swallowed it all, without saying a word or rapidly taking a swig from his Coke. I was impressed, but noticed that he did not take another slice. The wonderful dishes arrived and we set to with a will.

We recommended that Sr Portugal treat all his pigs with the antibiotic streptomycin, which is particularly good for the control of leptospiras, and suggested that if this did not work then he should consider vaccinating the herd. We had the specific fluorescent antibody for *L. pomona* and we were able to show that that was the problem. The treatment worked and it was not necessary to vaccinate the herd. However, ever after we received excellent service at *La Choperia* and when we left Perú they gave us the recipe for their wonderful *aguadito de mariscos* (shellfish soup) that still regularly graces our dining table.

There was a very different pig farm on the El Cural irrigation just outside the city. The pig unit was quite the most extraordinary that I have seen; it consisted of one building about five yards wide and a hundred yards long and set on the side of a hill above a sheer drop into a tributary of the Rio Chile. If there is a serious earthquake, pigs and buildings will disappear into space! All of the life cycle went on in this one building: service, pregnancy, maternity, weaning and fattening. Were this to be tried in Britain there would be a massive build-up of respiratory pathogens; as it was, there was a problem of neonatal diarrhoea. The management was excellent, quite the best I have seen in Arequipa; had it not been, their problems could have been very severe. The purpose of our visit was to advise them on the problems of joint abscesses and the diarrhoea in the baby pigs. The joint abscesses were associated with the concrete used for the floor: straw is almost unobtainable in Perú and using rubber mats was hardly practicable for piglets as they would almost certainly eat them. We partially solved the problem by using sheets of hardboard in the pens for the unweaned piglets. The boards were to be removed between litters and sterilised by the Arequipa sun. The only way we could stop the diarrhoea was by adding antibiotics to the food for the piglets.

The keeping of Angora rabbits for their fibre commenced during the life of the project and developed into a popular business, as their fibre made excellent stuffing for airline seats, being soft and very light. Along with Angora rabbits came Angora rabbit diseases and within a year the number of submissions from these animals increased twentyfold. It was an easy industry to enter as, for a few hundred dollars, it was possible to set up in business, and within a year it started to produce returns. There are two methods to harvest the fibre, shearing and plucking; in Arequipa it was the latter method that was used. When I saw how they did it I was horrified; the front legs are tied together as are the hind legs and the animal is stretched out on a board. Using a blunt edge like that of a ruler, the hair is pulled out of the skin until only the hairs on the head and lower limbs remain. Surprisingly the animals seemed little affected by this ordeal and were soon back eating. Since we had no idea of how else the fibre could be harvested, there was nothing we could do.

The greater the number of animals in a given space, the greater the opportunity for pathogens to multiply and diseases to appear. Because of its wonderful climate, warm, dry and sunny, livestock in Arequipa rarely suffered from respiratory disease; not so the rabbits. They were kept indoors, often in dark and ill-ventilated buildings, and so we saw pneumonia on a regular basis. They were kept in overcrowded conditions in hutches that were not adequately cleaned and so we saw diarrhoeas and the dreaded mucoid enteritis. When the craze for keeping these creatures extended to the local people, the Collaguas, in the Colca Valley, we saw rabbits dying from altitude sickness when they were brought too rapidly from the coast to 3,500 metres. I did not see a long-term future for the rabbit industry in Arequipa as I was certain that they would not be able to compete with the large producers in China, where one farm could produce more fibre than that produced by all the Arequipeños together. But while it lasted the animals suffered at the hands of people trying to make a quick dollar.

There were not many goats in Arequipa and the only large herd that we knew of was kept by the father of a friend of my daughter Claire. Victoria phoned me in the laboratory one day and in a worried voice she said:

"Dr Windsor, can you please come down to Mollendo immediately as my father's goats are dying."

"Hold on a minute, Victoria," I said, "before visiting a farm we need to have some idea of the problem. Please ask your father to bring a couple of dead animals to the laboratory and if it is necessary, of course I will visit the farm."

The following day Sr Leyva arrived at the laboratory with two dead nanny goats and both showed the same lesions, namely severe jaundice and massive cirrhosis of the liver. Neither showed evidence of hypersensitivity to sunlight, so commonly seen in animals with serious liver problems. I had no idea what the problem was and neither had my Peruvian colleagues, but we agreed that it was likely to be a poison of some sort, and this diagnosis became more of a certainty when Sr Leyva informed us that his goats grazed along the seashore.

A visit to Mollendo was arranged and Edilberto drove Milagro and me to the coast, where we met a worried Sr Leyva, who had three more dead nannies. One look at the membranes in the eyes showed by their tell-tale yellow that they too had succumbed to the same disease as their predecessors. Before disturbing the live goats, we sat in the Land Rover and watched them grazing on the foreshore. There did not seem to be much grass for them to eat but they seemed to be tucking in to the one plant present in great profusion, which was a low-growing plant with circular, rich green leaves. I had no idea what it was, but the goats were eating away at it. We found the leaves in the rumens of the dead goats and we took samples, which were identified by the biology department of the University of San Agustin as *Heliotropium aerosovicus*. Although we were unable to confirm the liver lesions by histopathological examination, I was certain that it was the cause of the problem. A close relative of the plant *Heliotropium europium* is known to cause severe liver lesions in sheep and goats in Europe, Africa and Australia. It seemed likely that this species was equally toxic. The animals had to be moved away from the shore and the poisonous plants. We advised Sr Leyva to find his animals some proper grazing, supplement their diet with alfalfa hay and inject them all with a vitamin B complex to boost their liver function. This solved the problem and Claire had a very happy friend.

There were many excellent rotisseries in the city, and on the nights when we had no electricity it was often easier to walk up the road and get an excellent chicken and chips, which came with its little bag of spicy sauce, than cook on the camping-gas stove. There were no poultry producers in Arequipa and the broilers had to be flown in from Lima or brought by road from Ica. Attempts to set up broiler farms in the region had all ended in disaster as it seemed almost every arrival of day-old chicks from Lima brought its own consignment of *Salmonella gallinarum*, the organism that causes fowl typhoid in birds of all ages, or *Salmonella pullorum*, which causes bacillary white diarrhoea (Pullorum disease) in young birds. It did not matter which: if the birds were treated with the right antibiotic they recovered, but they never performed as they should and so the enterprise was uneconomic. Potential poultry farmers were never able to source a supply of clean, healthy, infection-free birds and so the enterprise foundered. The whole time I was in Arequipa, the rotisseries depended upon imported birds.

The fame of the laboratory was spreading far and wide and before long we had doctors from the local hospitals asking if we could provide them with some laboratory services. After discussing the matter with Lucho and the board, we decided that it would be very good publicity for the laboratory and it would be even better if we provided the services without charge. This we did. We received many different types of sample from the doctors in the different hospitals: blood, faeces, urine and pus among others. I was amazed at the frequency with which we diagnosed *Ascaris* (roundworm) infection in faecal samples: it was obvious that there were problems with the sanitation in the *pueblos jóvenes* round the city.

One morning Dr Amalfi Gallegos from the public hospital Honorio Delgado came to see me and Aurora showed him into my office.

"What can I do for you?" I said rising from my seat. "Please sit down and tell me how we can help. Aurora, please could you bring Dr Gallegos a coffee? What's the problem?"

"My patient is a six-month-old baby with meningitis, and she is not responding to the usual treatment. I have taken a sample of cerebrospinal fluid and I would be most grateful if you could find out the organism causing the trouble and perform an antibiotic sensitivity test to give us some idea what drugs we should be using."

"That will be no trouble. By tomorrow we should have some idea what is causing the problem and in a couple of days we will have a sensitivity test result for you; although it might take longer to determine the identity of the offending organism."

Dr Gallegos was keen to find out exactly what the laboratory could do to help the doctors in the town and then the conversation turned to health in the city and how I was enjoying my stay in Arequipa.

On direct plating we isolated a *Salmonella* species and within forty-eight hours Dr Gallegos had the results of the sensitivity test. The identification of the organism took more than a fortnight. We had decided at the start that for reasons of economy we would not purchase the specific antisera for all *Salmonellae* but just enough to enable us to put the organism into a definite group; this organism belonged to group D, the 'enteriditis group'. Today the classification of *Salmonellae* is all changed but I have not changed with it and so the old-fashioned classification will be used. We sent the organism to the Public Health Laboratory in Colindale, England, who confirmed that it was indeed *S. enteriditis*. We were informed by Colindale that they were not really supposed to examine samples from overseas and so would we send no more.

It was not long before we received from Dr Gallegos another sample of cerebrospinal fluid from another patient with meningitis, this time an adult, but on this occasion we isolated a group B *Salmonella*. I packed it up and sent it to my old college friend Dr Clifford Wray who headed the Salmonella section at the Central Veterinary Laboratory in Weybridge, Surrey, England. The blast came by telephone.

"This is Cliff Wray speaking. Roger, what on earth are you up to?"

"Why? What is the matter?"

"Do you realise what you sent us?"

"Yes, it was a Group B *Salmonella* species."

"You're damn right it was a bloody Group B, it was *Salmonella typhi*, the cause of typhoid fever in man."

"But it was from a case of meningitis."

"I do not care if it was from a sore big toe, it was *S. typhi,* and *S. typhi* is a Group A pathogen and our laboratory is not registered to deal with such organisms. The shit really hit the fan when I informed the director [Dr Tony Little, who was also a classmate] what had happened and we have had the inspectors crawling all over the lab and staff for the past few days."

"I am most frightfully sorry," I said, "I had no idea that *S. typhi* could cause meningitis, and the last time we isolated an organism from spinal fluid it was *S. enteriditis*. I had no idea and we do not have the money to buy all the sera to identify them."

"Well, the next time you are home come in and see me and I will slip you the sera to prevent this happening again."

"Thanks so much, and my sincere apologies again. Do tell Tony that I am frightfully sorry."

And there the matter rested, but it was a most embarrassing incident; however, the patient recovered and there was no epidemic of typhoid in the city.

Sadly, both Cliff Wray and Tony Little are now dead, and they both were killed by prostate cancer. Both were microbiologists and had spent much of their professional lives working in the Central Veterinary Laboratory in Weybridge. Cliff was the pure academic and spent all his time working on *Salmonellae*. Tony was much more of a politician, and he led the 'strike' of workers which resulted in their receiving 'inner-London weighting'. This was a brilliant strike in that the workers carried on working, examining samples from sick animals and reporting the results to the vets, so that animals did not suffer. However, they refused to charge for the work they had done and so only the employer suffered; which is surely the point. This could be followed by other industries such as the rail industry, when the trains would run normally but the passengers would travel for free!

Together with John Gallagher, Tony had shown the important role that badgers played in the life cycle of bovine tuberculosis. When they made their important discovery, bovine TB was only present in cattle in Gloucestershire and Cornwall. The whole problem was completely mishandled by the Ministry of Agriculture and the 'badger lobby', instead of coming on board, were antagonised. As a result, bovine TB is now present in all the western counties of England, the whole of Wales and is moving into Scotland. The present system of shooting badgers will not work. The only way we shall obtain populations of healthy badger and healthy cattle is to eliminate infected setts by gassing them and then sealing them to prevent recolonisation by healthy badgers. The massive increase in the badger population is also responsible for the demise of the hedgehog as badgers enjoy eating them, spines and all. Tony went on to become the director of the CVL and was awarded the CBE for his efforts. It would be a great legacy for Tony were the badger lobby to come on board and assist in achieving a TB-free Britain.

Why is it that the military consider themselves above the law? We saw this in action in Arequipa when the army imported half a dozen horses from Brazil. They were flown into Arequipa Airport from somewhere in the Pantanal and the objections of the Ministry of Agriculture staff were ignored. We knew nothing of this until an army major came to the laboratory to report that some of the imported horses were off-colour and could we go and examine them. A round-table discussion was held in my office and Percy and a laboratory technician went off to examine the horses and take samples. Three of the six animals had a mild fever and were very depressed and some had haemorrhages in the skin of the mouth. Percy took blood samples for haematology and serology, and by using the Coggins Test we were able to demonstrate that the horses had brought equine infectious anaemia into the country with them. Fortunately, as this is an insect-borne disease, it was unlikely to be of great significance in the dry Arequipa climate, where there were very few biting insects. None died and all soon recovered but the Ministry of Agriculture were able to obtain a great propaganda victory, pointing out that had they been consulted they could have advised on testing the animals before they were purchased. An interesting aside to the Coggins Test is that when we first worked in Kenya, Maxine was secretary to Leroy Coggins who developed the test and was working in Muguga at the time, and she even partnered him at tennis!

What surprised me was how few small animal samples we received, but then the people did not really keep pets. We were unusual in that we had a dog and our beloved tortoiseshell cat. From the time we lived in Cambridgeshire our home has always been completed by a tortoiseshell cat, but we had difficulty in finding one in Arequipa until we came across a little old widow who lived near us and supplemented her probably meagre pension by growing and selling garden plants. When we moved into our house it had neat and tidy gardens at front and back, but they were neither exciting nor colourful until we met Sra Gata (Mrs Cat). We called her that because, unlike most Peruvians, she adored cats and was surrounded by them. We first visited her to buy plants to brighten up the garden when we saw that she had a young queen with several tortoiseshell kittens. Sra Gata was delighted to find a good home for one, although she charged us for it!

Arequipeños did not keep dogs as pets, they kept guard dogs and many of them spent their entire lives on the roof from where they were supposed to scare interlopers. As most houses had flat roofs it was not too uncomfortable but for those living on pitched roofs life must have been uncomfortable as well as lonely. Rabies was not a serious problem in the country, probably because of the low numbers of domestic dogs; because of the sparse rainfall, there were few feral dogs and cats in the cities. Although the virus was present in vampire bats, unlike their relatives in Argentina, they rarely transmitted rabies to pet animals or cattle.

From time to time we diagnosed mange, both sarcoptic and demodectic, in dogs, but because they rarely mixed, the disease was not common. One fascinating case was when we diagnosed *Microsporum gypseum* causing a type of ringworm in a dog; we were somewhat taken aback when the owner informed us that his son had similar lesions on his arms and we found the same fungus on the son! A course of the same treatment cleared the infection in both dog and boy.

One case involving a pet alpaca is worthy of mention here: Alfredo was owned by the Posada del Puente Hotel and it grazed freely along the river bank; it was always a delight of an evening to sit drinking a cold Arequipeña while watching the sun set. Alfredo would come to the table to greet the patrons, and this led to his undoing as the drinkers shared their beer with the friendly camelid. The problems really started when Alfredo acquired a taste for whisky and the locals thought it great fun to get him drunk. One morning I had a phone call from the manager of the Posada asking me to come and have a look at the alpaca who was behaving strangely. I called in on my way home to lunch and examined the animal, which was unable to stand, and appeared very anaemic, but there were no signs of jaundice; its abdomen was full of fluid. When I heard the history, I decided that cirrhosis was the likely problem and so blood samples were taken to carry out a liver function test. I gave the animal a large dose of B-vitamins and returned later in the afternoon and gave Alfredo intravenous treatment with glucose saline, but the manager phoned the next day to say that the alpaca had died overnight.

Despite the majority of our work being with samples from cattle, we had enough material from other species to make life interesting and to keep us on our toes. In this chapter I have tried to show something of that variety and in the next you will learn of our work with camelids.

7

Snow in the Tropics,
the Andes, the People and their Animals

I was greatly concerned: I could not come to terms with the fact that a British aid project was only working for the benefit of the richer (albeit poor) Peruvian farmers while doing nothing to assist the really poor peasants in the high Andes. Once the laboratory had survived the worst effects of the inflation and our routine work was paying the bills, I thought it was time to see if we could offer our services to the *campesinos*; I was also very keen to work with the camelids, those sort of ruminant animals native to the Andes. According to archaeological evidence they had originated from the forebears of the Bactrian camel that had migrated north and west across the great Asian landmass and crossed the land-bridge into America, where they turned south and east until they reached Florida. The group split into two and half retraced their footsteps back to Asia while the remainder continued their journey south until they found the Andes, where they decided to settle. The larger animals preferred the lower slopes and easier conditions and became identified as *guanacos*, while the smaller, finer-coated animals stayed higher up and were named *vicuña*. It is said that the domesticated llama was bred from the *guanaco* while the alpaca was developed from the *vicuña*. They are all considered to be one species and can interbreed producing fertile offspring. This has caused considerable problems for the breed societies that have recently developed in the USA, Europe and Australia, in trying to decide what is what!

Only sheep produce wool; other animals, including camelids, have hair but where this is very fine it is called fibre. Wool varies from hair in having minute scales on the surface that overlap, which causes them to stick together. Camelid hair has little crimp, much less than a fine sheepswool; Suri alpacas have almost no crimp at all, but it can be very fine, being less than 15μ in diameter (there being 1000 microns in a millimetre) which makes it very valuable. Fibre from *vicuña* and alpacas is said to be the finest while the coats of *guanacos* and llamas are coarser; there is a further problem in that they have coarse guard hairs, which have to be removed before the fleece can be used for spinning and weaving.

The first thing to do was to indicate to the two major exporters of alpaca fibre that we were interested in looking into the husbandry and production of these animals. Michell y Compania was the older of the two and was owned by a family of British origin. They purchased and processed alpaca fibre. As described in Chapter 5 the founder, Frank W. Michell, had fought in World War One and with his gratuity purchased a passage to Matarani; trading alpaca fibre gripped his interest and soon he had a flourishing business buying fibre from the *campesinos* and selling the raw fibre to the agents who shipped it off to Britain. Today it is one of the major producers of alpaca fibre.

The processing factory started by washing and combing the shorn fibre and the original British machine that did the job was still in use when I visited Michell's factory; sadly it was the only British machine still in action – the rest had all been replaced by those of Italian manufacture. The company was being run by the two sons of Frank, Michael and Tony, who were interested in our plans but felt unable to help as they had little direct contact with the farmers, buying from middlemen. The company later set up its own research ranch in the hills, but that was too late for us.

The second company was Inca Tops, a firm started by a Swiss company working with local people, and they had their own research farm in Sallalli in the hills above the Colca Valley: this would be a perfect place for us to make contact with the local farmers. The manager of the factory showed us round their gleaming factory, which was in complete contrast to the six Andean women sitting cross-legged on the floor, sorting by eye, into different degrees of fineness, the fibre that had just arrived at the factory. It was agreed that Ing René Rosas, the manager of the ranch, would come to the laboratory on his next visit to Arequipa to see how he could help us. A few days later I was informed by Aurora that there was an Ing Rosas to see me; he was obviously a man of the Andes, although much taller than the average, but he had the huge barrel chest and the darkened skin of the hill people. Despite this, he had studied at the prestigious La Molina Agricultural University in Lima and was a real expert in the management of camelids. A visit was arranged; he suggested that we stay in the hotel in Chivay and travel to Sallalli from there:

"The accommodation that we can offer is only very primitive as it is for the *campesinos* when we arrange courses, definitely not for Europeans."

Edilberto was called into the conversation as there were no maps showing the location of the ranch; the one consolation of this is that there are not many tracks to follow and so it is not too difficult to find the place you want.

Our first trip was a fact-finding mission; to learn about the management, the problems, and to see how the laboratory could help improve the production. We decided that it should be an all-male team and so Héctor and Fernando joined Edilberto and myself and we set off early in the morning not knowing how long the journey would take. Over many visits we tried all three routes to Chivay and all three had been opened as a result of the Majes project; two of the routes climbed directly up the mountain and over the shoulder of the Volcano Misti, the third went down towards the coast before climbing up, following the Majes/Colca River from the west. We took the one that started from Cayma and the climb began immediately; to get out of the Chili valley there were about fifty hairpin bends as we passed between the volcanoes of Misti and Chachani. It was noticeable as we climbed that there was more vegetation: grass and shrubs and then small trees made an appearance. Once on the *altiplano* (high plain) it was mostly coarse grass, devoid of trees or shrubs, and we saw many small herds of *vicuña*. When I arrived in Perú the *vicuña* was on the banned list of the Convention for International Trade in Endangered Species of Wild Fauna and Flora (CITES), which meant that it could not be traded at all. By the time we left the country the species could be traded, but only by governments, and thanks to conservation measures they are now widespread up in the mountains.

The Andes has its own typical vegetation: close to streams and watercourses grow the more delicate and palatable plants, while away from water the grass is much coarser and contains more silica, mostly of a species called ichu (*Stipa tebu*). Here you will find these strange plants that resemble a large green molehill and are solid to the touch called yaretta (*Azorella yareta*), a primitive member of the umbelliferae (daisy family) and used as fuel; how they evolved and what is their function I never ascertained. There were a few cacti but far fewer than we saw in the north and much smaller than those I had seen in Argentina.

However, everything changed as we descended into the Colca Valley; this was a place inhabited by its own people, the Collaguas, and what a people they are: the women, in their homespun bright red embroidered skirts with their waistcoats and straw boaters each bearing a large fabric rosette, easily outshone the men in their drab western attire (Plate 26). Many Andean peoples wear red: the reason for this is that the cochineal beetle thrives on the prickly pear cacti. The Collaguas proved to be simple people, hard-working people, people with a great zest for life, religious people, happy people... lovely people.

On one occasion we went to Chivay on the Saturday after Ash Wednesday, the first Saturday of Lent, to find the Plaza de Armas alive with dancing, singing people. They were all the worse for drink and Maxine and I were press-ganged into trying the fiery home-distilled liquor that was the cause of their intoxication, and to dancing to the one tune that the town band could play. There was no unpleasantness and we were able to find out that the party was to celebrate the end of Carnival, before embarking on the Lenten duties. Only the Collaguas would celebrate the arrival of Lent with a drunken party. Lovely, lovely people...

It was difficult to believe that this town and all the other villages in the valley had been cut off from Perú for so many years, as they are constructed in the same way as most Peruvian towns with a Plaza de Armas and the streets radiating along a grid pattern. All the churches in the valley are of a similar design, constructed in the seventeenth century by the Franciscan monks and all painted white. It was the Majes Project that opened the whole Colca Valley to the rest of Perú. Had an Australian pilot not flown off course, this jewel might have remained 'lost' for many more years. On his return the pilot commented that he had seen this valley with a large number of small villages each with its own white-painted church. When the engineers were looking for a water supply for the Majes irrigation, proper roads were made to Chivay and up into the mountains, and the valley was opened to the world.

The *conquistadores* had obviously found the valley and to control the Collaguas they had moved them into villages, where the missionaries had built their beautiful churches. The steep banks of the Colca River had been terraced magnificently; for some reason these terraces were not destroyed by the Spaniards and today some of the best terracing in Perú is to be seen in the valley. Prior to the Majes Project the Collaguas communicated with the rest of Perú through their llama trains that took produce of the valley down the river to the coast and brought back building materials and cooking pots. The town of Chivay consisted of simple, rough stone houses surrounded by stone walls; like so many Scottish stone houses, doorways and windows were picked out by dressed and polished stone. Roofs were of thatch, tile or the ubiquitous corrugated iron. There was a developing commercial centre and a fairly dire hotel. However, there is not much that you can do to destroy chicken and chips and although the hen might have died of old age it was still edible and the Cerveza Arequipeña tastes as good at 3,500m as it does at 2,400m above sea level.

The two-hour drive to Sallalli was incredible as we were driving towards the snow-capped volcano Ampato (Aymara for 'the toad') towering at 6,288m above the sea; as we got closer we could see the glaciers. This was an active volcano and from time to time a great cloud of steam and smoke would issue forth from the summit, like a North American Red Indian sending a very slow tribal message. The track twisted and turned and the surface was dreadful, full of sharp rocks that could and did do serious damage to the tyres. There was one rock in particular that we tried without success to remove (it was the tip of a buried boulder) and after it had written off two Land Rover tyres Edilberto took a can of white paint so that in future he would be able to see it.

The ranch itself was on the foothills of Ampato and covered a huge area of more than 1,500 hectares (Plate 20). The herds were mixed, both alpaca and llama, which was normal in the area, although adult males and females were herded separately. The reason for this is that the alpacas seek out the soft herbage by streams while the llamas prefer the rougher ichu grass. From the herdsmen's point of view it was much simpler to take the animals out in the morning when they would find their own grazing. They were brought into pens at night and when I asked why, I was informed that it was the predators:

"What predators?" I asked.

"Mostly two-legged," replied Ing Rosas, "but we do have four-legged ones as well. This is mountain lion or puma country and there are foxes everywhere."

In my six years in Perú, I only ever saw one puma and it was too far away to film.

A mob of animals which had been kept in the pen that morning was put through a crush for our inspection and they were fine, fit animals (Plate 20). As with the cattle in the lowlands there were no lame animals: the dry conditions underfoot make for healthy feet. What stately animals they are, looking down with their supercilious approach to man. When handled their coats felt very rough and that is because to rid themselves of skin parasites, they take sand baths, where they lie on their sides in the sand and wriggle to work the sand into their coats. This plays havoc with shears to such an extent that electric shearers cannot be used (Plates 21 & 22). The old iron shearers are the most efficient, but still need regular sharpening; I saw the local farmers shearing with the lids of old tin cans, or even with glass from broken bottles.

On examination even the old animals had good teeth, although a few had incisor teeth (the ones at the front) that projected at very strange angles.

A large number of the animals were carrying lice (*Microthoracius praelongiceps*) and these were such as I had never seen before, being orange and blue in colour and of a large size (2–3cms). A few animals showed the tell-tale signs of mange, usually in the armpit or groin – loss of hair and crusty skin with a hint of blood at the margins – and so we took samples to identify the mites responsible (in our examinations they were always *Sarcoptes* species, the type that burrow into the skin). A very few were carrying *Amblyomma* ticks; I recognised them from my Africa days because of the beautiful patterns on the outer shell. We took numerous rectal faeces samples which we would examine for worm eggs on our return to Arequipa.

Microthoracius praelongiceps

Discussions with Ing Rosas informed us that there was no policy for dealing with internal and external parasites, but problems were treated as they arose. Liver fluke was not a problem in the *rabaños* (herds) of the south but there was a worm that played a similar role and which could cause havoc if it became established in a herd. During the examinations my mind had been mulling over how we could use this ranch for the training of local people in disease prevention, and ways to improve the economic management of their herds. After we finished work we adjourned to the nearest stream and there I got a real shock: I had expected the water coming from a glacier to be bitterly cold at that high altitude (4,300m), but it was scalding hot; it was not the run-off from the melting glacier that I expected but an underground stream heated by the volcano. We later found out that just outside Chivay there was a public swimming pool supplied by a hot spring (Plate 27).

Sitting in René's office and drinking a welcome cup of coffee I asked René what we could do for him.

"Well, Roger, you could examine routine samples to check our worm and external parasite problem and from time to time you could examine blood samples for their mineral content; we get the odd deaths among *crias* (newborn) and I would be grateful if you could carry out a post-mortem examination if I bring you the carcasses. Having the laboratory behind us will be a big boost for us, and so I am grateful for this visit."

"I think that we can do more than that to help you," I said, and outlined my suggestions for an economic study. "You mentioned that you will soon be weaning a batch of *cria*, and from what you tell me these youngsters will all be grazed together, male and female, alpaca and llama. I propose that we set up a project that will measure the productivity of the animals."

"How will you do that?"

"We will need to weigh the animals at regular intervals; we will treat half of them with a drug that will control both internal worms and skin parasites. We will measure the effects of this drug by checking the parasite burden. At the end of the trial we will ascertain the costs and the economic benefit or otherwise of the treatment."

"That sounds like a really useful study," said Ing Rosas.

"Let me work out the details of the exercise and I will put it into writing for you to show your bosses what we plan to do. It should involve little expense for Inca Tops other than the labour, as we will provide free all the testing and drugs."

On that happy note we set off back to Arequipa but it turned out to be a longer journey than we thought. We had set off late in the afternoon and it became dark when we were crossing the *altiplano*. For some climatic reason or other the mist descended upon us as we began the descent, and Edilberto considered the visibility too poor to drive the road safely and he suggested that he get out and walk with a torch and I drive the Land Rover in his footsteps. For several kilometres we made slow but safe progress down, until

Edilberto considered that the visibility had improved enough for him to start driving again. We arrived home all in one piece and so we were very satisfied with our first foray into the Andes proper.

Richard had just completed the first term of his A level course and was studying mathematics, chemistry and biology, and for biology he had to undertake a project in his holidays. I suggested to him that he might think about what we were planning to do at Sallalli and told him that we wanted to measure the economic benefits of controlling parasites and determine how the economic benefits could be calculated. His suggestions formed the basis of the project: the animals would be identified and weighed; each animal would have its external parasite burden assessed by the examination of five selected areas of the body, in which the fleece would be parted and we would then count the numbers of lice seen (again Richard's idea). Evidence of mange was to be recorded and samples taken; a faeces sample would be taken and the number of worm eggs determined. By a random method the animals would be divided into control and treatment groups and the treatment group were to receive the calculated therapeutic dose of ivermectin. This was a newly developed injectable drug that killed intestinal worms, lice, fleas and mange mites living on and in the skin. It was said to have no effect on ticks. However, there were so few ticks on the animals that their effects could be ignored; unlike their African cousins they were not known to spread diseases.

A round-table discussion with the laboratory staff was held and after the wildest of Richard's suggestions were removed, a solid project was produced and written up for Ing Rosas to give to his board, which quickly gave its assent. The first problem was how could we weigh the animals; by the end of the project they could be expected to weigh almost 50kg. The solution was to construct a large tripod from which we could hang a spring balance to which we attached a sling made of rope and old hessian sacks which could be used to hold the animal by its chest and belly. We found that if the support was wide enough the animal did not struggle too much, which meant we were able to read the weight accurately (Plate 24). While we were making our preparations, the animals were weaned into a group of fifty alpacas and twenty llamas which by the time we visited were beginning to adjust to their new companions. Ear tags had been put in by Ing Rosas.

We had found a new place to stay in the old camp from the Majes Project which had been turned into a hotel/motel. On this occasion we rented a furnished house that had been formerly occupied by a member of the senior staff and which was reasonably comfortable. Richard joined the same team that had made the previous visit and Maxine had prepared lunch for the five of us for three days – bread rolls with various fillings all wrapped in foil and stacked in a cold box along with oranges and apples. We allowed for two days working on the ranch to ensure that we had time to process all the animals. It was hard physical work at the altitude of 4,300m (>14,000ft) and lifting the animals in the sling onto the weighing machine soon made us pant. They were all weighed (Plate 24), sexed and a skin examination made, then the faeces samples taken – a hand enclosed in a rubber glove was inserted into the rectum and a pellet of faeces grasped. The hand was removed and the glove turned inside out enclosing the faeces sample within. The number of the animal was written on the glove which was put into a cold box (not the one containing the lunch!). The animals were paired with ones of similar sex and weight and using playing cards they were assigned to a group. There was no recommended dosage rate of ivermectin for camelids and so we used that given for sheep, and the appropriate quantity was injected under the skin of the animals in the treatment group (Plate 25). Animals in the control group seriously affected by mange were also treated.

This exercise was repeated at monthly intervals for five months (Plate 26 shows the team). Unfortunately, the work was undertaken during a period of very severe drought, which interfered with pasture growth. The animals were all sheared for the first time and we were able to compare the fleece weight in the animals: there was no difference between the fleece weights in the females but treated males had heavier fleeces. The treated male animals, both alpaca and llama, put on much more weight than their untreated counterparts, but this was less evident in the females. When we took into account the cost of the drug, the treated females increased in value by $1.4 and the males by $3.5, an important difference to a farmer with an average income of $100 per year. Richard did all the statistical calculations and produced a well-illustrated report for the A level authorities, but they would not accept that the planning and writing were his, and his grade was reduced to a 'B'. Nevertheless, he must have the satisfaction of knowing that his schoolwork resulted in two published papers in peer-reviewed scientific journals.

One of the interesting findings of the project was that over its life, the parasite burden of the control animals decreased in parallel with that of the treated animals. We assumed that the treatment of half the herd reduced the contamination of the pastures and so there were fewer worm larvae to infect the animals. This did not explain why the lice burden was also reduced…

Once we had shown the economic benefits of parasite control we decided that we had to tell the farmers the good news. Ing Rosas organised a meeting in a community hall and sent word to all the *campesinos* that they should attend, and to make sure they came, Inca Tops put on a free lunch. This would be our first opportunity to try and win the support of the camelid owners and show them what we could offer. Percy Zambrano suggested that we should give the participants a guide to the common diseases and what samples to take for the laboratory to examine. After some discussion it was agreed that the booklet be written in Spanish and not Quechua, because the people able to read would be those that could speak Spanish. A working group of Héctor, Percy, Milagro, Aurora and I set to, to produce this booklet. At the crucial time our photocopier decided to stop working and it was not repaired until late afternoon on the day before the meeting. I asked for volunteers to stay behind and help print and assemble the booklet; without a word the whole team bound for the Andes set to and started the work. It was obvious that this was going to be a late-night job and so I phoned Maxine and asked her to prepare dinner for the six of us: by 8:30 we were tucking into chilli con carne and rice washed down with beer and as soon as they were finished Edilberto drove the team home: we had to be on the road by 6:30 the next morning. I thought what a wonderful team they were; all perfectly happy to stay in the laboratory without being paid overtime until 8:00pm to get the job done, even though they had to be on their way to work at the crack of dawn the next day. This was team loyalty, everyone working for the benefit of LABVETSUR and the *campesinos*; this was the sort of loyalty that money could not buy. I felt proud to be their leader.

The following morning, there were no sleepyheads; they were all excited about going up into the hills. The weather was good with no fog to slow our progress and we arrived at the venue in good time. There was a great crowd of people there for the meeting, men, women and children, and they filed into the meeting room and sat on long benches while the team from LABVETSUR sat on chairs behind a table. As there was no electricity, instead of photographic slides we produced the information on large charts that could be displayed on the blackboard. Ing Rosas began the proceedings by telling the meeting in Quechua that the British Government had sent me to Perú to help them and to that end we had opened a big laboratory in Arequipa which could do wonders in telling the farmers why their animals were sick. We had come to them to tell them about the work we had done at Sallalli for Inca Tops and how they could get the same benefits if they followed our instructions. I spoke to them in Spanish, while René translated: I had decided to do very little talking and to allow the Peruvians to tell the story. And so I restricted myself to a few platitudes about how much I enjoyed working in their beautiful country and how happy I was that the laboratory would be able to assist them to improve the health and profitability of their animals.

Milagro, Héctor and Percy then described the work that we had done and the results that we had obtained; they explained how the improved production could be turned into money for them, to pay for school fees, to buy clothes and perhaps an extra bottle of Cerveza Arequipeña. They talked about other problems of keeping camelids and what we could do for them. There were a great deluge of questions and all the time one or other would translate for me so that I could follow the proceedings. Aurora then told them about how we had prepared a guide for them and there would be one per family. The meeting then stopped for lunch, not surprisingly, alpaca stew, after which we said our goodbyes and returned home.

Richard had done a good job with the project and I was saddened by the attitude of Oundle School, in that they would not countenance their boys failing and rather than risk failure, they would not allow the boy to enter the race. Previously, in the term in which Richard had taken his O level examinations, he had come home with a dreadful report, by far the worst that he had ever had; but had proceeded to show the incompetence of the staff by obtaining five A-grade passes and five B-grade passes in the ten subjects, which put him in the top ten boys of his year. I had wanted him to follow in my footsteps and become a veterinary surgeon, but the school put him off this object by telling him that he was not clever enough. He turned his sights towards biology and I advised him that his best bet was to study at Cambridge, still glowing with the Nobel Prizes of Crick and Watson. Oundle did not consider him clever enough to try. As I informed him:

"The worst that you can do is not get in, and if you do not apply you will certainly not get in."

He was not allowed to apply. He studied biology in Edinburgh (where, as he said, he had a great social life) and then did a fine doctorate at the National Institute for Medical Research at Mill Hill in London, on apoptosis, a condition associated with the development of cancers. This topic is also called 'Programmed Cell Death'. He had come a long way from the student working at 4,300m in the Andes in Perú. He was ever an entrepreneur at school and he always returned laden with cigarettes to be sold at a huge profit to his fellow inmates. He was obviously not liked by the staff at the school because he had talents that he would not use. He could have been a fine horseman as he showed when we were in Argentina (described in *More Sherlock Holmes than James Herriot*). I watched him playing hockey for the school third eleven and he was undoubtedly the star on the pitch, but it did not appeal to him. Perhaps it was this refusal to use his talents that upset the masters at Oundle School. My view was that, at a fee-paying school, the masters had to find ways of drawing out the talent.

It was a far cry from the masters at Bancroft's School where I studied; there, the staff relished boys who were different, and who had something about them. There were many pranks throughout our schooldays of which the Bell Saga was the greatest success. By the time we reached the fourth form there was a clique that was almost inseparable; Tom Barker, Richard Crouch, Brian Ranson, Ian Williams, Barry Yoell and myself.

How, or where or why Brian obtained the bell, is lost in the mists of time but this was a brass bell about a foot high with a clanger and was a relic of World War Two.

Richard Crouch, Barry Yoell, Tom Barker, Brian Ranson, the author, Ian Williams

Bancroft's was one of the first schools to have a science block which had been built at the turn of the twentieth century. There was a combined physics classroom and laboratory on the ground floor and a similar set-up on the first floor for chemistry. Both had been designed for thirty boys, with a blackboard, a master's demonstration desk and rows of desks for the boys at the front of the class, with practical benches occupying a large space at the rear. There was also a small preparation room and store. Above the chemistry laboratory there was a large loft accessed by a trap-door. One autumn Tuesday afternoon when the ground was too hard for rugby, and we should have been on a long cross-country run, the clique sidled off and we made our way up into the science building. By means of a human pyramid, Brian and I were able to clamber in, the bell was handed up and Brian tied it to a beam directly above the master's desk. I took the pink string that Brian had also acquired and while he tied it to the clapper, I took it over the beams to the very back of the practical class. With the aid of a biro pen I bored a small hole in the plaster of the ceiling, close to the wall, tied some transparent nylon fishing line to the string and fed it through the hole, hugging the wall close to an electric conduit pipe down to ground level; unless you knew it was there, it was completely invisible. A tug on the bell-rope and a few seconds later the bell would toll. This inertia was perfect because it enabled a boy to creep on hands and knees to the back of the class, give several hefty yanks on the bell rope and be back in his seat before the bell sounded. This was the signal for the whole class to shout, "Fire, fire!" and charge for the door. Clanger Clayton, the chemistry master, screeched out in his nasal, high-pitched tones:

"No, no, boys, it's not a fire – probably a police car!"

By the time the mayhem was sorted out we had lost a good five to ten minutes of the lesson. We were able to play this game for several weeks before a technician up in the loft spotted our handiwork and then there was hell to pay, not for the misdemeanour but for the pink string. Unfortunately a similar type of string had been stolen some time before from the physics department. It was this that saved us. Brian's father was known to Mr Matravers, the head of Physics, and when Brian assured him that the string came from his father's shed, he believed us, and the authorities were so pleased that we were not thieves, just pranksters; Mr Matravers admonished us saying:

"You can thank the Christmas spirit for our taking no further action," and nothing more was said. The reason for the concern that we had been stealing was that there had been a spate of thefts of school property culminating in stealing of keys to the art department; a group of senior boarders and day pupils were caught having a party in the art room one weekend and as the thieving culprit would not own up, all were expelled.

The retaking of the school swords was an episode that occurred when we were in the sixth form and again the masters took it in good part. The monitors' room had been adorned with a pair of light cavalry sabres which, in a dawn raid, had been stolen a year or so previously by sixth formers from Chigwell School, our neighbouring public school across the valley. By now, Ian had gone off to join the army and was at officer training school, and Barry had gone to study engineering in New Brunswick University in Canada on a Beaverbrook scholarship; he later changed course at university and ended up as a physician. That left Tom, Brian, Dick and me and we were joined by Peter Pennick, then captain of rugby who possessed a Morris Minor Tourer, and Willie Gevaux from the year above. We met up late at night. In front of the school was a strip of open grass that belonged to the Epping Forest Conservators, across which ran a wide drive up to the school gates. The conservators had recently erected 'No Parking' signs on this drive which, for some reason, incensed us. These were wrenched from the ground and the six of us set off for Chigwell School, all packed into the Morris Minor with its roof down, along with two ten-foot signs that projected over the windscreen. We entered Chigwell School from the football field, depositing the signposts in the goalmouths. For some reason the white paint used for marking the pitch had been left by the side of the pitch; where we found the brush I do not remember, but there was a strip of tarmac (or so we thought) alongside the pitch and in huge letters we painted 'CHIGWELL IS A HOLE'.

From having friends at the school, Tom knew the whereabouts of their prefects' room, which like most rooms in schools in those days was not locked, but we entered through the window. And there were OUR swords on the wall; they were removed. The Chigwellian prefects had a great number of cooking pans and so we purloined those for good measure. And we left.

The next day the shit hit the fan. The Epping Forest authorities were furious and the headmaster of Chigwell was incensed at the desecration of their all-weather cricket pitch and said it would cost thousands of pounds to sort out.

I suspect that the response of Sidney Adams, our headmaster, was that the writing would soon wear off. The word came that the head wished to see members of the dayboy monitors' room in his office and all twelve of us trooped in: we were informed in no uncertain terms that he was not pleased and that this was a serious matter. The culprits were asked to own up. Peter, Willie, Brian and I put up our hands; Richard and Tom were not monitors. Those monitors not involved in the incident were sent away and those remaining were asked to request the non-monitors to own up. Richard and Tom joined us in the study for a wigging. I do not remember exactly what the Head said but it would almost certainly have gone something like this:

Mr Sidney Adams

"You boys have had a highly privileged education and this is not the behaviour that we expect of the young men about to leave this school. Regaining the school swords in itself was a worthy aim, but you were foolish to link it with the removal of public property, namely the parking signs, and the wilful damage to the Chigwell School all-weather cricket pitch." At that he asked Dick and Tom to wait in the ante-room while he dealt with the monitors. Again I do not know what he actually said but I remember the gist:

"And so what am I to do with you miscreants? My major problem is that you involved non-monitors: officers should not misbehave in the presence of other ranks; consequently, you will all be reduced to the ranks until the end of term. Should you not blot your copy books further, you will then be reinstated. Do you understand?"

We assented and so he went on:

"You may not use the monitors' room and you will relinquish the ability to administer punishments to the junior boys. That will be all: you can go, but send in Barker and Crouch so that I can deal with them."

In fact they were let off any punishment because they had been 'led astray' by monitors.

We went directly back to the monitors' room and were soon joined by Tom and Dick. Those monitors not involved in the prank were all there and a discussion ensued. It was decided that it would not be good for school discipline if the de-monitoring story got out: in those days school discipline was mostly enforced by the monitors and so we decided that the whole matter would be kept deadly quiet. We continued to use the monitors' room and slid into a cubby hole when a master came by. Pupils who had to be punished were passed on to another monitor. To our amazement no word of what happened got out and at the end of the term we were all reinstated.

But that was not the end of the story as the Chigwellians wanted revenge. Luckily we had a mole in Chigwell School: Tom Barker's parents were friendly with parents of a boy at the school. It was half term and the boy was staying with the Barkers as his parents were going away. Tom thought it was strange when the lad informed the Barkers that he would not be with them one night and Tom felt sure the swords were at risk. Fortunately, on the afternoon prior to the night of the planned raid, Tom met Lou Baker (a large second row forward from the year below) and recruited him to assist, and they took guard that night in the monitors' room. Settled into one of the large comfy armchairs, Tom soon fell asleep, but about midnight was woken by a cry from Lou that there was a face at the window. Tom donned the school's prized First World War German helmet, and Lou took possession of the 'beat stick' – the cane used by monitors on miscreants' backsides – and they went in search of the enemy. They saw shadows behind the buttresses round the quad and headed towards them. As they got to the war memorial in the centre of the quad, the Chigwellians broke cover and ran out of the quad towards the field; one short, fat Chigwellian, not knowing that there was a six-foot drop from the quad to the field, went head over heels down the bank. Tom, not noted for his valour, did not want to catch up, so slowed down to allow the invader to escape. When Tom got to the road outside the school he saw a car pulled into the roadside, with his house guest at the wheel – the getaway car! It had several Chigwellians around it but as Tom and Lou approached they were received with great good humour and the friendly banter of rivals, despite the failure of their mission. The swords saved, they drove to Tom's house where it was a convivial cup of cocoa before they went home to an early morning bed.

Despite these youthful indiscretions, the school wanted us to succeed and exhorted us to reach for the stars. We were actively encouraged to try for Oxbridge and so I applied to numerous Cambridge colleges to study veterinary medicine (Cambridge vet school was in its infancy in those days) and I pinned my hopes on Downing College where a senior fellow was Admiral Charles Harris who had been a member of the Worshipful Company of Drapers and chairman of the school governors. I thought the connexion might be beneficial and so I wrote a long and detailed application, stressing my Bancroftian background. I received the following curt reply:

'Dear Mr Windsor,
Thank you for your recent application to study at this college. I regret to inform you that we do not admit veterinary students.
Yours sincerely...'

The university veterinary course was very new and it was twice as long as the standard science or arts degree which meant that the college's intake would be reduced. Only the larger colleges showed any interest and I was offered a place at Trinity College, but to take up the place I had to do my national military service first. That, together with the course being a year longer, made me decide in favour of a place at Edinburgh University. A fifth of our intake studied at Oxbridge or Imperial College London, while a further fifth went to universities such as Edinburgh, Birmingham, Bristol or Nottingham. This, at a time when going to university was far from the norm. Our teachers wanted us to aim for the top. This I compared to the attitude of the staff at Oundle School...

But we must return to the Andes. The project calculating the economic benefits of treating parasitic infestations in camelids resulted in regular trips to Sallalli and much work checking for worm eggs. Milagro Terán, who had studied for her veterinary degree in Puno, joined the team as she was very keen to be involved with the *campesinos,* and I readily turned over to her the day-to-day control of the project and the organisation of the field visits: she was an able lieutenant and did a fine job collecting the samples and tabulating the results while Richard was away at school. She lived with her family in a *pueblo jóven,* Alto Cayma, which was several miles up the hill beyond our suburb of Yanahuara. I often took her home in the evening as she did not have her own transport. The name Milagro means 'miracle' and it was not difficult to understand why she was so named, as she was the first daughter in the family and she had twelve older brothers. During our journeys home I got to know her well and I was very touched one day when she told me how happy she was that I was working in Arequipa:

"Why is that?" I asked and she replied:

"Because you teach us so much."

"But that is the reason I am here, to help you to make a success of running a veterinary laboratory."

"But our teachers in the veterinary school in Puno were not like you."

"What do you mean?"

"They do not want to teach us all they know, they always keep something back so that they always know more than us."

"What nonsense!" I expostulated. "I want my students to do better than me. Nothing gives me greater pleasure than to be able to boast that a particularly successful vet once worked with me; the present dean of the vet school in Bristol saw practice with me in Kenya when he was a student."

"Thank you for coming to us, I only wish our university teachers had the same attitude as you."

Most Peruvians genuinely wanted to learn and at the time none wanted my job; it was all so different from working in Africa. That conversation with Milagro opened my eyes to the problems of the people; most wanted to make a success of their work but there were a few who felt that, if they could not succeed, then they wanted no one to succeed. I was later told by a Peruvian a story that summed up the problem. There were teams of mountaineers racing to the top of the highest peak on the continent – Aconcagua. The Peruvians soon had a commanding lead over the Argentines and the Chileans but as they neared the summit they could not agree who should be the first to actually reach the top; while they were squabbling they were passed by both of the other teams. The Peruvian people are a delight but this defect in the national character is the cause of so many of the country's problems. As will be told in the Epilogue, it almost destroyed LABVETSUR and did destroy FONGALSUR.

Llamas are said to spit, and I learnt the proof of this the hard way. Richard was busy taking rectal faeces samples and I was standing behind him recording and labelling the samples. The llama was held, Richard lifted the tail, the llama turned to watch him with its customary look of disdain on its face and gathered a regurgitated dollop of food in its mouth. Just as it spat, Richard bent down to put his hand in the rectum; I received the offering full in the face. Partly digested stomach contents are unpleasant and I had to retreat to the stream to clean my face; my son thought the whole incident hilarious! We had a more serious problem of the trial animals dying. Not one died at a time convenient for them to be brought to the laboratory and so the cause of death was never determined. As it was the smaller and weaker ones that died, and as it had been a very dry summer, we decided that they had died from starvation. It was neither desirable nor feasible to give the animals supplementary feeding: such foods were not readily obtainable nor economically viable in the *sierra*.

The trips to Sallalli were not all plain sailing. I have mentioned the dreadful track to the farm and the written-off tyres, the fogs have been described, but we also had snow to contend with. Perhaps the most fraught journey we ever experienced was when we were taking the ODA project inspector Dr Archie Hunter to view the work that we were doing with the camelids. Guy and Claire were home for the holidays and Claire had brought her friend Jackie Brown with her. It was decided that if we left early on the Saturday morning and took the Chachani route, we could get there before lunchtime, do the work and get to the hotel before dark. This would leave the Sunday free for tourism so that we could show Archie the condors and the church processions. Another reason for taking the Chachani road was the possibility of seeing the resident *guanaco* herd that often grazed near the road; on this occasion we did not see them.

We set out in the usual glorious summer sun of Arequipa, but before we had climbed very far we were in the clouds and visibility was poor. I do not know why, but I stopped. I had had a sudden premonition of danger, I did not know why. I got out of the Land Rover and walked on up the hill to be confronted by... nothing. There had been some summer rain and it had washed away the road. In front of me there was a drop of more than a thousand feet. Had I not stopped, we would have crashed to our deaths. It was obvious that the landslip had occurred some time before but the traffic authorities had done nothing to put up warning signs. However, vehicles had circumnavigated the void and so we followed slowly in their tracks and without further incident made good time to Sallalli where we received a warm welcome and a hot cup of coffee from Ing Rosas. We ate the rolls prepared by Maxine followed by some fruit and were soon ready to work. No sooner had we commenced the examination and the sampling than the skies darkened and within the hour it had started to snow. René suggested that we should leave straight away before it got too deep unless we were happy to spend the night with them – but we had no food with us to provide for dinner for six. We set off in the blizzard and soon were driving on a wing and a prayer as it was impossible to see where was the track, until we went off it and got stuck in the mud by its side. All passengers got out and I put the truck into low-ratio four-wheel drive and tried to reverse straight back from whence we came. It was no good: the wheels spun but we did not move. All five passengers put their shoulders to the wheel and, inch by inch, we crept straight back until we were out of the gloop, after which the truck moved more easily and I got us back to the track.

We were several miles from the ranch and twenty or more miles to the village and it was no place to be stuck without any means of communication. In later years the embassy indicated to ODA that to improve our safety we should have a shortwave radio station at the laboratory with a mobile station for the Land Rover. But when we were with the ODA adviser on board, we were on our own. However, without more mishaps we found our way to the track leading to the Colca Valley and by then it had stopped snowing and we got to the hotel without further delay.

The following day was once again glorious sunshine and it being summer the Colca Valley was full of flowers, perhaps the most surprising were the lupins; the smallest was barely six centimetres tall, even with its spike of flowers, while the largest was more than five metres high, a real lupin tree, with branches twisted and gnarled. Whatever the size of the plant the flower spikes were the same (even if different in size) and the colour was always the same, a beautiful, deep sky-blue. It was not just the lupins, there were prickly pears with their pale yellow flowers, the majestic *Cereus* (the organ-pipe cactus) with its white trumpets that opened for just one day. One disappointment with nature was the absence of songbirds and I suspect that this was because they were trapped and eaten by the local people. Mauricio de Romaña, in his wonderfully illustrated book *Descubriendo el Valle del Colca*, describes more than a hundred different species of bird in the valley, but I believe that you have to get well away from habitation if you wish to see them.

We drove along the valley going into the villages as we passed to look at the churches and watch the Collaguas with the women in all their finery making their way to or from the church. Horses were tied to the church fences giving the place the air of a western movie. We finally arrived at La Cruz del Condor and sure enough the birds gave us a stunning performance of swooping and gliding and we even saw young on the cliffs waddling and flexing their wings before their first take-off. This to me is a magical place, said by the Peruvians to be the deepest canyon on earth. If you stretch the imagination and take the top of the canyon as the summit of the volcano Ampato on one side and the mountain Mismi on the other, then they are correct, as it is 5,000m from the summit down to the river, and from where we stood on the edge of the cliff, it was more than 1,000m down to the river – a long way to fall (Plates 23, 28, 30). What I never understood were the settlements on the far side of the river: there were houses and outbuildings quite close to the river, with seemingly no means of access from the *altiplano*; certainly there was no access to motor vehicles and yet the houses had tiled roofs, which must have been brought by pack llama. How do people survive when they have a 1,000m climb to get away from home? Perhaps they communicate by walking along the riverbank, but by any account it must be a lonely existence.

From La Cruz del Condor we set off back home. We did not retrace our footsteps but carried along the Colca River taking the long road home, a longer journey but a much easier drive as there were fewer hairpin bends and no harsh gradients. The road links up with the Majes irrigation and then joins the Pan-American Highway back to Arequipa; the trip made a complete circle. The Colca Canyon became our regular haunt when we had visitors. I can hear the children saying: "Not again!"

From the ambassador to the sons of old school friends they were taken to this quaint outpost. Unfortunately the management of the hotel where we stayed became so corrupt that the owners turned it into a lodge where you had to provide your own food. This coincided with a visit from the ambassador, Keith Haskell, his wife Toni and their four children, Luisa, Jonathan, Paul and Anne-Marie (Plates 29 and 30). They drove down to Arequipa during the week so that Keith could do all the official visits to the mayor, prefect, FONGALSUR and, of course, LABVETSUR (Plate 31). For these he was driven round by the honorary consul, Reggie Roberts, in his 1956 Cadillac, with the Union Jack flying. Normally the honorary consul would have thrown the 'cocktail' for the ambassador, but because the whole family were staying with us, Reggie agreed that we could be the hosts. It was a time when electricity was a serious problem with cuts on a daily basis. As previously mentioned the city was divided into two, and one half had no power from 5:00pm until 9:00pm while the other half had none from 9:00pm till midnight. The party was going to be held by candlelight. When Lucho heard of this he was appalled as this would show Arequipa in a really bad light and so he phoned the head of the electricity company and pointed out that the British Ambassador, the honorary British Consul, the alcalde, the prefect, the archbishop, and the heads of the armed services in Arequipa would all be there and what an embarrassment it would be for the nation. Our lights were switched back on. Pride in the nation is so important in Perú. The party went with a swing and as a result nobody was supervising the boys, so they were able to indulge themselves with the pisco sours; they were definitely the worse for wear at the end of the evening.

A trip to the Colca had been planned and so Toni and Maxine busied themselves working out menus and acquiring the ingredients (Plate 29). With the boys in one vehicle and the girls in the other we went up the switchback road between the volcanoes. The journey was uneventful and we saw a large number of herds of *vicuña* grazing on the *altiplano*. Just before the descent into the Colca Valley, by the side of the road was a huge 4x3m concrete slab, which had obviously been designed as an advertisement hoarding, but never put to use. Héctor, ever the entrepreneur, had come to me and asked for money to buy paint and brushes. On one visit to Sallalli, he and Edilberto had painted a huge sign advertising the services of LABVETSUR: the ambassador was duly impressed. Our visit was purely for tourist purposes and so he was spared the awful road to Sallalli. Instead he had the hotel at its worst: the first night was fine but on the second night Maxine and Toni had to fight the staff to keep our food for us; the staff wanted to use it for other guests who had not been so provident. It had just got dark when the lights went out: the generator had broken down. For the next hour Keith, the boilerman and I tried to get it working, but all to no avail. We dined in the candlelit dark – luckily the cookers were run on kerosene.

To amuse ourselves after dinner we played Film, TV or Book Charades. The Windsors were totally outclassed by the Haskells, who were obviously regular players of the game. It was a most entertaining way of passing an evening but we were all early to bed. A whole range of events had been planned for the next day including a visit to a Catholic mission soup kitchen where Sister Antonia fed several hundred Collaguas on a daily basis. From his 'Ambassador's Fund', Keith had purchased solar panels to provide electricity to make her life easier when cooking at night or when she was delivering babies. Sister Antonia was a down-to-earth Yankee from a poor home in New York, who loved her God, her Order, her life and her people, but this did not preclude her cursing them when provoked. It was a fascinating visit for the adults but the young ones were getting bored and so we set off for La Cruz del Condor and again these majestic birds did not let us down. En route we crossed one of the canals feeding the Majes irrigation scheme which we stopped to examine and stayed rather longer than we anticipated because both families got hooked playing Pooh Sticks: I do not know whether it was an invention of A. A. Milne, or whether he just described it. We collected our 'boats' from the local bushes and we all leant over the bridge and at the command of Keith dropped our sticks into the water and then rushed to the other side to see whose stick had won; harmless entertainment but great fun. The highlight of the trip from my children's point of view was watching the British Ambassador having to hand-pump the fuel into his Range Rover.

The hostel became so bad that on one visit to Sallalli we decided to camp on the farm overnight: a big mistake. We took all the food necessary for Maxine to prepare dinner and breakfast and we had wine, beer and fizzy drinks, to make it a party. Guy, who was perhaps the fittest member of the family, suffered dreadfully from *soroche* (mountain sickness) which made him very miserable. We all slept in the big dormitory where there must have been a hundred straw mattresses, in piles ten high. Rather than bring them down we decided to sleep in our sleeping bags on the top. It was a terrible night: the dormitory was unheated although we were warm enough in our sleeping bags; as the night wore on the temperature dropped well below zero and this is what caused the problem. At 4,300m the oxygen available to the lungs is much lower than at sea level and although Maxine and I were accustomed to living at 2,500m, the oxygen level was much lower than our lungs were used to. Consequently the brain was sending signals to the body to open all the blood vessels in the lungs to increase the uptake of oxygen. Opening the blood vessels in the lungs rapidly reduces the body temperature and so there are contrary signals telling the lung vessels to close down. This affected all of us and we could not sleep and we all got up the following morning with desperate headaches. In order to sleep comfortably at high altitude it is necessary to have a high ambient temperature, so that the lung blood vessels can open fully. We had our breakfast, thanked René for his hospitality and got down into the Colca Valley (3,500m) as quickly as possible. We did not repeat that mistake and thereafter we always stayed in the Majes Project Camp.

Going to work one morning I noticed that there was at least an inch of dust on the roof of the Land Rover and a sprinkling of dust over the entire garden! It was not until I got to the laboratory that I found out the cause: the volcano Sabancayo (an active volcano on the north ridge of Ampato) had erupted in the night, spewing millions of tons of ash and debris in the air. I did not realise immediately that that was the end of the Sallalli project. There was volcanic material spread at least a foot deep over the whole ranch. Grazing would have to be found, and quickly, if the animals were not to starve. They were taken more than 100kms before grazing could be found. The eruptions from the Sabancayo continue sporadically to this day.

Reports started to come in from farms further from the volcano of deaths in camelids and poisoning from the ash was suspected. Examination of dead animals and chemical analysis of the ash told us the true story. The ash was not toxic as it consisted almost entirely of silica, but it was the cause of the problem. The silica was in sharp, pointed crystals which were damaging the lining of the gut, causing haemorrhages and also allowing pathogens to enter the body proper, causing widespread infection. This was the sad end of the research project in Sallalli, but not the end of our work with the people of the Andes and it did not curtail our visits for work and pleasure to the Colca.

When we lived in Willingham, all visitors were taken to Ely Cathedral and the Stretham Steam Engine; when in Perú, visitors were taken to the Colca. During our stay in Perú we received many visitors from home. In addition to school friends of our children, my old boss from the Cambridge Veterinary Investigation Centre, Sherwin Hall, and his wife Jenny visited us twice; they were with us for my fiftieth birthday, which was celebrated with a great party at the lab (Plate 32) as well as a party at home with family and Peruvian friends. The Halls left us to fly to Tacna to catch the plane for La Paz in Bolivia, where they had lived when Sherwin was working for FAO twenty years previously. The following day they were back! Flights to La Paz had been cancelled and so they took a tour to Cuzco and Macchu Pichu to make up for the disappointment at not being able to revisit their old haunts. Our old friends from the village of Willingham, Jim and Hilary Potter, were delightful guests as they enjoyed everything and both were very interested in Andean art, and they just adored wandering round the many markets that southern Perú has to offer.

My godson, William Crouch, the son of Richard, and his school friend Alex Long, were good company; Alex had South American connexions and they had visited some of his relations in the Pantanal in Brazil before coming to us. Alex was most loquacious and both Maxine and I noticed that when we were driving up the mountain the altitude began to affect him; his conversation slowly dried up and for the first time he was silent. However, he soon recovered his equilibrium and he and William were able to walk the Inca Trail to Machu Pichu.

Daniel (Dan), the son of Tom Auber, another old school friend, brought Chris Boomer, his trade union mate. Dan had an amusing experience on the journey. There was a complete dearth of Tampax (sanitary tampons) in Arequipa and Maxine had asked Jenny (Dan's mother) to send some out with Dan. Jenny had packed Dan's bag for him and to save space she took all the tampons out of their packaging and stuffed them inside refills for a vacuum flask which we had also asked for. The first that Dan knew of this was when his case was opened by a suspicious customs officer, who insisted that Dan take the vacuum flask refill out of its box and open it to show that it was empty; to his horror out spilled all the tampons. Of course the custom's officer had no idea what they were. However, there was a female officer nearby who explained to their man what these offending items were, and that no duty was payable on them! It was excruciatingly embarrassing for Dan as it would be for any young man of that age. However, Chris spread the story round and thereafter Dan was known to his friends as 'Dan the tampon smuggler'.

On a working visit to farms along the Majes (Colca) River I had discovered a wonderful hotel on its banks near the town of Aplao and we decided to take Dan and Chris there on our way up to the canyon. We were sitting with the owner of the *Posada*, who spoke excellent English, and was telling us about farming along the river, where a great deal of rice was grown. I was so used to translating for our guests that as the owner spoke I was translating, without thinking, until Dan pointed out that he was speaking in English!

One reason for stopping there was the *camarones* – freshwater crayfish – for which the river is renowned; specimens of body length 25cms or more were not uncommon and they were wonderful to eat cold with a salad, but much better was to have the Peruvian dish of *chupe de camarones* – crayfish soup – which is to die for, although I prefer mine served without the topping of a fried egg. Our visitors were suitably impressed with the condors and enjoyed the trip. They, too, walked the Inca Trail to Machu Pichu.

Aurora suggested that we should have a 'works outing' and go for a picnic. In order to take as many people as possible, I took my car with Maxine and a couple of staff members while the rest packed into the Land Rover (there was no rule in Perú that there must be a proper seat for each person) and so one Sunday we set off for the huge reservoir, Aguada Blanca, in the Salinas and Aguada Blanca National Reserve. Héctor, who seemed to know everybody, had obtained permits for us to fish for trout in the dam: Maxine had made a picnic for a dozen, the Land Rover was well supplied with beer and there were folding chairs for Maxine and me in the car boot. The journey took about two hours along a good, if unmade, road and we set up base by the side of the reservoir. Three or four of us tried our hand at fly fishing and we caught absolutely nothing, not even a nibble. We did not come home empty handed; once the picnic was done we filled the cold box with rainbow trout, each about a foot long, which we bought from a little old Indian fishing with a homemade bamboo rod, who was pulling them out of the water as fast as he could. The penny dropped, the fisherman was using worms while we were using flies: at 4,000m there are NO flies, no flying insects of any sort at all. The trout were not taking our flies because they did not know what they were. It was a wonderful day out, great for team building and for building friendships among the staff. With Maxine handing out the picnic, it felt not like a works outing, but more of a family party. This feeling was reinforced by the fact that I could never persuade any of my senior Peruvian colleagues to call me by my Christian name; the best I could do was to get them to call me Dr Roger, and to this day that is how Aurora, now the mother of a vet, still addresses me. However, we were one big happy family and even today more than twenty years after I have left their country I still have the same feeling of affection for my former colleagues and their beautiful country.

I was never able to fulfil my obligation to the department of Cuzco; because of the terrorist problem it was not possible to undertake any farm visits. There was no veterinary school in Cuzco and no professional organisation with whom we could deal. Puno possessed a veterinary school and so my visits there and my teaching of their students went some way towards my obligation to that department.

I had come to the conclusion that the best way to popularise camelid meat was to persuade the hotels to serve it as a special dish for tourists and on one trip to the mountains I had been present when an alpaca was slaughtered. I had inspected the carcass and found that it was perfectly healthy and fit for consumption and as a result I had purchased a hind leg, which we put into the freezer to be used on a suitable occasion. When the ambassador visited Arequipa he and Toni usually stayed with us and during one such visit we decided to have a dinner party in their honour and so we invited Reggie and Evelyn, Lucho and Roxana and Lewis and Christina Vaughan. Lewis was an Australian volunteer vet helping to set up the veterinary practices in the irrigations. This was the time to get out the leg of alpaca. I had eaten the meat on several trips to the mountains and found it very similar to venison, being lean meat with little fat, but with a pleasant, delicate flavour. We had finished the first course and Maxine brought in the leg of alpaca which she had marinated for two days before pot roasting it. Without saying what it was, I carved and served it and we were giving them *Casillero del Diablo*, a heavy Chilean red wine with it. The conversation was general when Lewis looked up from his plate and said in his broad Australian accent:

"This sure as hell beats alpaca stew." He and Christina were living on a missionary salary supplemented by his local earnings. Reggie turned to Maxine and asked her if she had ever eaten alpaca, because he had not. Keith said to Lewis:

"Nobody eats alpaca because it is always full of parasites." In the circumstances not a very diplomatic remark! I then felt that I had to own up and tell them what it was.

"I can assure you that this animal was not infected with parasites because I examined the animal myself when it was slaughtered." A somewhat embarrassed silence engulfed the table before the conversation resumed. Keith and Toni tactfully had second helpings, as did Lewis and Christina and Evelyn, but all of the Peruvians declined. We decided that we had better not try to introduce more Peruvians into the delights of eating camelid meat but to continue working away on the hotels. On a recent visit to Perú, I found that alpaca was on the menu in the more expensive restaurants, and so it seems that our missionary work has paid dividends.

8

Cajamarca

One of the delights of my contract with ODA was that I was required to visit the laboratory in Cajamarca four times a year. This delightful, rustic city was where Pizarro, the Spanish *conquistador*, captured and murdered the Inca Atahualpa. At the time of the Spanish arrival Atahualpa was engaged in a bloody civil war with his brother and he thought that the Spaniards would help him win. Instead he was captured and Pizarro offered to exchange him for a room filled with gold and silver. The locals duly filled the room up to the mark indicated by the Spaniards, who then reneged on the deal. By converting to Catholicism, Atahualpa was not burnt alive; instead he was garrotted before being burnt.

Cajamarca is almost as far north of Lima as Arequipa is to the south, and like Arequipa it is more than 100kms inland, up an inter-Andean valley. Even travelling by air it was a two-day journey each way as there were only flights to and from Cajamarca in the early morning. Landing a plane in the narrow valley was a real problem and once the sun was shining the cross winds made the exercise problematic, not to say dangerous. The aerial approach to the valley was through a narrow pass in the Andes and when there was cloud about, the pilots had difficulty seeing where they were going and I remember on one misty flight an announcement coming over the aircraft's sound system asking the passengers to look out of the windows and warn the pilot if we were getting too close to the mountain…

At the time there was no industry in Cajamarca and so it depended upon agriculture and in particular milk for its wealth. Today the province is being exploited by the Chinese for its minerals while Newmont Minas Buenaventura and the International Finance Corporation are mining gold. When forced to choose by the Peruvian Government, Nestlé had retained its plant in Cajamarca (INCALC) in preference to Arequipa, despite there being only a third of the number of dairy cows; the Cajamarca plant produced baby milk powder as its main product and the remainder was made into condensed milk. It is a city of uncluttered streets and open spaces, of simple houses with tiled roofs and greenery.

Cajamarca is far enough north on the continent for the effects of the Humboldt Current, which brings cold water from the Antarctic, to be weakening. Unlike in the Department of Arequipa, which has no rainfall and hence no natural vegetation until 2,000 metres or more above sea level, the Pacific Ocean is beginning to warm at Cajamarca and so the winds are able to pick up moisture from the sea and it has its own natural vegetation. As a result the farms are all together, not separated into irrigated zones. In order to rear cattle, the pastures are irrigated and the animals are raised on grass rather than alfalfa. The farms are much longer established than those in Arequipa and much larger in area and stock numbers. Because of the value of its livestock, at the time Cajamarca boasted one of Perú's five veterinary schools, the others being Lima, Ica, Chiclayo and Puno; today they are springing up all over the country like mushrooms.

On my first visit to Cajamarca I spent a day in Lima visiting La Molina Agricultural University where I met the future President of Perú, Alberto Fujimori, who at the time was the director of the university. When Lucho heard that I was going to Lima he decided to join me. We spent the day visiting the various departments of this important university, and it was here that I first saw the giant guinea pigs (three to four times the normal size) which were being bred to improve the nutrition of the people in the Andes. It was a vibrant place but the staff all complained that they were starved of funds with which to work. I spent the night with John and Joan Taylor in their delightful house in the ambassador's residential complex and we had a great swim in the large pool. John was the second secretary in the embassy and had responsibility for my work in Cajamarca as well as the LABVETSUR project. They became good friends and as mentioned in an earlier chapter were indispensible to us for looking after the children on their journeys to and from Arequipa. The same problems arose with connexions from Europe;

they all arrived after the flight to Arequipa had left and so the children had to spend a day in Lima both going and coming.

After the bustle of the airports in Arequipa and Lima, it was a delight to arrive at the small, friendly airport in Cajamarca, with no carousel, and porters who were happy to carry the bags for a few intis. I was met by two cheery faces who seemed delighted to see me. Over the years they were to play important roles in the development of the northern laboratory and from the start they were of great assistance to me. Dr Enrique Lopez worked for the Centre for Investigation and Promotion of Agriculture (CIPA) and was in charge of the local artificial insemination centre where they collected and froze bull semen, which was used throughout the department. He was also the head of the local veterinary association and was a suave, debonair ladies' man, always smartly dressed with immaculately polished shoes; he was very bright and industrious and much more of the extrovert than Dr Marcos Chávarry of the laboratory, who was from a very different mould. I suspected that Marcos came from much humbler stock than Enrique and he was much more introverted and closed but bright and enthusiastic, if less well dressed. We became firm friends. First I was taken to the *Turistas* hotel to deposit my bags and have a wash and brush up after the flight. Then we sat in the café and had a long chat. They knew all about LABVETSUR and wanted to know how they could go about doing the same in the north.

"Hold your horses," I said, "first I have to have a look at what you have and what is the system in the laboratory, but rest assured I would like to see Cajamarca have a similar management system to what we have in Arequipa."

With that we drank up our coffee and set off for the laboratory, which was in a small village called Baños de Los Incas (Baths of the Incas) a couple of miles from Cajamarca. Once out of the town the houses died away to be replaced by farmland with trees round the houses and cows grazing in the fields. Everywhere there were delightful women in their colourful local dress each with a straw trilby hat on her head, some even wearing two, one perched on top of the other; most had babies on their backs and without exception they were all spinning wool via a spindle that hung by their side. All too soon we came to the delightful laboratory standing in its own grounds, which were neat and tidy (Plate 33).

I was taken into Marcos' office and another cup of coffee was brought; between them they gave me a garbled history of the laboratory and its British origins. I was later shown a large wooden box which contained all the old

141

papers from this project, which had not been destroyed as they should have been when the British Government closed it down. At a later date I went through the box and discovered the confidential file, which I removed and kept. The remainder of the papers I destroyed in the laboratory incinerator. It is from the stories of Enrique and Marcos and this salvaged file that I pieced together the history of the laboratory.

The British aid organisation ODA set up a project called PRODAC in Cajamarca in 1973 and the laboratory work was a small part of the aid, the aim of which was to improve arable farming, livestock farming and hence milk production in Cajamarca. Because of the total mismanagement on the part of the British this project was a complete disaster and all that remained of the British investment was the laboratory, which was hobbling along without much support by either the national or local government. Marcos and his staff received miniscule salaries from the Department of Cajamarca but they had no money to buy reagents or media and were still using those left by the British. Nestlé, aware of the benefits to their suppliers, helped out where they could with different material.

The laboratory had been established to provide a diagnostic service to farmers and veterinarians in the project area, but in reality this help was restricted to those farmers who joined the project and was not universally available. The laboratory was to undertake surveys of diseases reducing productivity. The first team leader was Dr Tim Cheyne, an old friend of mine who had extensive experience of field veterinary work in Africa but had never worked in a laboratory. Tim's lifestyle upset the Peruvians and this was reported by a team member to the embassy, and at the end of his contract, just as Tim was becoming useful, the British Government dismissed him. The mole, in his turn, was dismissed by ODA. The next project manager, Dr George Calderbank, was another veterinarian with extensive experience in Africa, who treated the Peruvians in the same manner that the more reactionary colonials treated their African staff. This did not endear him to the Cajamarquinos; his refusal to allow them to travel to Baños de Los Incas in project vehicles with their British counterparts caused great disquiet. Relations between the British personnel and the Peruvians became so bad that the local staff went on strike demanding the removal of the British staff and in particular a Dr Brian Smith. This is the only example of a strike against a British aid project of which I have ever heard. After much toing and froing by the British Embassy in Lima, relations were patched up.

I have been unable to determine when the role of project manager and laboratory head was split, but a British veterinary surgeon, Dr Clive Woodham, with whom I worked in Cambridge, was recruited to run the laboratory and at last they had a man trained to work in one, but Calderbank informed Clive that he was only to work with cattle and the owners who submitted samples had to be members of the project. It is difficult to find a more stupid set of regulations because unfortunately diseases did not know which farms were signed up to the project, animals continued to be sick and Clive thought it was the duty of a veterinary surgeon to try and heal sick animals, particularly when he was part of an aid project. The final straw came when a dead dog was brought into the laboratory having shown nervous signs. Clive had the temerity to carry out a post-mortem examination on the animal and then carried out tests that showed the dog had died from rabies; the telephone lines between Cajamarca and Lima must have hummed. Letters were sent back and forth and Clive, who had stopped an outbreak of rabies in its tracks, was dismissed. They did not wait until the end of his contract, he was just sent packing.

In 1976 Clive Woodham was replaced by a young veterinary surgeon, Andrew Newitt, with no laboratory experience. Despite this he seems to have performed a reasonable job and was responsible for the design and construction of the laboratory building. One day, he did not turn up at the laboratory. He was not seen again for several weeks and it appears that he went walkabout in the Andes; luckily this was at a time before the *Sendero Luminoso* were seriously active in the Andes… He had to go. His replacement was Dr Tony Williams, a man with considerable African field work, a South American wife and some training in laboratory work. Tony was popular with the staff, Marcos still had a photograph of him on the wall of his office. Tony made a start on fulfilling the objects of the project. In 1980 Calderbank left and he was replaced by the agricultural specialist Dr Brian Smith about whom the Peruvians had previously complained. I have been unable to find out why Tony left but he was replaced by Dr Lindsay Bell. Dr Lopez has informed me that Dr Bell was dynamic, spoke excellent Spanish, was very popular with the local staff and was responsible for the importation of British Friesian embryos and their implantation in local cattle. She was also responsible for sending local staff for formal training overseas. Unfortunately she arrived with the instruction to end Britain's involvement in the laboratory and in 1984 the project closed down. Dr

Lopez believes that had she been there from the start, PRODAC would have had a more successful outcome.

I have no idea how much money was spent on the PRODAC project but its legacy was almost nothing: Perú's only tasty cheese, a shell of a decent laboratory with reasonable equipment and material that they had purchased, but no academically trained staff. Until the arrival of Dr Bell not a single Peruvian received any formal training as a laboratory technician; no vet received postgraduate training and no youngsters were sent for veterinary training by the project. I was unable to determine whether a British laboratory technician had been employed; there is no one mentioned in the records, but this could account for the lack of local technical staff being sent away for formal training. I could not help but wonder why the project had been set up and how it had been judged in London. My short acquaintance with the enthusiastic staff had been enough for me to know that they had enjoyed working with the British vets, wanted the laboratory to be successful, and were very keen to do a good job. I had to set about rectifying the total failure of the project.

Enrique and Marcos had outlined an ambitious programme for me with visits to FONGAL Cajamarca, INCALAC (Nestlé), and trips to visit some of the more influential farmers, plus the faculty of veterinary medicine, and the departmental Minister of Agriculture. The Peruvians had a strange system of government: there was a national minister of a department, eg. agriculture, in Lima, and each department of the country had its own Minister of Agriculture who was autonomous but at the same time subservient to the boss in Lima! As all senior posts were of a political nature, every time there was a change of minister, all the senior staff changed! But we started off with lunch and my first visit to Salas, the café/restaurant in the Plaza de Armas: a huge, bleak rectangular room with a bare wood floor, set with about fifty tables and looking more like a canteen than a restaurant. The cashier, Sra Salas, dressed in black, sat with her cash register by the entrance. This was to become my regular place for breakfast, lunch and occasionally dinner on all visits to the city. The food was excellent, the service good and the prices cheap: breakfast in Salas cost half that in the *Turistas*, and you always met somebody you knew. You did not need to read the newspaper at breakfast in Salas because a great drama was played out before your eyes every morning as the locals brought in their produce: a small man would stagger in beneath a great haunch of beef, immediately followed by another with a large tuna fish from the Pacific on his back and then would come the procession of women bearing large baskets of fruit and vegetables. Woe betide any supplier of inferior goods as they were sent packing taking their poor-quality produce with them. My favourite lunchtime dish was *choclo de los Incas* which was a simple corn cob: the cob was the normal size but the grains were the size of the top joint of my thumb. Served with butter, salt and pepper it was lunch in itself. It was delicious, but I have never seen this variety of corn in any place other than Cajamarca.

After lunch we were off to the faculty where we were met by the dean, Prof. Elio Delgado, but known to all as 'el Chino' because of his Asiatic appearance: all people with oval eyes were called 'chino'. The school was fairly impressive with its well-maintained buildings. Like most Third World veterinary schools, there was a dearth of accommodation for animals and the students were expected to gain practical experience in the field. I was most impressed with the parasitology department and in particular Dr Cesar Bazan Vasquez, whose speciality was fascioliasis (liver flukes) and the snails that act as the intermediate host.

"Liver flukes!" I exclaimed. "Do not tell me that liver fluke is a problem in a country where you have to irrigate the grass."

"It is a massive problem here," replied Dr Bazan, "and not just in cattle. Twenty-five per cent of the human population is infected with the fluke."

"I cannot believe it," I said.

"It is easy to understand," said Dr Bazan, "the lakes and streams in the sierra are alive with snails, and when the rains come the snails are washed down in the rivers and irrigation canals. Come back during the rains and I will give you a bucketful of snails taken from the flood drain by the laboratory door." (I did and he did!)

"But how do the humans become infected?" I asked.

"This whole area is criss-crossed with irrigation canals which are opened three or four times a week and so they never dry out. Watercress grows in these canals and it is a staple food for the local people; the women harvest it as they walk to and from the market. The liver fluke larvae leave the snails and climb onto the watercress where they encyst on the leaves. However, they are so small as to be invisible unless you are looking for them. The vegetable is eaten uncooked and so the parasite is able to infect the human. It is a massive problem, and I do not know what we can do to stop it. We cannot put chemicals in the water because it is drunk, not only by the cattle but also by the people. This is one condition that the government is giving us some money to investigate."

I had worked in several different countries and I knew the liver fluke could infect man, but this was the first time that I had heard of large-scale infestations in humans; but then, where else is wild watercress a staple food?

The microbiology and pathology departments were keen to be involved in efforts to resuscitate the laboratory as they considered that it could be a useful source of teaching material and of course a good place for the students to work during the vacation. I was taken back to the hotel and was told that they would collect me for dinner at eight. The restaurant, La Cajamarques, was next door to the hotel and was a fine blend of rusticity and sophistication and the food was excellent. A fine end to a very busy day.

Back in my hotel bedroom I thought over the day and the enthusiasm and interest shown by all the people that I had met. I was saddened by the way the British project had failed the people it was supposed to assist, and I decided that it was as important to me to make a success of the Cajamarca laboratory as it was LABVETSUR. To achieve this I would need to receive the active support of the ambassador: Peruvians are very status-conscious and no politician or administrator would listen to me without backing from the top.

It was an eye-opening trip, and my feet never seemed to hit the ground as we visited Nestlé, FONGAL Cajamarca, the Ministry of Agriculture, CIPA, La Región Noroeste Marañon, and several dairy farmers. With the exception of the ministry staff, everyone was in favour of trying to set up the laboratory as a self-financing organisation with its own board of directors. The battle was about to begin. On my last afternoon in Cajamarca, Enrique, Marcos and I sat round in the laboratory and discussed their immediate needs. I was certain that LABVETSUR could spare some reagents and chemicals to help our struggling sister, while I set to and put in train measures to ensure the long-term survival of what came to be called LABRENOR (Regional Veterinary Laboratory of the North).

On my return south I had a meeting with the ambassador; John Shakespeare had gone and had been replaced by Adrian Beamish who did not seem greatly interested in British aid to Perú. This was my first meeting with him as he had not been to Arequipa, and I had great difficulty in interesting him in the problems of Cajamarca. It did not seem to bother him that Britain had had a large agricultural project in Northern Perú over a period of more than ten years and that there was almost nothing to show for the huge expenditure. Reviving the laboratory and making it a useful tool for farmers in the north did not appear to interest him. Saving the money that Britain had poured into Cajamarca interested him even less; however, he spoke with great animation about the air-conditioner he was having installed in the residency to keep his wine cellar cool. I hammered home the point that without his support we would achieve nothing; it was only when I pointed out that it was the efforts of John Shakespeare that had got LABVETSUR off the ground, and that the project was giving great kudos to Britain and his predecessor in the corridors of power in Arequipa, that I was able to arouse his interest. He finally agreed to assist in prising the laboratory out of the grasp of the Ministry of Agriculture and setting it up as a self-financing organisation, but only on two conditions: first, I had to prove to him that there was a demand from the farmers that this should happen, and second, that there was political support in parliament for the privatisation of a state-owned organisation.

This was not the support for which I had been hoping.

It was just a few weeks later that the ambassador made a visit to Arequipa; he came to LABVETSUR to see what we were doing, and gave the appearance of being interested in the work and the staff. Reggie Roberts, the honorary British Consul, threw a cocktail party for him in his house. This was the big one – the British Ambassador was an important figure among Peruvians, and the whole of Arequipa 'society' turned out for the man. The party started at 7:00pm and because it was a British party all the dignitaries turned up on time. No ambassador. The party went on without him: at 7:45pm he arrived, having fallen asleep at the end of his busy official day. He had the temerity to ask Reggie to set up a reception line again, but Reggie quite rightly refused. Were that not enough, the next day he was due to return to Lima, and Maxine and I were at the airport to see him off. He was driven to the airport in Reggie's wonderful 1956 Chevrolet with ambassadorial flag flying. On arrival at the check-in, Mr Beamish was unable to find his ticket. He searched his luggage and it wasn't there; he had insufficient cash and so Reggie had to pay for a replacement ticket. On arrival in Lima he remembered that he had put the ticket in the breast pocket of his jacket ("I never put it there") and he had not checked that pocket. I do not know whether or not he refunded Reggie with the airfare.

My next visit to Cajamarca was in the company of John Taylor from the embassy and Dr Tony Irvin who was a senior adviser to ODA and who had been a close neighbour in Muguga, Kenya when we were there in the late 60s and early 70s. Tony was on a whistle-stop tour of ODA projects in Latin America and the Caribbean, and so when he was in Arequipa we only had time to show him the laboratory and take him to the nearby irrigation schemes to see the work we were doing with the dairy farmers, before we had to dash off up to Cajamarca to start the move towards putting their laboratory on a similar footing to LABVETSUR. No sooner had we arrived in Cajamarca than word came through that the day we were to fly back to Lima, Aeroperú would be on strike, and Tony's next meeting was in Bolivia with the Minister of Agriculture. Panic. Thank heavens that we had John Taylor with us, as he took on the job of getting Tony to Lima in time for his flight to La Paz. It was lucky that Perú had a good telephone service, as John had to make calls to Lima and London to get authority to charter a plane to fly us from Cajamarca to Lima and then he had to call Lima again to get the plane. While John was phoning away, Tony and I were doing the rounds of the people who were to be the key players in the meeting the following day. Enrique and Marcos showed Tony and me what the laboratory was doing, and Tony was impressed with the work being carried out in what was to be called LABRENOR. He approved of our plans for the laboratory and for its financing. Tony thought that it might be possible to obtain some 'pump-priming' money from ODA. All was set for the meeting of the parties.

The round-table meeting was a very one-sided affair with Ingeniero Hidalgo of the Ministry of Agriculture being the sole opposition. I decided that the only way to tackle the man was to mock him: since I had to translate for Tony, I was able to stop Hidalgo whenever I wanted by using the translation pretext. I further infuriated him by calling him Ingeniero Hígado (liver in Spanish). Although we had won the technical fight, the political battle was still to be won. However, I would be seeing the ambassador, who could apply the political pressure, when I got back to Lima and I knew that I had all the ammunition that he had requested.

The small jet was waiting for us at the airport early next morning and at precisely 8:00am we took to the air. This was the first and only time that I flew to or from Cajamarca in a jet plane as even small commercial jets were unable to land. We had an uneventful flight to Lima Airport, where I left Tony to continue on his journey to La Paz while I set off with John for the embassy to brief the ambassador on our technical success and explain that we still needed his political assistance. The boys in Cajamarca had been busy and obtained official letters from FONGAL Cajamarca, and from the dean of the veterinary school; several farmers with both large and small farms had written letters of support and they even persuaded one of the local politicians to write. Meanwhile in Arequipa with the aid of Lucho a meeting had been set up with his cousin, Senator Jorge Lozada Stanbury, who had just been appointed to the Agricultural Committee of the Senate. He, of course, was very much in favour as he had been party to the setting up of LABVETSUR and he had agreed to sound out senators from the north. For my meeting with Ambassador Beamish I had all the material of support which even the most doubting of Thomases would have to accept. Being so well armed I met Mr Beamish in his office, presented my case to him and handed him the letters from the various people...

I waited for some time as he looked at the various documents. He looked up and dropped his bombshell.

"I do not think that the embassy can take up this case because it would be interfering in internal Peruvian matters and it is our government policy not to do this."

"But why did you ask me to collect evidence from farmers' organisations and politicians that they would support such a move? I have collected more than enough to convince any clear-thinking person that there is Peruvian support to save this laboratory and you are not prepared to help. You know full well that without support of the embassy I will achieve nothing. Meanwhile money spent to aid this country will go to waste."

I could not believe it: after I had done everything that he required, he had completely reneged on the agreement. I would have to face my Peruvian colleagues and friends and tell them that our man was not going to help us. We were all very depressed.

Salvation came in the form of the Madrid Treaty that brought peace for the time being between Britain and Argentina. Beamish was removed as ambassador to Perú to chair the talks. As it was not known for how long the talks would continue, the government decided to appoint a new ambassador and a man who cared about the countries in which he lived was appointed. Keith Haskell CMG, CVO, not only became a great ally, he became a great friend; he was accompanied by his wife, Toni, who was of Portuguese origin, but you would never have known, as her English accent was perfect. They had four children, the younger three of whom complemented our children in age and whenever they were together they made a good fighting unit. Under Keith's direction the embassy became a different place as he set about improving Britain's relations with the people of Perú, small things in the wider scheme: he arranged for not only a discarded London fire engine to be sent to Lima and persuaded a shipping company to send it free of charge, but also a set of kitchen equipment for a British woman running a children's home in Piura, solar panels for an American nun running a soup kitchen in the Colca Valley and music stands for the Arequipa town band were all provided. Each cost little but had a massive impact in the community to whom they were given and the name of Britain became, once again, one of respect after our war with Argentina.

Keith came to inspect the LABVETSUR project and he and Toni came to stay with us; it was holiday time and so they brought the children. Reggie Roberts drove his 1953 Cadillac to meet the ambassadorial party but Maxine and I had to drive Keith and Toni home as the children decided that they had to travel in this glorious car with ambassadorial flag flying. Reggie took Keith on his official rounds, while Maxine looked after Toni and family and I waited to meet him in the laboratory. His first meeting was with Lucho and other FONGALSUR dignitaries to which I was not invited; I suspected that this was to enable them to discuss the performance of the project leader who now went under the title of *gerente* (managing director) of LABVETSUR. Keith endeared himself to the staff; he had done his homework and knew about them from the various laboratory reports. After his tour of the laboratory (Plate 31) and a chat with each member of the team, we adjourned to my office with Lucho and Reggie, and Aurora brought us coffee. We had weathered the inflation storm and so the four of us discussed how we should develop our services.

Once the future of the laboratory had been settled, I turned to the subject of the laboratory in Cajamarca. Lucho, Reggie and I told the saga of the northern laboratory and what we had done to try and preserve something from the wreck of the former British project. I outlined the work we had done to provide Ambassador Beamish with the necessary ammunition and Lucho told of the meetings he had had with the senator and how we had been let down. I suggested that Keith should accompany me to Cajamarca to see for himself and this was agreed to. Lucho said that once we had selected a date, he would alert his counterpart in Cajamarca and ask him to set up a meeting between all the interested parties.

With the agreement of Reggie, we had arranged a party for the ambassador in our house. When we started giving these parties, Maxine and I prepared everything ourselves, but when our landlady Kuki heard about this she informed us that she had a small company that could take the organisation (and the washing-up) off our hands, and so she was contracted to provide the party, which she did very well. On this occasion there was no hitch to the reception line and Keith and Toni duly met the archbishop, the prefect, the mayor, and all the heads of the armed forces as well as most of the British community in the city. It was a great party and Guy Windsor and Johnny Haskell imbibed a little too much pisco.

The next day the Haskells were back to Lima and again the ambassador had to travel in the Windsor Nissan, while the children went in the Cadillac. A date had been set for the Cajamarca trip: I would fly up to Lima on the Sunday and on the Monday, Keith, Toni and I would fly to Cajamarca to be met at the airport by Keith's driver in the official Range Rover; he would set off on the Saturday. There was an amusing incident in Lima Airport on the way north; we had gone through the diplomatic check-in and were on our way to the departure gate, when I was stopped by a security guard and asked if I was carrying! It took me some moments to work out what he was after: he thought I was the ambassador's bodyguard and had asked me if I was carrying a weapon. I assured him that I was not armed and that I was not a bodyguard and I was allowed on my way. The driver was waiting at the airport along with Enrique and Marcos. It was decided that I would bring the ambassador to the laboratory after we had settled into the Hotel Puruay, booked by the embassy, which was a new eco-hotel in the Cajamarca countryside, built into the side of a hill. There were great views, but the stairs to the rooms were very steep, and to get to the en suite bathroom meant another descent of four steep steps; I could see myself taking a head dive down them in the middle of the night.

Keith was impressed with what the laboratory was doing, and having talked to the staff, he was even more keen to help. He spent the afternoon making his official visits with Winston Barber the honorary British Consul in Trujillo who had driven up to join the party. A meeting had been arranged in the municipal chambers for 10:00am on Tuesday morning. The regional Minister of Agriculture would open the meeting and there would be delegates from the ministry, and from CIPA; from the Faculty of Veterinary Medicine the dean, Prof Delgado, was coming, and FONGAL Cajamarca would be represented by the president and the *gerente*. The technical manager of Nestlé was coming, Enrique would be there on behalf of the Colegio Medico Veterinario de Cajamarca and Marcos would represent the laboratory. Keith and I would be there more as advisers rather than decision makers. The meeting was not as I had expected: the ministry staff were as nice as pie and agreeable to everything that I suggested. They had drafted an agreement for Keith to sign and I was able to advise him that it was to our taste; all that was required was to fill out the details. By 11:00am we were in accord and it was agreed that all should sign the *convenio* (agreement) once the work was completed. Keith left with the brass while the technocrats got down to business of fleshing out the details.

It became rapidly apparent that we had been conned. To this day I am not sure whether it was deliberate or accidental. The deputy for Cajamarca, Ing Pablo Sanchez, read out a second document in which they discussed the control of the laboratory, and it was obvious that it bore no relation to that discussed while Keith was there, and had been prepared before the meeting: all that was going to happen was that there would be a substitution of the bureaucrats of the region for those of the Ministry of Agriculture!

I was furious. The board to run the lab was to consist of the president from the region, a member from the Ministry of Agriculture, one from the Ministry of Health, one from the Ministry of Social Services, a representative from the *Municipalidad*, one from the vet school and one from FONGAL Cajamarca. One board member from a private institution, one from a semi-private one (the vet school), to five bureaucrats. I told them that there was no way that my ambassador would accept such a weighting. There had to be at least parity between state and private. They were horrified when I suggested that FONGAL should have two representatives and that Nestlé (INCALAC) as the only purchaser of milk should also have a say.

"But they are only interested in making money," the bureaucrats said.

"So are we," I replied. "If the lab does not cover its costs then it will not survive." No agreement was reached and I had to leave after a lunch in Salas as we were driving down to Chiclayo for the ambassador to meet more of the northern hierarchy. Because of the numbers travelling we went in two vehicles and Keith travelled with the honorary consul, so I had to wait until the evening to discuss what had happened. The journey was uneventful, delightful as ever with wild flowers everywhere. I said to myself, *Before I leave Perú I have to write a book on the wild flowers of Cajamarca*, but I never had the time.

In the hotel I told Keith what had happened and I briefed him what to say the following morning when he had breakfast with the regional president. I set off for the airport and flew down to Lima arriving at the house of Michael Pawley, a new secretary in the embassy, at 11:15 with a flight confirmed the next morning at 6:30. I was pleased to be home after another frustrating visit to the north.

9

Casa Grande

During one of my regular visits to Cajamarca, Dr Llontop came to see me: he was a small wiry man with black curly hair and a short moustache. He explained that he had heard of what I was doing in Arequipa and what was happening in Cajamarca and thought that I could help. I asked Marcos to join us while he explained.

"I live in Trujillo where I have a private veterinary practice. My largest client by far is La Co-Operativa Casa Grande, which lies about 40kms north of the city. Today Casa Grande is a town of 40,000 people with a large commercial centre, some light industry, churches, schools and a police station."

"I thought we were talking about a farm?" I said.

"We are, it was not always like this. Hans Guildmeister bought the existing Casa Grande estate in 1887. The success of his enterprise enabled him to buy the neighbouring estates of Lache, Sausa, Jagüey, Viscaíno, Gasñape and Molino, forming Sociedad Agricola Casa Grande Ltda, which was possibly the largest sugar producer in the world and easily the largest farm in the country with almost 110,000 hectares of land being used to grow sugar cane."

"That sounds enormous to me, I have never heard of such a large farm," I interjected.

"At one time in the 1950s Casa Grande was producing enough sugar to supply the whole of Perú's needs and so the sugar produced by other growers could be exported with great benefit to the country. The whole town has grown up and is built on land once owned by the Guildmeisters. They also developed a dairy herd of more than 100 cows, and they have a beef herd but I do not know its size because the land extends to more than 75,000 hectares inland in the hills going towards Cajamarca."

Marcos explained, "This unimproved land is called '*monte*' and is very poor in quality and has a low stocking capacity because the rainfall is very low and unreliable and so the grasses consist mostly of silica."

Dr Llontop continued, "There is also a herd of wild horses, of which a few are rounded up each year and brought to the house for breaking. There is a pig unit and egg producing and broiler poultry units. Tilapia [bream] are raised and we have our own veterinary laboratory with a high-security negative pressure section for making our own foot-and-mouth vaccine. That is to say there was..." His voice trailed away.

"This was all before the Velasco era: in 1968 General Juan Velasco Alvarado overthrew the democratic government and installed a communist military regime that destroyed agriculture throughout the country. Nobody was allowed to own more than ten hectares of land and so all the productive farms in the Andes were divided up and given to the peasants who had no idea of how to run their portion of the farm. As Casa Grande could not be divided in this way the Velasco Government decided that it should be given to the farm workers to be run as a single unit in a co-operative. The foreman and charge hands were all appointed to the board and do you know what was the first action of this new board?"

"No," we replied in tandem.

"The board decided that every farm worker should be given a colour television set. This was duly done and several hundred colour TV sets were purchased. This was sheer madness because there was no colour TV transmission in Perú! And so they could only see the picture in black and white on their colour TV sets." I shook my head in disbelief.

"Since then it has been downhill all the way; no money has been spent on anything of value. The plant that takes the cane and turns it into sugar has not been upgraded and so it costs a fortune to run and the co-operative loses more and more money.

"When Guildmeister ran the place, the laboratory employed two expatriate German veterinary surgeons and in addition to the foot-and-mouth vaccine, they made vaccines against anthrax, pasteurella, blackquarter and other diseases that I never knew or have forgotten. Today there is no money to buy media, reagents or chemicals and we are still using the stock of cattle dip that the family left, but when that runs out I do not know what will happen to the cattle in the *monte*. Every time there is a crisis the *gerente* is sacked and a new one brought in but the board do not realise that they are the problem; the workers do not work and they are all paid too much. Perú now imports sugar!"

"What a fascinating place," I said. "But how can I help you? You have not come all this way just to tell me the history of Casa Grande; what do you want me to do?"

"I would be most grateful if you could plan to visit us the next time you come to Cajamarca. There is a guest house on the *estancia* [farm] where you would receive free accommodation. I would like you to make a complete examination of the livestock and its management. I am certain that we have several important disease problems which you might be able to help us to control."

I had a short conversation with Marcos:

"I am due to fly out on Saturday morning but if I could get the bus on Thursday afternoon, I would be able to spend the Friday looking round the *estancia* and fly from Trujillo to Lima on Saturday."

"Do you think that this could be a useful source of income for LABRENOR?" asked Marcos.

"I think they might need your services if Dr Llontop has given us an accurate picture of what is going on."

It was agreed that I would take the afternoon bus to Trujillo, which stopped in Casa Grande, and that Dr Llontop would meet me at the bus stop and take me to the guest house where he would have arranged for me to spend Thursday and Friday nights.

The journey to Casa Grande was fascinating with stops in several of the small towns on the journey. The bus was full, mostly with women bearing large bags of produce together with the odd hen or guinea pig. Perhaps what was the most interesting aspect of the journey was the lesson in Darwinian biology. The Andes is a mass of valleys and although the road followed the main Jetequepeque valley down to the coast, there were numerous (probably more than fifty) small side valleys that joined; each of these valleys had its own vegetation. Shrubs and cacti differed in some way from those in the next valley. On later trips when I was in my own Land Rover I stopped and was able to look at these differences in more detail and take photographs. Had I been a better scientist I would have devoted more time and effort to documenting the plant life. I am certain that each valley was unique and like so many things in Perú it is definitely worth further investigation. My priorities, unfortunately, lay elsewhere.

Dr Llontop was waiting at the bus station in Casa Grande and drove me to the guest house where a large single room had been booked for me. Over a beer before my meal we planned the programme for the next day, starting with a visit to the *gerente*.

The drive up to main farm buildings and house was lined by mature trees, the trunks of which were painted white for about three metres. I was told that this was from the days before there was electricity available and transport was by horse, but it was both grand and elegant. The farm offices were close to the sugar extraction plant and full of people working away. The *gerente*, Ing Roeder, greeted me warmly:

"I hope you found the guest house comfortable and the food to your liking. We have so many problems on the *estancia* and now there is no money to invest in new equipment, or even drugs for the cattle. The members of the board are constantly seeking to raise their salaries and privileges despite there being no money to pay for them. Please do your best to advise Dr Llontop what needs to be done to improve the health and production of our livestock." After a discussion of our plans the interview concluded.

"He's a good man," said Dr Llontop, "but his hands are tied as the board are determined to squeeze every inti out of the farm. In some ways Casa Grande is a microcosm of Perú; nobody is prepared to invest and wait for a return; they all want to get their money out before it devalues. This inflation we are experiencing does not help. But when I see what Guildmeister built and what it has become I want to weep." He stopped and wiped his eyes. "A wonderful farm providing good wages for the staff, good conditions for them to live in, good schools, good sports facilities, everything; the farm producing and making good profits, and now everything is turning to rust and the animals die... But let us go and see the laboratory."

As with the rest of Casa Grande, the laboratory had been built to last and had superb facilities; whether the system of reducing the air pressure in the high security laboratory would still work was a moot point as it was likely that the seals would have perished from lack of use. Despite the excellent facilities it was obvious that nothing was going on in the building. The store was full of unused media and chemicals that had been there for many years. What a waste. From the laboratory we went to the dairy and again no expense had been spared on the building or the equipment, but it was an old side-by-side parlour rather than the modern herringbone type. The cattle were brought in from the fields for my inspection and they were a motley crew with a real hotchpotch of breeds, sizes and colours. It was obvious that the man in charge was not a cattleman and Dr Llontop had little say in the breeding policy. I had seen a similar problem in the Orapa Diamond Mine in the Kalahari Desert in Botswana, where they had dairy and beef cattle, pigs and poultry to provide fresh food for the staff of the mine. There, the farm was being run along the same rules as the diamond mine, which meant that they had two shifts of staff milking the cattle each day and two more at the weekends, which made the costs astronomical; it was little wonder that the farm had been losing almost half a million dollars per year. In my report to the farm manager I suggested that different rules apply to staffing a farm and an industrial plant. The diamonds were much more important than the cattle; nevertheless, different managerial techniques needed to be used. In Casa Grande the different managements were both agricultural but one was livestock and the other was growing and processing sugar cane.

Without carrying out a detailed clinical examination, I was fairly certain that some of the animals were suffering from tuberculosis and Dr Llontop explained that there had been a serious tuberculosis problem in their cattle: it had first been diagnosed eight years previously and more than 200 cows had been slaughtered. Thanks to the total incompetence of the Ministry of Agriculture there was never adequate tuberculin to test on a regular basis and in fact they had not tested for a couple of years until the previous September when they found that more than 110 cows were positive to the test. The ministry wanted to slaughter them straight away and that was why Dr Llontop had come to Cajamarca asking for my help. The ministry agreed to delay the slaughter until I had made an investigation. The calves showed poor development suggesting faults in their nutrition, which was not surprising on a farm where the board did not like to invest money.

We visited the pigs and the poultry and saw the fish ponds and we looked at the fields of cane almost ready for harvesting; the water supply had been turned off to allow the plants to wilt and so increase the sugar content of the sap. Finally before harvesting they would set fire to the standing canes to burn off the leaves; it would then be ready for cutting and processing. There were stands of perennial cane and stands of the annual crop and there was a railway line to take the cane to the plant and the refined sugar to the coast for shipment, as it was cheaper than sending the sugar by road to Lima. I was staggered by this *estancia*: I had never seen anything quite like it. When working in north-west Argentina I had seen a smaller *estancia*, Los Lapachos, in Jujuy, owned by Ricardo Leach, which produced sugar, tobacco and milk and about which a small town had developed on the farm, but Casa Grande was on a different scale: where the Leach family had a large guest wing as part of their house, Casa Grande had a large self-contained guest house with its own staff; it also possessed its own railway line with rolling stock which transported cane from the land to the plant and refined sugar to the docks for onward transport. It also owned a huge area of grazing land for the beef cattle. It was many years later and thousands of miles away before I saw a larger farm, and that was also a co-operative; it, too, had once been a single large estate, growing rice in South Vietnam, but was converted by the Ho Chi Minh Government to a highly successful state-run unit. I agreed with Dr Llontop: it was tragic to see a wonderful production unit destroyed by such ineptitude. It was obvious to me that without a major overhaul of the management, the farm was destined for bankruptcy.

I informed Dr Llontop that I would send him a report and outline what we could do to try and sort out some of the problems. In my report I recommended that I visit the farm with a Cajamarca colleague to undertake a complete evaluation of the dairy herd, carry out a tuberculin test on all the cattle, and take samples to examine in Arequipa for enzootic bovine leucosis. I pointed out that we could carry out the tuberculin test without charge as I could obtain the tuberculins from Britain without incurring any costs to LABVETSUR, and I could give my services without charge, but we had to buy the leucosis tests and so would have to charge for those.

My next visit to Cajamarca would have to be an extended affair as I would have to spend two weekends away from home; Monday to Wednesday I would work in LABRENOR and travel with Enrique to Casa Grande on the Thursday afternoon. On Friday we would examine the cows one by one and tuberculin-test them all; from animals with enlarged lymph glands we would take blood samples and separate the sera in the laboratory. There would be nothing to do over the weekend, but on the Monday we would have to read the results of the tuberculin test.

A visit by Tasmin Little, the internationally known violinist, with her regular accompanist Piers Lane, to the embassy decided the date of my next trip to Cajamarca, as they would be playing in the residency and I was keen to hear them. Because there would be a formal reception in the residency I wore a sports suit for the visit, not something I normally wore for work, a blazer and flannels being my preferred working gear – men did not wear shorts in Perú, even of the colonial variety; long trousers were *de rigueur.* I took with me a pair of working trousers for carrying out the clinical work. Being on my own I stayed in the *Turistas* hotel in Cajamarca. A visit to some farms of *campesinos* up in the hills was the only thing of note. We had to leave the Land Rover and walk the last few miles as we could not get the vehicle across the rivers. It meant that I experienced two of Perú's rustic bridges. The first was over a very wide river running not more than two to three metres below its banks. The bridge consisted of a steel hawser slung between concrete pillars on either side of the river with a suspended basket that could carry two people. By means of a second hawser and a lever on either side, the basket was hauled back and forth across the river. This was quite a scary experience as the basket swayed from side to side and I was certain that it would tip its contents into the river, but we crossed safely. The second bridge was even more frightening; this was like a rope ladder laid horizontally with rough tree branches about 12cms in diameter as the steps. This was a narrow bridge with a rope handrail on either side. The distance was shorter, not much more than thirty metres but there was a fifty-metre drop to the river and the bridge swayed in every conceivable direction as I made my tentative way across. The Peruvians scampered along not bothering to hold on to the hand ropes. Some rivers had both types of bridge and some had wide bridges without a handrail (Plate 34). I wondered to myself how could proper services be brought to these people? The terrain was much more demanding than any I had ever seen in Africa. Vehicular access to some of these Andean settlements would never be possible.

We were able to solve their calf problem and we were invited to lunch. It was a most interesting visit and our hospitable hosts killed the best guinea pigs for our lunch. For *Cuy chactado,* the guinea pig is killed, dressed (all its innards removed), flattened between two stones and then roasted in the fire. It was served with freshly dug *papas picantes* (boiled potatoes with a spicy sauce), with ice-cold well-water to drink. I have found all over the world that it is the people who have so little, who are so generous and will give you all they have. Many people are squeamish at the thought of eating guinea pig but it is not unpleasant and has a very similar taste to chicken; however, I was never able to do the Peruvian trick of eating all the bones, but left them on my plate...

Development towards independence for LABRENOR was painfully slow as Ing Hidalgo from the ministry kept finding more 'insurmountable' obstacles to handing over control. Marcos and I had a meeting with him in his office but it was like a brick wall.

"Government property could not be given to non-governmental organisations." He could not see that they did not need to 'give' the building and its equipment to LABRENOR, but allow them the use of it. I pointed out that we had equipment in LABVETSUR that belonged to the Ministry of Agriculture and although we used it, if the laboratory closed down, then it would be returned to its rightful owners. We were going to need a big hitter again to change his thinking! However, I knew that Dr Archie Hunter, a veterinary adviser to the Overseas Development Agency, would be in Perú in time for my next visit, and so Marcos and I agreed that we would set up another meeting with all interested parties to force the *ingeniero*'s hand.

Enrique and I set off by road to Casa Grande. A few kilometres outside Cajamarca, in an area of dense bush, Enrique stopped the vehicle and pointed to a shack hanging precipitously over the side of a hill.

"Look up there, Dr Roger: some months ago there was a moderate earthquake, but part of the hill collapsed, exposing this building to general view. It is a 'coca' laboratory."

"What do they do there?" I asked.

"They take the leaves of the cocaine plant, and using sulphuric acid and acetone, extract the impure drug to produce the *'pasta basica'*, which is then transported along the River Amazon network to Colombia where it is refined into the pure drug ready for export to the USA or Europe."

Examining the cattle on Friday morning was a bit of a pantomime; although they were used to being milked they were not accustomed to being handled for a clinical examination and the staff were a little afraid of these large beasts. Clipping the hair and measuring the skin thickness for the tuberculin was yet another problem; two sites have to be prepared because a small dose of bovine tuberculin is injected into the skin of the upper site while the lower site receives a dose of tuberculin made from the avian strain of the bacterium. The reason for using the two different strains is to aid the elimination of 'false positive' reactions: the reaction to the bovine tuberculin is always much greater if the animal is suffering from tuberculosis. Taking a blood sample from the tail vein was quite straightforward as they stood quietly in the milking stall and munched away at some food in the trough. The calves and heifers were also tested and the premises examined; we noted that the adobe walls of the calf pens were being eaten away by the calves, a sure indication of a nutritional deficiency.

In historical times much of the building in this part of Perú was in adobe and the local tribe, the Chimu, built exclusively in it. Not far away was the incredible archaeological site of Chan Chan with its nine buried palaces, only one of which has been reclaimed from the desert sands (Plate 35). They also built the largest adobe structure in the world, The Temple of the Sun. When the *conquistadores* arrived they realised the religious significance to the Chimu of this building, and they attempted to destroy it by diverting the river in order to wash it away, but only succeeded in removing one corner of this solid adobe structure. The sand and the wind in this part of the world do some fantastic things: in the desert you can see massive '*medias lunas*', each a giant croissant made of sand. These can be found in many parts of coastal Perú but it is only in the north that you find *media luna* stacked on *media luna*, forming gigantic pyramids of sand that drift across the road with the wind. These must have been the inspiration for the Chimu to build their massive temple.

To return to the calves of Casa Grande, eating the walls indicated a nutritional deficiency in the calves, which would explain their poor growth. Calves that do not reach their potential are unlikely to produce good yielding cows. It would be necessary for me to produce dietary recommendations to ensure that the calves grew well until they were weaned. It had been a long day and Enrique and I found the baths in the guest house – they did not have that modern invention, the shower – a welcome relaxation after the heat and the dust. Over dinner Enrique informed me that the American Ambassador would be up in the hills the following day, opening a rebuilt irrigation scheme. He suggested that it might make for an interesting day out.

At 10:30am on the Saturday we set off for the two-hour drive to an Andean village whose name I have forgotten. In a similar manner to the valleys running into the Cajamarca road, the side valleys each boasted their own flora and so we had an interesting journey up to the village. Even the smallest Andean village possesses its *picanteria* (a café/restaurant serving local dishes) and the first beer washed away the dust from the dirt road. We were soon joined by local dignitaries including the *alcalde* wearing his chain of office and with his gown over his arm. The chairman of the irrigation company was the next to arrive with his great moustache and his enormous straw sombrero; they joined us at the table and from the discussion I found out what had happened. The *Sendero Luminoso* had totally destroyed the irrigation canal from the hill to the fields, which meant the end of agriculture for the village as the half a million dollars required to replace it was not to be found from local or national resources. In desperation the chairman of the irrigation committee had written to Ronald Reagan, then the President of the USA, and explained the predicament of the villagers: without the canal there could be no agriculture; the village would die and all the people would have to migrate to Trujillo to try and find some means of subsistence. Apparently the president had written to the ambassador and instructed him to finance the reconstruction project and that was why he was coming to open the rebuilt irrigation canal.

Another round of beers was ordered – my rounds seemed to be getting bigger and bigger. The ambassador was due at 2:30pm and the opening would commence at 3:00pm. At least that was the plan, but this was rural Perú. I had steak and chips for lunch while Enrique was more adventurous and went for a dish that seemed to include little tubes of small intestine. From where we sat in the bar we could see the Plaza de Armas, the centre of every Peruvian town, and promptly at 2:30pm the town band arrived and started by practising the *Star Spangled Banner* and then the beautiful but interminable Peruvian national anthem. No American Ambassador. Three o'clock came: no American Ambassador. By 4:00pm, it was obvious that His Excellency Tony Quainton was not going to come but by then there was a huge crowd including representatives of the Trujillo press.

The chairman of the irrigation was getting desperate and said to me:

"Dr Windsor, will you be the ambassador? You are a white man not a Peruvian and the people will not know."

"Will I play the part of Tony Quainton?" I replied. I weighed up the pros and cons; it did not matter to me because I was unlikely to be prosecuted for impersonating Ambassador Tony Quainton: by the same token it was better for the image of the American Embassy that somebody purporting to be the ambassador should open the irrigation scheme than that the crowd should be sent home disappointed.

THE VETERINARY DETECTIVES: A VET IN PERU

"OK," I said, "I'll be the ambassador."

The *alcalde* donned his gown and he, the chairman of the irrigation and I made our way to the dais which had been erected for the occasion, while the band played *El Condor Pasa* which I have always thought was the national anthem of the Andes and which was popularised for a western audience by Simon and Garfunkle as *El Condor Pasa (If I Could)*. The three of us stood on the dais while the band played the national anthem of the USA and then that of Perú. The alcalde welcomed H. E. Sr Tony Quainton, the 'Ambassador' of the USA, and thanked the great American people for helping their poor relatives in Perú and the chairman went into great paeans of praise for El Presidente Reagan who had come to the rescue of this poor village high in the Andes. He went into great philosophical detail about how this demonstrated the brotherhood of man when such an important person in the world should give time, thought and money to people that he did not know, many thousands of kilometres away. And then it was time for the 'Ambassador' to speak. I do not remember exactly what I said because it was never written down. I thanked the speakers and the crowd for the warmth of my welcome and said how important it was for rich nations to help those in need. I stated that President Reagan was very disturbed by the seemingly endless problems of terrorism in Perú and would do all that he could to counteract the effects of these disgruntled people; I could not resist the temptation to throw in some propaganda for Britain by saying how the American Government was co-operating with the British in bringing development aid to this and other South American states. I said how proud I was to be there, while thinking at the same time how the USA was happy to throw money at a problem while not being prepared to take a risk of its people being injured. One sees this magnified in many conflicts today where the western powers are happy to drop bombs and kill innocent women and children, while not risking putting in their soldiers to fight. My speech was considerably shorter than those of the other two speakers. And I concluded by wishing the project well and I hoped that it would help the people in the village lead better lives; I congratulated them all on working so hard to bring the irrigation canal to life so quickly. And then I sat down to great applause.

The following morning Enrique and I were eating breakfast when into the dining room rushed the waiter waving the local paper:

"Doctor, you are famous – your picture is on the front page of the paper."

My speech, together with a photograph of the "American Ambassador", was there for all to see in *Noticias Trujillo*, and I waited to get complaints from the Americans, but none ever came. I suspect that the American Embassy was only too happy to let the matter drop as it would have been of some embarrassment to them, were it published that their ambassador had just not turned up to open an American project.

Back in Casa Grande on the Monday we were joined by Dr Llontop to read the test. Only five animals were positive to our test, a very different picture from that seen in the previous test when more than a hundred animals reacted. It had been agreed that all would be slaughtered and Dr Llontop would be present and send any lesions to us in Arequipa. From our discussions it was obvious to me that there was more to things than met the eye. There were animals showing obvious lymph gland enlargement indicating the presence of enzootic bovine leucosis virus in the herd; this was not surprising as several of the animals were from the USA (a country in which the disease is endemic). Dr Llontop said he would attend the slaughter and examine the animals for evidence of tuberculosis and take photographs. All the slaughtered animals showed evidence of the disease and we were able to demonstrate mycobacteria in the samples sent to Arequipa. This gave the board confidence to continue with my programme, which was for the staff of LABRENOR to test the herd every three to four months with slaughter of all positives until the herd had had two clear tests, when testing would be reduced to once a year. However, this policy became impossible to carry out and had to be modified because we found other factors that interfered with the tests (see Chapter 10).

Dr Llontop took me to Trujillo Airport where I caught the plane for Lima and was met by Keith's driver in the bulletproof Range Rover with windows that did not open. The Bentley of John Shakespeare was steel-clad as a protection from terrorists, the Range Rover was protected by Kevlar, which is a much lighter polyamide fibre with immense tensile strength. This enabled the vehicle to attain the same speed as the unprotected Range Rover. I was taken directly to the residency where I was to spend the night. The stars of the evening were Tasmin Little with her accompanist Piers Lane. The main reception room in the residency was prepared for the concert and as a very junior member of the audience, which was packed with ambassadors and their wives, I selected a seat near the back but which gave me a good view of the musicians. It was a delightful concert and both musicians gave excellent performances. Miss Little not only pleased the ear with her music but she delighted the eye. The concert began with the Kreisler 'Praeludium and Allegro' and concluded with the 'Tzigane' by Ravel. It was an excellent end to a long, arduous trip away from home, but I was very happy to fly home to Arequipa the next morning.

We had demonstrated only a low level of infection with tuberculosis in the herd, but the same was not true for enzootic bovine leucosis, as almost every sample that we had taken in Casa Grande was positive to the ELISA (enzyme linked immuno-assay) test for the presence of the virus. As only a small percentage of animals that are infected go on to develop full-blown leukaemia, I thought that the slaughter policy should not be used; instead, attempts should be made to prevent the transmission of the infection. The virus could be transmitted in blood, milk and possibly uterine fluids, with the virus being present in diseased lymphocytes (one of the common white cells in the blood). My report recommended that the infected animals be managed as a separate group, which should be milked and fed last. When an infected animal was handled then the rubber glove used during the examination should be discarded after use. To eradicate the disease in this way would take several years and would require a high standard of husbandry, which I was not sure would be maintained. However, the Peruvian worker, if properly trained, could be relied upon to do a good job, and so there was some hope of success; in the meantime the losses from the disease would not be very high.

We heard that the project was to be inspected by a veterinary surgeon from the Overseas Development Administration, Dr Archie Hunter, a consultant from the Centre for Tropical Veterinary Medicine in Edinburgh. Enrique and Marcos set up a similar meeting to that attended by the ambassador: Keith thought it better if he did not attend as this might detract from the importance of 'the man from London'. Archie and I travelled up to Cajamarca with John Taylor from the British Embassy. The Cajamarquinos arranged another meeting of the interested parties and had sensibly invited the Regional Minister of Agriculture (still the same man) to close the meeting rather than open it, and to give his blessing to the new structure; at least that was the plan. Archie was suitably impressed with the work being carried out in LABRENOR. He approved of our plans for the laboratory and for its financing and said that he would ask Tony Irvin to obtain some 'pump-priming' money from ODA. With Enrique and Marcos,

I took Archie and John round the various officials who would be present to ensure that they were all on side.

The round-table meeting was a very one-sided affair with Ing Hidalgo being the sole opposition. As I had done in the previous meeting, I decided that the best way to attack the man was to mock him when he was being intransigent. I showed the meeting a copy of the directive from Lima to Ing Hidalgo in his position as regional director of agriculture, instructing him to proceed with the privatisation of the veterinary laboratory along the lines of LABVETSUR in Arequipa. John and I were translating for Archie and so again I was able to stop Hidalgo whenever I wanted by using the translation pretext. Again I infuriated him by calling him 'Ingeniero Hígado'. Nothing would budge him. By now feelings were running high as he kept evading the issue: finally I actually lost my temper as I had had enough, and threw my papers on the table and stated that if he continued to refuse to carry out the instructions from his minister in Lima, he had no alternative but to resign his post.

Archie recalls that at this point, the shit hit the fan, and he thought a mini war was about to break out and that Ing Hidalgo was going to be lynched. John, the diplomat, calmed the meeting down, and Ing Hidalgo agreed to implement the directive. Because of how things had gone, it was decided that an agreement should be drawn up there and then, and a secretary was summoned to whom someone dictated the constitution of LABRENOR. I then had one of my occasional bursts of inspiration and suggested to the locals and our adviser that I should propose that Ing Hidalgo chair the board of directors for LABRENOR; he was bound to accept, which he did. This would give him massive power over the laboratory, but which he could only use for the good of LABRENOR because he would have no supporters on the board. He would have to make sure that the laboratory was a success because his reputation would depend upon it. The meeting concluded by deciding on the composition of the board: Hidalgo in the chair, Enrique as secretary, one of the agricultural advisers as treasurer; Nestlé were given a seat on the board, along with FONGAL Cajamarca, and because of its history and the potential financial support, the British Embassy was asked to appoint a board member. I filled this for the remainder of my time in the country. A very impressive certificate with seals and stamps was drawn up, which all participants including John and Archie signed. At some point during all of this John Taylor slipped out and reappeared with a bottle of whisky. Once the document was signed by everyone, John unscrewed the stopper, which he scrunched up and threw away, meaning that nobody would leave till the whisky was finished as we toasted the new constitution. Some of the senior agricultural research officers must have told the minister over lunch of the problems because he finally arrived when the dust had settled with a speech handing over the laboratory to this consortium.

The two Peruvians, John, Archie and I had a splendid meal in La Cajamarques well washed down with good Chilean wine. We had an uneventful flight to Lima Airport, where we left Archie to continue on his journey to Santa Cruz in Bolivia where he was to visit the LIDIVET project, while John and I set off for the embassy to brief the ambassador on our success.

In retrospect it seems crazy that we had to battle for more than two years to resuscitate a laboratory that everyone agreed was essential to improve livestock production in northern Perú. Yet it had taken the combined efforts of the British Ambassador, the president of FONGALSUR, his cousin Jorge Lozada Stanbury, the senator for Arequipa, the senior animal health adviser to ODA and several consultants from Britain working with the dedicated band of young vets in Cajamarca, Enrique Lopez, Marcos Chávarry, Pedro Ortiz and the veterinary staff from the faculty, together with the staff of FONGAL Cajamarca, the technical team from INCALAC (Nestlé), and the local farmers, to bring about the rebirth.

Once we had been given the go-ahead, it was a different story as the dedicated staff from LABVETSUR set about helping their colleagues in the north. The first to make the long journey was Elio Cruz who set about ensuring that the computer systems in the laboratory were compatible with those from INCALAC and FONGAL Cajamarca, and writing the programmes for charging the farmers through their INCALAC accounts. Aurora was the next to make the journey, to set up the recording and reporting systems. She was followed by Denis whose job was to determine what equipment and reagents were required to set LABRENOR on its feet (Plate 36). When all was ready Keith Haskell and I went north for the official opening of the revitalised laboratory, and once the celebrations were over I remained to get the veterinary work up and running and the *Brucella* testing system under way, which, as in LABVETSUR, would form the basic income for the laboratory.

I remained in Cajamarca for three weeks and as in LABVETSUR I was delighted with the enthusiasm of the LABRENOR staff; if their efforts were rewarded, then I was certain of the success of the northern laboratory. I decided to spend a weekend in the jungle and so on the Saturday morning I set off for the Amazonas town of Chachapoyas. As I was driving towards Celendin I thought how delightful it was to come to Cajamarca to do some veterinary work, rather than take part in the endless battles with Peruvian bureaucracy.

I remember little of the weekend, because I was by myself, and met nobody who sticks in my memory. What I do recall is that I spent most of the weekend driving the long, long journey on a very bad road through the most glorious Andean scenery, at one time climbing up and up bare hills, and at others in the most beautiful forest. The province Amazonas takes its names from the River Marañon, which is Perú's principal tributary of the Amazon. I stayed in the Hotel Marañon, which was comfortable and cheap, but my abiding memory of the hotel was a very smart waiter presenting me a very lengthy menu but it turned out that all they could offer me was the eternal chicken and chips!

I returned to Arequipa with a great sense of achievement, not my achievement, but that of all those Peruvians, members of the veterinary profession, laboratory staff and farmers who had fought to revitalise something that they had had, but which had almost been torn from them. They deserved to succeed.

I first met Dr Aurelio Málaga Alba in Cajamarca as he was descending from the pillion of Pedro Ortiz's small motorbike. We were all in Cajamarca for the annual conference of the *Colegio Medico Veterinario del Perú*. I had timed my regular visit to LABRENOR to coincide with this meeting. I was about to enter the vet school when Pedro rode up with the great man. Dr Málaga was the father of veterinary medicine in Perú, having founded the first veterinary school in the country in San Marcos University in Lima; he had been director of the State Veterinary Service and also Minister of Agriculture. He leaped nimbly from the motorcycle, belying the fact that he was in his eighties. He was small in stature with receding white hair, a large moustache, bright sparkling eyes and a wicked grin that went with his sharp sense of humour. He greeted me warmly and I took to him instantly and the more I knew him the more I was impressed with him. He was a man of great integrity, the grandson of a former president of Perú and a veterinary research worker who added greatly to our knowledge of rabies in vampire bats; he was currently working for the Pan-American Health Organisation at the Instituto Nacional de Salud in Chorrillos, a suburb of Lima. I was very interested to find out that he was a Dick graduate of 1926 (that is, he graduated from the Royal (Dick) Veterinary College), my old college in Edinburgh. He had chosen Edinburgh as it was the only vet school in Europe in the 1920s that offered a course in virology and he had been and remained passionately interested in the subject. His father had sent him to Britain with enough money to purchase an Austin 7. He told me how he had written to his father saying that he did not want to shame the family by driving around in such a small car when all his classmates were driving Jaguars and Bentleys. His father duly obliged and sent him more money.

The stories about him were legion: his most recent exploit was told to me by Dra Norma Nöe. She had been with Dr Málaga and a younger male colleague in the northern jungle looking for vampire bats. On their return to camp the mist had come down and they took the wrong turning coming down the hill and were lost in the jungle for almost a week. According to Norma it was Dr Málaga that kept them alive and found them jungle food to eat. Once they had found a stream, he insisted that they follow it downhill as eventually it would lead them to civilisation or at least habitation; sure enough they ended up at a Peruvian air-force base that was watching the border with Ecuador. Of the three it was Dr Málaga who suffered the least, and within a short space of time was back to normal, whereas Norma had still not fully recovered. Among his other exploits, the one that most impressed me was that when he was director of veterinary services there was an outbreak of foot-and-mouth disease in Ecuador and Dr Málaga imprisoned the sister of the president for illegally bringing cattle across the border. When he refused to have her released he was dismissed by the president.

Also at that meeting was Professor Michael Clarkson, who was head of the veterinary parasitology department at Liverpool Veterinary School. He, Dr Málaga and I drafted a telegram to the president of the *Colegio Medico Veterinario del Perú* (which combined the functions of the British Royal College of Veterinary Surgeons and the British Veterinary Association) which purported to come from the president of the British Veterinary Association and read:

"On the occasion of your annual conference, the British Veterinary

Association sends you greetings and their best wishes for a profitable gathering. The veterinary professions in our two countries have a great connexion in that it was a graduate from a British veterinary college that founded the first veterinary college in your country, thus establishing a direct line from the founding fathers in Britain. We wish your profession every success. Walter Beswick, Honorary President."

When this 'telegram' was read out at the conference it raised a huge round of applause from the delegates and so Michael and I were pleased with our little deception.

The great problem that I found listening to the scientific talks was that I could understand every word that was said, but that at the end of the talk I had no idea what the delegate had been talking about. I formulated the view that when you listen in your own language you do not concentrate on every word spoken but you listen to the overall content and discard what you consider unimportant, enabling you to analyse the content as you go along.

Michael and I had to attend every social function, and dancing with the young veterinary students on cobblestones at 3,000m was exhausting. Guinea pig was served at all official dinners and I found it quite palatable, rather like eating a scrawny old chicken. We were the only non-Latins present and consequently the centre of attention; luckily for me Michael had a reasonable command of Spanish and so I did not have to translate for him as he was able to make himself understood. It was a good meeting and I was able to explain to many vets what we were trying to achieve in Arequipa and Cajamarca, and the concept of self-financing was generally understood.

On my return to Arequipa I felt that something was needed to cement the relations between the profession in the two countries and it seemed to me that to honour Dr Málaga would fill the bill. Consequently, I wrote to the dean of the veterinary college in Edinburgh and suggested that Dr Málaga be given an honorary doctorate of the university. I was able to provide them with sufficient evidence of the merit of the man and they readily agreed. I then turned my attention to the Royal College of Veterinary Surgeons and suggested that they offer Dr Málaga an Honorary Fellowship of the College but was greeted with a blank wall of indifference.

"He has never been a member of this college," was the reply.

"Since he is a Peruvian and returned to Perú on his graduation, it is not surprising that he never joined." I was so disgusted by this action that I wrote and told them by failing to honour a great man, who had done so much for veterinary medicine, they were the losers and not him.

Dr Aurelio Málaga Alba with vampire bat

On my frequent visits to Lima I often called in at his laboratory. One Thursday morning I picked up Dr Málaga at his apartment and I drove him to his workplace in the Instituto Nacional de Salud in Chorrillos. Dr Málaga was very sad at what was happening there: with few staff and no money, slowly the whole place was falling to pieces. Dr Málaga introduced me to his colleague Dr Rodriguez who was testing rabies vaccine by injecting live virus into the brain of vaccinated mice. There was no anaesthetic for the mice, he had no gloves, no mask and there was no food for the mice! National Institute, poor Perú! Dr Málaga took me to see the snake colony, where the various poisonous snakes were kept so that their venom could be collected to make protective sera for human treatment. This whole unit was in a much better condition than that for rabies and I suspected the commercial company that made the antivenin were financing their activities.

Edinburgh University came up trumps and not only gave the degree but they provided the flights for Dr Málaga and his wife from Perú to Edinburgh, accommodated them in the George Hotel, threw a lunch party in his honour after the morning graduation ceremony and gave him the necessary gown and hood to keep (Plate 38). That afternoon the vet graduates were admitted to the Royal College by its president in a ceremony at the Dick, after which Dr Málaga delivered the William Dick Lecture to a packed audience (Plate 39). I was in Britain on leave at the time but Maxine was in Texas with our younger son visiting his godfather and so with my daughter Claire as my partner I attended all the ceremonies. I had hired a large limousine in which to chauffeur our guests. Claire and I stayed with our dear friends the MacLarens in their beautiful Georgian house in Newington. The night before the graduation, Professor David Brocklesby, the director of the Centre for Tropical Veterinary Medicine, gave a party at which there were a large number of overseas guests. On the night after the ceremonies the MacLarens hosted a dinner party, to which they invited members of the medical profession with an interest in neuroscience or brain disorders. The whole affair was magic and Dr Málaga and his Cuban wife had a wonderful time, and as I helped him from the car on his return to the hotel from Newington, he put his arms round me and said:

"Roger, this has been the proudest day of my life."

I could not have received a better thank you.

Some months later Dr Málaga came to Arequipa to see what LABVETSUR was doing and he stayed with us. He was very impressed with our facilities and not a little jealous (Plate 40). While in the laboratory he presented me with a copy of his book on rabies (Plate 41). He asked after Claire and said that he had a little present for her fifteenth birthday (in Perú a rather special birthday for a girl); he also asked us if there was anything that we could not obtain in Arequipa and Maxine and I both replied – 'mushrooms'. A week or so later a shoe box arrived in the post; on removing the paper it was found to be a polystyrene box containing a large number of excellent mushrooms. In the midst of the mushrooms was a small polythene envelope inside of which was a beautiful emerald for Claire. Thereafter, whenever I was in Lima, I would make a point of visiting Dr Málaga either in his laboratory or in his elegant apartment in Miraflores. In May1991 I phoned his laboratory to arrange to see him, but was informed that he was ill and had not been to the laboratory for more than a week. I called at his flat and he opened the door, a pale shadow of his former self. He made me coffee and we sat in the sitting room looking out over the Pacific Ocean and I told him that Maxine and I were about to go on leave to the UK. Once again he reminisced about the wonderful time that he had had in Edinburgh and we discussed the party at David Brocklesby's house and the dinner party given by the MacLarens. I had to drag myself away; I did not want to go. As I was about to open the front door he put his arms about me and we hugged each other; I knew then that I would never see him again. Maxine and I went to Britain and on 22nd July 1991, Aurelio Málaga Alba died. He was a delightful man and had done so much for his country. A leading veterinary surgeon and with his passing, Perú lost one of their truly great countrymen. It is my hope that a biography of this fine man be written before all those who knew him die.

10

Caballos de Paso

When in England on leave I met a farmer who wished to import *caballos de paso* (pacing horses), similar to the quarter horses used in the American west for working with cattle (Plate 42); these are ambling horses that you can ride all day without getting tired because you do not have to rise and fall as you do when trotting. The horses do not trot, which is the movement when the diagonal limbs move in unison; instead it is the two limbs on the same side that move together. Ambling is a much more comfortable ride for the horseman than the constant movement at the trot; it is very tiring trotting for a long period of time.

The problem for exporters is that Perú is said to be infected with the three types of virus of equine encephalitis and these viruses also cause the same type of brain disease in humans. The Europeans are therefore concerned about the importation of the virus with the horses. I thought that if LABVETSUR set up a serum survey of horses, mules and donkeys from Piura to Tacna, it could be a new source of income for the laboratory. At the same time, showing that large parts of the Peruvian coast were not infected would help the European authorities to make a favourable decision. Discussions with aficionados in Arequipa suggested that the diseases had never been seen in southern Perú. I decided to visit the north of Perú to find out if the horse owners were interested in paying for such a survey.

There are three different viruses producing Eastern, Western and Venezuelan equine encephalitides and all three are spread by biting flies and mosquitoes in particular. These diseases in horses can result in death and the virus can be transmitted to humans. Despite their name these viruses primarily infect birds and only occasionally spill over into the horse and human populations. Unfortunately, the birds affected are migrating birds that travel backwards and forwards between the USA and South America. Most infections are in passerine birds (a group including most of the songbirds) and appear to be asymptomatic, although a few species become ill after experimental inoculation. Clinical cases have been reported in some non-passerine birds including partridges, pheasants, turkeys, ratites (emus, ostriches), some psittacine birds, pigeons, house sparrows, and egrets, among others. Among mammals, these viruses mainly cause disease in horses and other equine species, but clinical cases have also been reported in sheep, cattle, dogs, South American camelids (llamas and alpacas), pigs, and deer.

As the visit would have to include all the major cities of northern coastal Perú it would be necessary to carry it out by road; John Taylor from the embassy agreed to lend me an old fisheries project Land Rover and so I flew off to Lima one Monday afternoon and of course the plane was late; nevertheless, I managed to get to the meeting with the National Association of Caballos de Paso on time and it was a very useful meeting. The members were very keen to export horses and agreed to co-operate in any way possible, including paying for the survey. It was their idea that the survey should be financed by a tax on all horses exported. Thus the people who made the money would pay the bulk of the costs; the problem for me with this suggestion was that LABVETSUR would have to underwrite the cost of the survey until the first export of a horse took place.

On Tuesday I collected the embassy Land Rover and drove up to Trujillo with no problem and in the evening met with their association in the Central Club; the Arequipa Club is housed in a large, elegant Victorian building but the home of the Central Club was positively regal, which was not surprising since it had been the viceroy's Palace and was built in the old Spanish *casona* style: you pass from salon to salon to patios with fountains and fishponds and all beautifully furnished. It was enormous, occupying a whole street block (100m x 100m). After the meeting I was entertained to an excellent meal of *chicharrones de pollo* (these are chunks of chicken marinated in a spicy sauce and then deep-fried) followed by prawns in batter, all served in their grand dining room. That evening I met a delightful vet from Chiclayo called German Gorbitz (a Peruvian of German origin) and we set up the meeting with the Chiclayo Association for the following evening. The Central Club is very grand but I preferred the Arequipa Club, which was not so grand but a more convivial place to go with friends.

Dr Gorbitz arranged for the meeting to be held in the house of the chairman of the *Associación de Caballos de Paso de Chiclayo*; the meeting was preceded by a splendid dinner. The chairman was in a jubilant mood as his wife had just been selected as, not *Señorita Perú*, but *Señora Perú*! She had won the National Beauty Competition for married women. She was certainly a beautiful woman and an excellent cook; I believe that that was one of the qualifications for the prize, along with looks and dress sense. After a great meal we set to discussing how to go about obtaining permission to export their horses to Europe and to Britain in particular. According to the horsemen, Venezuelan equine encephalitis was the only type that had ever been diagnosed in Perú and that it had only come as far south as Piura, the second most northerly department in the country. Apparently, birds from further south in Perú did not migrate to North America and there was no evidence of infection in the resident population of birds. They were all prepared to pay for a survey if that would aid in the export of their horses. I undertook to contact the British and European veterinary authorities and report back to them. We agreed I would meet them again on my return from Piura. It had been a most enjoyable and productive evening.

The next afternoon I set off for the two-hour journey to Piura but was directed via the old road and so instead of two, it took me more than five hours! However, it was a most interesting journey and very reminiscent of Botswana, with thorn trees and long, dry, yellow grass; barbed wire was strung from old wooden posts and even the grazing cattle were of the zebu type with their pronounced humps. This road had been in large measure washed away during the floods of 1983 and a new one constructed. I would be driving along when the road suddenly ended with a sheer drop and I had to drive off onto a track to where the tarmac started again. All the roads in the north were terrible but this was the worst that I had seen. However, the journey was enlivened by a couple of young ladies to whom I gave a lift. They were hitchhiking, having missed the bus to Piura. They were both extremely attractive, one was of African descent and the other was definitely pure *latina*, and both were in their late twenties. They informed me that they were 'working girls' or 'ladies of the night:

"We have been working in the house in Chiclayo for the past two years,

177

THE VETERINARY DETECTIVES: A VET IN PERU

but recently the manager has increased the number of girls and there is not enough work and so we contacted the house in Piura, and we start tonight; we had a party in the house last night to bid us farewell; we overslept and missed the bus."

"And we are most grateful to you for getting us to Piura in time," butted in the African girl.

During the journey I received a detailed explanation of the system operated in Peruvian brothels. Most coastal towns in Peru have a brothel on the outskirts of the town and, I was informed, all operate to the same system. Girls rent a room from the owner/manager and the house opens at 7:00pm and the girls solicit from their rooms – the clients walk down the corridors and discuss terms with the ladies. At 11:00pm the system changes and as the girls become free they congregate in a large meeting room with music playing and set about with small tables. There is a bar and couples can dance or go off to their private rooms. At 2:00am the house "closed"; however, the client can remain with his partner in the room until 6:00am when they have to leave. Their description of the house, the clients and their style of life certainly helped pass the time on the extended journey.

Piura is a pleasant city, one of the oldest in Perú, but clean and neat. Much of the city was damaged during the floods and so there are many new buildings to be seen. I dropped off the young ladies at their new home and was offered a 'quickie', which I declined.

Because I was so late, the people had given me up for lost and most had gone home; the meeting was reprogrammed for the next morning. The hotel was in the Plaza de Armas in an old *casona*, a beautiful old building with a large patio in the centre where I had dinner and breakfast. About a dozen men turned up to the meeting and their response was very similar to those on the previous day. I returned to Chiclayo after the meeting, by the correct road this time. It is an incredible road: unlike the old road it went through a total desert with almost no habitation along the 200kms between the two cities. I was about 50kms from Chiclayo with the Land Rover going like a bomb... when it suddenly stopped. I knew that the petrol was low but not that low. As luck would have it, we came to a halt outside one of the half dozen cafés on the road. I got some more petrol but that did not do the trick. I had borrowed the Land Rover from the embassy and there was not a single tool in it. I thought that the problem was dirty petrol blocking the carburettor. After a while I decided that the best idea was to get a lift into Chiclayo and take it from there. I locked up the Land Rover, and with my suitcase set off with a couple of fruit salesmen who dropped me at the hotel. I phoned German who was horrified that I had left the vehicle on the road. He insisted that we set off immediately to get it started or tow it back.

"What about the meeting?" I said.

"They won't mind, I'll phone them and tell them we will be late."

We got back to the vehicle about 8:00pm to find that a mechanic had arrived to repair another truck that had also come to a stop. He had a look at mine and decided that the problem was the petrol pump. As soon as we set up a supply of petrol to the carburettor the motor fired and it was running; it was decided that we would rig up a tank with a gravity feed to the carburettor which should get me home. This was duly done and as we were checking we noticed the petrol pump was again working and that the petrol was pumping out from the tank. Hurrah. We dismantled the temporary feed, connected up the main petrol pipe and left the engine running while we went and had a Coke. Off we went. Half a mile down the road the engine stopped again! The mechanic had gone off with his temporary tank and so there was nothing for it but to put on the tow rope and spend an hour behind the wheel. It was a horrendous journey, I could not use my lights because that might drain the battery so I could see very little. What really worried me were the sand dunes which migrated across the road with the wind. We got back into Chiclayo just after midnight by which time the meeting had been abandoned. We found a café that was still open and had some fried chicken. And so to bed.

German, who worked for the Casa Real Brewery, organised a mechanic to examine the car on the Saturday morning and he decided that the petrol tank had to come out. The car was towed off to the garage and out came the tank and then the pump. Once the pump was cleaned up, primed with some petrol and a current applied, it was obvious that it was working perfectly and so all was replaced. The electrician was called; a huge blackman wearing the most filthy oil-stained dungarees came to examine the situation. It was hilarious: he lifted up the bonnet and stood with his arms folded, a vacant expression on his face, looking at the mass of wires all tied together which makes up the Land Rover's electrics. After a long silence, he shook his head, licked his lips and finally spoke. Had he spoken in English it would have been:

"Dat is de wire to de pump!"

He was right. He crawled under the truck, and with a small wire and light bulb did strange things. He dismantled several circuits under the bonnet and finally connected two different wires together, stood up and said:

"De truck will go now."

Sure enough it did! It was almost black magic! I was staggered, he certainly knew what he was doing but gave the appearance of being a hobo!

The visit to the horsemen had been arranged to fit in with a routine visit to Cajamarca and a short visit to Casa Grande. Because of the problems with the Land Rover I did not get to Casa Grande until 5:00pm. Luckily they had received my telephone message. The whole of Sunday was spent driving round the farm; they were using the effluent from the pig farm to feed tilapia and *camarones* (crayfish) in ponds. The whole enterprise had improved beyond measure since the advice that I gave them and the milk production had increased from eight litres a day per cow to sixteen... can't be bad!

The tuberculosis problem in the cattle of Casa Grande was serious: it had been present for more than eight years and 200 cows had been slaughtered. When we started discussing the problem it was obvious to me that there was more to things than met the eye. It finally transpired that not only was *Mycobacterium tuberculosis* involved in the problem; it was possible that the human strain was involved. Was it possible that the enzootic bovine leucosis was playing a part? At the back of my mind was the problem we had seen on the Orapa Diamond Mine dairy farm in Botswana, where, if the herd was tested when a certain plant was in flower, all the cattle showed a positive reaction to the test. There had to be other factors at play. Discussions with Dr Llontop and the ministry vets that Monday morning resulted in the decision that only animals that had reacted positive to two consecutive tests, three months apart, would be slaughtered. On that happy note I set off in the Land Rover for Cajamarca.

Halfway up the Jetequepeque Valley there was a loud bang and I thought that the silencer had fallen off, but it was a rear-wheel tyre blowout, and so I had to cross the Andes with no spare wheel. As I climbed the final ascent to Cajamarca the rain fell down and before starting the descent I was driving in thick fog. However, I managed to get in with no further problems.

I had an excellent meeting with the *Association of Caballos de Paso* and then had dinner with Marcos and his fiancée Betty. Just as we were finishing dinner the MP for Cajamarca came in and we started talking about the problems of the laboratory; he assured us that he was on our side over the privatisation issue. Five pisco sours later and I fell into bed.

I managed to find a new tyre and persuaded FONGAL CAJAMARCA to pay the 800,000 intis (about £130) until I could get the bill to the embassy. Because of the problems with the Land Rover, the second meeting with the Chiclayo association was rescheduled for my return journey. I spent the night in Chiclayo instead of Trujillo which added an extra 250kms onto the journey to Lima the next day. However, I had an excellent meeting with the association and they entertained me to a superb *chifa* (probably the best Chinese meal I ever ate in Perú).

And so it was time to return to Lima. I was up at 6:30am and as the hotel restaurant was open I decided to have breakfast and ordered toast and two glasses of orange juice. I received two plates of bacon and eggs and coffee, none of which I wanted. I did get my orange juice!

When I arrived at Casa Grande to collect my specimens, dear old Dr Llontop insisted that I go to his house because he had a present for Maxine and so that was more time lost. In Trujillo there was no petrol and I drove round for about half an hour trying to find some, finally finding a garage that had the expensive '95', which was what I wanted. When I arrived in Huarmey, there was no petrol to be had, not even '84'. And so I set off across the last stretch of the coastal desert with my heart in my mouth hoping that I would have enough fuel to get to Paramonga. At one point there were six crescent dunes across the road and a truck stuck so that there was a pile up of cars, lorries and buses stretching for a good kilometre. After waiting for about half an hour with nothing happening, I decided that I could be there all night and so I set off across the sand; keeping the revs up and the gear high I got right past the whole lot with not the slightest trouble and wished that I had not waited so long.

I made Paramonga with plenty of petrol to spare but was again unable to get '95'. The last hour into Lima was a nightmare with heavy traffic, no street lights (as they had all been turned off) and pedestrians coming at me from all directions. There were police and army everywhere, *pasa montanas* (these are the anti-terrorist soldiers) in armoured cars, and soldiers with machine guns at every road junction. I later found out that the reason for the military presence was that the *Sendero* had announced that there was to be an armed march on the Friday! There had also been a terrorist-inspired riot a couple of days earlier, which left several dead in Lima; the forces were not leaving things to chance. I finally arrived at the Taylors' house about 8:00pm after almost thirteen hours' driving. I was knackered but the Taylors were having a farewell dinner party and some guests had already arrived, and so I had to have a rapid shower and change and appear at my charming best! It was a pleasant evening even though Justin Gilbert of the British Council informed me that with John's departure the British Council were taking over the management of the project. I told Justin just what I thought of that; I explained what I thought of the British Council and its management skills. I quoted a *Guardian* editorial to him which was headlined 'Limp Wrist over the Empire' which I thought summed up their management skills. I was never known for my tact.

I cancelled my meetings on Friday and brought my flight forward because I thought the airport might be targeted. And on the Friday I returned and as usual waited at the airport for four hours (about average for that time), and arrived home late in the afternoon absolutely dead.

I wrote to the powers that be in the State Veterinary Service in Tolworth, England and to the authorities in Brussels, and asked how the export of horses could be arranged. From the latter I received a curt reply telling me that individual countries made their own policy, and from Tolworth it was a blanket refusal, because horses in South America were likely to be infected with the equine viral encephalitides and Venezuelan equine encephalitis virus in particular. In order to export horses to Britain they would first have to be quarantined in the USA for a month, while there they would be tested for the virus.

On my next visit to Chiclayo I told them of the reply that I had had from the British authorities. The Chiclayans were not happy at the thought of having to ship their horses through Miami as this would make the whole venture unprofitable. It also seemed illogical to me, because these infections were all endemic in the USA and it struck me as mad to take animals from a disease-free area and quarantine them in a country where the disease was endemic. But, such are the ways of bureaucrats and so often disease controls are used as a means of preventing trade. It all boiled down to the fact that the vets in Britain trusted their counterparts in the USA but not those in Perú. There may be some justification in this belief. When I left Perú, no horses have been exported to Britain. I understand that today there have been direct exports to Europe, although none to Britain.

1. The volcano Misti from the Puente Grau, Arequipa

2. The Plaza de Armas, Arequipa

3. Arequipa – The Sunday raising of the flag, author with city officers

4. FONGALSUR, Dr José Diaz del Olmo, Dr Aldo Meza and author

5. Our house in Avenida Lima
– front gate

6. Our house in Avenida Lima
– front door

7. The study on mezzanine floor

8. The patio

9. The rear view of the house
from the pool

10. Round the kitchen table: Guy, Victoria, Father,
author, Fernando, Claire, Marisol

11. The volcano Picchu Picchu – 'The Sleeping Indian'

12. Christmas in La Posada del Puente

13. Elio Cruz with Ma in the garden

14. Interplast doctors, Graciela de Bedoya, Jorst Emmel,
FRONT: author, Eduardo Bedoya

16. The wedding of Lita and Alejandro with LABVETSUR guests - Aurora, Milagro, Maxine, Alejandro, Lita, author, Hipólito, Fany

15. The wedding of Lita and Alejandro

17. The vicar, Alan Winstanley, and the Archbishop of Arequipa, Monseñor Vargas Ruiz de Somocurcio

18. The Gang in the kitchen: Marisol, Guy, Victoria, Claire, Pedro, Rosarel, Carmen, Caroline, Fernando

19. The Arequipa Club on Richard's 18th birthday: Claire, author, Guy, Richard

20. Camelids at Sallalli: volcano Ampato towering above

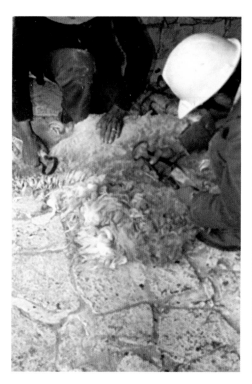

21. Shearing an alpaca

22. Alpaca after shearing

24. Richard
weighing an
alpaca

25. Richard
injecting an
alpaca

26. Héctor and Richard with Sallalli team, note Collagua traditional dress

28. Richard, Guy and Claire at El Cruz del Condor

27. The hot springs in Chivay: author,
Maxine and Hilary Potter

23. The Colca Canyon: Jim and Hilary
Potter with author

29. Maxine, Keith and Toni Haskell in the kitchen preparing the picnic; the maid Teresa in background

30. Anne-Marie, Claire, Luisa and Toni Haskell at El Cruz del Condor

31. Author in LABVETSUR demonstrating the cell counter to the ambassador, Keith Haskell, the consul, Reggie Roberts and Dr Manrique Laborde of Uruguay

32. The author's 50th birthday party at LABVETSUR: seated: Reina, author, Maxine, Roxana Lozada, Jenny Hall, 1st Row: Percy, Fany, Roxana, Rosa, Elsa, latest girl friend, Richard, Aurora, Elio, Cruz, 2nd Row: Hipólito, Fernando FF, Sherwin Hall, Claudia, Fernando FAP, Héctor

33. The Cajamarca Veterinary Laboratory

34. Maxine negotiating a rustic bridge in Cajamarca:
note the basket bridge to the left

35. Marcos pointing out the frieze on the Chan Chan palace wall

36. LABRENOR: Marcos with the new sign

37. Maxine giving a concert in Belén Church, Cajamarca

38. Dr Málaga with the vice chancellor, Honorary Degree Ceremony of the University of Edinburgh

39. Dr Málaga with Professor Ainsley Iggo, dean of the Dick Vet, Edinburgh

40. Dr Málaga in LABVETSUR: Percy in background

41. Dr Málaga in LABVETSUR: presenting author with his book on rabies

42. Caballo de Paso, a watercolour by Evaristo Callo Anco

43. Marjorie Michell, Maxine, Michi Searle and Roxana Lozada
at the opening of the La Joya Posta

44. The LABVETSUR Stakes: Lucho, Roxana, Aurora, author, Maxine

45. The LABVETSUR Stakes: presenting the trophy, Lucho, Roxana, Maxine, winning trainer, Aurora, author

46. The ruins: Machu Picchu

47. On an uncomfortable bench in Madre de Dios: Guy, Louise, Claire and the author

48. Guy in 'Sanders of the River' mode on the launch

49. Richard with the statue of Atahualpa, overlooking the city of Cajamarca

50. Marcos, Ma and Maxine at the graveyard near Cajamarca

51. Claire riding a caballo de paso on Ing Zingg's farm

52/53. Two views of the excavated palace at Chan Chan

54. Ma and author descending from viewing platform, Nazca

56. The Embassy New Year's Eve Party: Claire as Prospero, Maxine as Caliban, Paul as a native, Johnny shipwrecked, Luisa a hula-hula girl, Richard the pirate, Anne-Marie a native girl, Guy, Saving the Whale, Toni as a Polynesian islander, author as King Neptune

55. Maxine and author as Caliban and King Neptune at British Embassy New Year's Eve Fancy Dress Party

58. Paraguayan Bottle Dance

57. Meeting of Projects – Andrew Coe (Brazil), Carole Mullen (Paraguay), author, Donal Brown (Bolivia)

59. Dinner in Asunción – Denis, Milagro and author

60. LABVETSUR team at Iguazú Falls: author, Milagro, Maxine, Lita, Denis

61. Peruvian team in Santa Cruz – Maxine, author, Denis, Jim McGrane,
Fernando, John, Daniel

62. Hotel Urbana, Santa Cruz, Bolivia

64. Examining alpacas in Sta Cruz

63. Bolivian meeting of ODA South American Projects: Participants'
'team photo' in LIDIVET

65. Richard, Guy and Claire cleaning the pool and cover

66. The Endellion Quartet in El Gato Vitoreño: Ralph, author, Andrew, Garfield, Maxine and David

67. The Barbican Trio at Arequipa Airport – Robert, Rebecca, Sophie, Maxine, author

68. Father in the sitting room with Victoria, Lita and Aurora

69. With Father on the altiplano looking for vicuña

70. Father getting the football match under way

71. Guy playing his trumpet with Socrates in the music room

72. Dr Mario Vargas Llosa in LABVETSUR: Hipólito, author, Roxana, Dr Vargas Llosa, Aurora, Omar, Rosa

73. The 450th Anniversary Concert: cleaning the piano

74. The 450th Anniversary Concert: Hugo Cueto, Maxine and Alejandra

75. Preparing for the fashion show: Richard adjusts Guy's tie

76. Claire and Richard on the catwalk at the fashion show

77. Addressing the Diploma de Honor meeting: dignitary, Lucho,
Keith, alcalde, author, dignitaries

78. The Diploma de Honor: Keith, alcalde, author

79. The Diploma de Honor: Sonia and David Hallenbeck, Roxana (L),
author, Maxine, Lucho

80. The Diploma de Honor: Roxana (B), Milagro, Reyna, author, Maxine, Elsa Moran, Cecilia Aquize

81. The Diploma de Honor: Reyna, Fernando, John, Lewis, Percy, Elsa Moran, Dr Angel Linares, Christina

82. One of the many lunches given to mark the departure of the author

83. The new LABVETSUR building

84. Original LABVETSUR staff who are still working in the lab: Edilberto, Claudia, Roxana, Fernando (FAP), Hipolito: Milagro was on holiday.

11

Las Postas – Setting Up Veterinary Practices

It was becoming obvious to me that for LABVETSUR to succeed in the long term, it was essential for clinical veterinary practices to develop in the various irrigations, as they were needed to supply the laboratory with samples. As the farmers realised that sending samples to us produced economically beneficial results, the routine work was increasing. When Dr Archie Hunter the ODA adviser came to see how we were getting on, I put the suggestion to him that we needed extra staff to make sure the project had the potential for long-term survival. Not only did he recommend that a chief technician be appointed but he reported that a vet was required to set up field services. ODA accepted his recommendations and set about recruiting the necessary people.

Before this came to pass I received a letter from a missionary society in Australia asking if I could find a use for a young Australian vet and his wife. I asked John Taylor in the embassy whether I needed to clear the matter with ODA in London and his advice was that it would only cause problems and since I did not notify London when I employed Peruvians, he could not see why they needed to know about Australians! John was ever a great pragmatist. I wrote accepting the offer and was informed that Dr Lewis Vaughan and his wife Christina would be with us as soon as he could arrange his release from the Adelaide Agricultural College. I decided that Lewis should work in the clinical practice rather than the laboratory because this would give him the opportunity to earn money to

183

supplement the little that he would receive from the missionary society. Lewis's previous experience had been in large animal practice as well as teaching in the Adelaide College of Agriculture.

Denis Gosden was the first to arrive and he came to work in the lab as chief laboratory technician. John Claxton arrived to set up the field services; he was young and inexperienced but had been the best student in his year doing the masters degree at the Centre for Tropical Veterinary Medicine at the Edinburgh Veterinary School. He set about his task of developing a veterinary practice in La Joya with skill and energy. We decided against using the Spanish equivalent of 'veterinary practices' because the word 'practice' to the Peruvian implies 'unqualified', so they were called *Postas de Medicina Veterinaria*. We decided that our first *posta* should be in the La Joya irrigation, because it was an old established one with many good farmers and indeed sufficient farmers to make the exercise viable.

Discussions were held with the management of the irrigation, who were greatly in favour of the venture. At one end of the irrigation there was a football field with an empty building that could be put at our disposal. It was decided to add on a second floor to provide a flat for John to live in; FONGALSUR agreed to pay for it and work started immediately. Leche Gloria were happy to allow us to use their computer system for charging the farmers. The *posta* had to be self-financing; this was a key condition. An advertisement was put in the press for a field veterinary surgeon to work alongside John. From the numerous applications, four were chosen for interview and a panel consisting of John and myself with Lucho in the chair selected Alberto Plasencia for the job.

The opening of the veterinary centre in La Joya was the cause of some friction between Reggie Roberts and myself. After the date for the opening had been publicised, Reggie informed me that he was going to Lima for an operation to remove a mole on his neck. Because Reggie could not be present to perform the opening ceremony, I asked the ambassador to send a junior member of staff to officiate and Russell Baker, John Taylor's replacement, was instructed to come. It made sense for him to combine some business with his trip and so he asked Reggie to set up some visits for him. Reggie was further upset because he was not going to be here to show him round and again asked me to change the date of the inauguration so that he could be present. This I refused to do. He did not seem to understand that if he was going to be here then there was no need for Russell to come. I was dismayed at having to upset Reggie, not only because he had been so kind to me personally, but he had been most useful when there were bureaucratic and other problems in the laboratory. Nevertheless, I felt it important to show the Peruvians that once an appointment had been made, it was essential to stick to it.

The inauguration went well. Lucho was also away but Roxana his wife was able to be present. She and Maxine, Marjorie Michell and Michi Searle all drove down in Marjorie's limousine (Plate 43). I took Russell Baker down in the Datsun and the laboratory staff were driven down by Edilberto. Miguel Rivas, the man who followed Lucho as president of FONGALSUR, arrived for the opening of the *posta* one and a half hours late without a word of apology. Large numbers of words were spoken, most of them superfluous, and then Russell declared the centre open. He and the director of agriculture then cut the tapes to the offices and the flat. FONGALSUR had made a good job of the accommodation, with plenty of windows and a superb patio. The party that followed was fun: pisco sours galore, *choclo* (corn on the cob) served with melted cheese and then a *parrillada* (steak cooked over a charcoal grill). As always, the Peruvians threw a good party.

John, Héctor and I had worked out a scale of charges. Each visit would have a charge consisting of three components:

- the cost for the professional time
- the price for the drugs or other consumables used
- the cost of transport to and from the farm

The veterinary surgeon would receive 75% of the professional fee, the other 25% would go to the *posta* to pay the costs of a secretary and the overheads of the building. The money for material and drugs used would be paid to the *posta*, who would provide all drugs and equipment – everything. If the *posta* provided the transport then the visit charge would go to the *posta*, but if the vet used his own vehicle, this charge would be paid to him. LABVETSUR undertook that the professionals would receive a guaranteed minimum salary each month, but there was no upper limit to what they could earn. A daily small animal clinic would be held in the *posta*, which would be cash only, and the vet would reimburse the *posta* for drugs used but keep all the money that he took. Vets had to live in the irrigation and a rota was produced to ensure that there was twenty-four-hour coverage, seven days a week. This was a concept completely new to the Peruvians: there were no veterinary practices in Arequipa and veterinary services were only open to farmers during office hours, as the larger farmers often employed a vet, invariably in a subordinate role to the farm manager. At the end of the working day the vet would return (probably by bus) to his home in the city and it was a Monday-to-Friday job.

Thanks to John's drive and efficiency and the work of all staff, the *posta* flourished and the vets were soon in great demand. When the farmers saw that investment in keeping their animals healthy paid dividends, the work mushroomed; the concept was a great success and John and Alberto soon required a third vet to cope with the work. Percy, who by now was employed in LABVETSUR, was asked if he wanted to transfer to La Joya but declined as he was building a house in the city and was beginning to make a name for himself in the control of mastitis. Héctor, who had his father's commercial eye, saw that the vets were earning good money in the *posta*, much more than LABVETSUR paid, and asked to join the team. Not long afterwards there was enough work for yet another vet, and Hugo Zea made the fourth. The services offered to the farmer were increased by adding artificial insemination to the list of work carried out. Ernest Carden from the Milk Marketing Board in Britain had become a regular visitor to the laboratory and was keen for dairy farmers to use the MMB 'Bull Power' brand British Friesian semen in place of the American Holstein. Friesian cows did not produce as much milk as Holsteins, but the male calves were better suited for beef production as they were not so tall and much more solid; they were also reputed to be much hardier and required less food. Once we found a supplier of liquid nitrogen, we were able to purchase storage and travelling containers and a selection of semen from various bulls. Soon there was enough work to employ a full-time inseminator, José Cornejo. Within a short space of time John had a large and very busy team. Part of the reason for this success was that John was able to persuade the authorities that the *posta* should undertake the campaign to control tuberculosis by tuberculin testing, and the vaccination campaigns for foot-and-mouth disease and anthrax.

At no time was LABVETSUR called upon to subsidise the salaries and the vets were soon earning more than one thousand dollars a month, which was an unheard of amount for a vet in Perú. There were calls coming in for us to open *postas* in the other irrigations. The next one, however, was not in Arequipa but in Tacna, the southernmost province of Perú, which borders

Chile. Dr Angel Linares was a vet of some clinical experience who had been trying to get a practice going in Tacna and we were approached by FONGAL Tacna to see if we could help. John Claxton and I travelled down to Tacna to meet the co-operative and to discuss with Dr Linares how and where the *posta* should be put. The site in the La Yarada irrigation had already been decided by the Tacneños. It was agreed that Dr Linares should spend a week with John in La Joya seeing how we operated and again Leche Gloria agreed that we could use their services for charging in Tacna. The concept of veterinary practices was developing in southern Perú and together the teams were building a proper veterinary service for the region.

Lewis and Christina Vaughan arrived and they lived with us while they got themselves settled in. It was decided that they would move into John's flat once he had moved on to Tacna, and that Lewis would join the La Joya *posta*.

I do not know how he did it but Ernest Carden managed to persuade ODA to donate to FONGALSUR eighteen pedigree Friesian heifers. We were visited by Tim Berrington from Greenfields, a cattle purchasing agency, who had been charged by ODA with purchasing and shipping to Perú eighteen in-calf British Friesian heifers. FONGALSUR decided to keep the cattle in a covered yard, which they erected at the bottom of their grounds. Lucho considered that the cattle in the grounds would have great publicity-value for FONGALSUR.

There was great excitement among the staff of FONGALSUR as the day of arrival drew near. Tim described to us the problems of getting the cattle to Arequipa. He collected up the in-calf heifers round farms in southern England and they were herded together to get them used to each other and to the keeper, who was employed to bring them to Perú. They were put into a lorry to be transported to Charles de Gaulle Airport in Paris for a direct flight to Lima on a passenger Boeing 747. The rear end of the plane was walled off from the human passengers and the animals were bedded on deep straw. According to Tim the heifers were as good as gold on the journey and were perfectly happy on arrival at Lima Airport. It was there that the first problem arose when it was found that the plane chartered to fly the cattle to Arequipa could not land at Arequipa Airport as the runway was not long enough. There was no way that the cattle could be brought by road because the journey was more than 1,000 miles and the road was atrocious. The Peruvian Air Force agreed that the animals could be landed at the La

Joya airbase but these negotiations lasted most of the day and so it was dusk before the animals resumed their journey, having spent the day out in the open, grazing by the side of the runway. From the airbase the heifers had to be put into another lorry for the fifty-mile journey on a reasonable road to their final destination. It was 10:00pm before they arrived and were unloaded into their yard. I saw that they were all fit and happy and went home to bed. At 8:00am the next morning I was at FONGALSUR expecting to find them all bunched together under the cover, but not a bit of it; every one of them was lying on the sand out in the sun and chewing away as if they had spent all their lives there. They were an idyllic picture and the stockman was thrilled at how well they had travelled. They soon became accustomed to their new life and adapted without the slightest problem. There were no calving troubles and all calved without assistance; unfortunately twelve of the eighteen calves were male but they were all of very respectable pedigrees. The whole exercise was a great success and increased the interest in British dairy cattle and also increased the sale of Bull Power semen, which was in great demand at the La Joya *posta*.

Both Guy and Claire were learning to drive and so we decided one Sunday to take a picnic to La Joya and eat it on John's patio; Guy would drive there and Claire would bring us home. On arrival at La Joya I was informed by John that a farmer had three dead cows and so off we went to see what had happened. This was a farm that I knew well: the previous year he had lost five animals from 'ruptured spleens', a condition not mentioned in the text books and one that had me flummoxed; the rest of the staff were equally puzzled. One cow had been opened on my arrival and it too had a ruptured spleen. There was a huge clot of blood in the abdomen. We collected some organs from the opened cow and suggested that the other two be taken unopened to Arequipa. After our picnic lunch, Claire decided that she did not have the confidence to drive round the hairpins and since we were in a hurry, I drove.

Guy assisted at the post-mortem examination and again one of the cows had a clot of blood in her abdomen that weighed 12lbs! The second one did not have a ruptured spleen, however, it was very pulpy but I still failed to put two and two together. The following Wednesday another animal dropped dead and again this had a pulpy and ruptured spleen; finally the penny dropped and it dawned upon me that we were dealing with an atypical manifestation of malignant oedema and sure enough the spleen was solid with *Clostridium novyi* together with a few *Clostridium septicum* (these are bacteria that cause gas gangrene in man). I could have kicked myself for my short-sightedness and lack of lateral thinking.

It was decided that the second *posta* in Arequipa would be in the San Camilo irrigation. There were two reasons for this: Lewis could run this *posta* and continue to live in La Joya while building up the work, and in San Camilo there was a large agricultural research institute run by INIA which required veterinary input on a regular basis. I had been concerned that this government institute would present us with a problem of non-payment, but thanks to our agreement with Leche Gloria, we controlled the charging. With Lewis also working in San Camilo, when John moved to Tacna, Daniel Gandarillas was recruited to work in both irrigations. I was worried that we were expanding too fast and that the *postas* needed time to consolidate their progress and ensure that each *posta* was solidly based before moving on. It was obvious that there was a great need and demand for clinical services but at the same time it was essential that the veterinary work paid dividends for the farmers, and that the foundations for a long-term future were secure.

It was not all smooth-going and we were shown another side of the Peruvian character. Sr Julio Salas had been the chairman of the committee that ran the irrigation and had been responsible for the first *posta* being sited in La Joya; however, he had been replaced as chairman of La Joya farmers, which upset him, and he set about doing his best to destroy the service he started. At short notice I was asked to go with John to a meeting in La Joya arranged by Julio Salas, and for almost two hours he slanged John off about what a disaster the *posta* had been and how he rued the day that he signed the *convenio*. I found his attitude impossible to understand: in the previous month a total of almost one hundred farmers, of a total of about 400, received 170 visits from the vets and we had never yet received a complaint from one of them. Even Salas himself used the *posta* for all his veterinary work. I think that John and I had upset him by not showing sufficient deference towards him! On a previous occasion when he shouted at me over the telephone about how he was a self-made millionaire and how I knew nothing about veterinary work, I put the phone down. He went on about closing down the *posta*: one of his complaints was that when the *posta* started, the vets both lived there and so that if a farmer wanted help all he had to do was go to the *posta*. Now there was a board outside stating which of the vets was on duty and where they lived; neither lived more than 500 metres from the *posta*! Since he was no longer in charge he wanted to pull down what he had helped build up:

the old Peruvian problem of jealousy was now affecting our project. We did not intend to allow him to succeed. The following day I had a delegation of farmers from La Joya in LABVETSUR to talk about the organisation of a vaccination campaign against anthrax. We discussed the matter in great depths and this time, since Julio Salas was not there, there was no problem. I had a real week of the La Joya irrigation as on the Friday we had a meeting of the new committee controlling the *posta*. It was scheduled to start at the dreadful time of 4:00pm but did not actually commence till 4:45pm, as we had to wait for the chairman to arrive! Thanks to the absence of Sr Salas it went pretty well with the participants all very positive about the service they received from the vets in the *posta*. Like most Peruvian meetings, it lasted for ages and we did not set off back to Arequipa until 8:00pm.

The large quantities of clinical material coming in from the *postas* for examination was of great value as it increased the income of LABVETSUR as well as providing us with useful teaching material for our *practicantes*. Making consultancy visits with the *posta* veterinary staff became a regular event, which showed the farmers that their clinicians were working as part of a large team dedicated to help them.

I have not given much detail about the work carried out because I had no involvement in the day-to-day running: that was left entirely up to John and the great success of the *postas* was due to his work and that of his team. All the technical advisers sent by ODA to inspect the field services were highly impressed with what we had achieved. The administrators in London should have been delighted with the success of their project, but they never commented.

12

Agricultural Fairs, Meeting People, Expanding the Work, Changing Administration and Bureaucratic Problems

In order to get LABVETSUR known, we regularly took part in agricultural fairs and shows, usually as part of the FONGALSUR stand. In the second year of the life of LABVETSUR, when the organisers were informed that we were participating, they decided to have a 'British Day' at the fair and the embassy were asked if the ambassador would open the 'British Day'. Mr Shakespeare was making plans for his departure and so sent his deputy to do the honours: a pleasant man but not a great advertisement for Britain and luckily for Britain he never became an ambassador. One problem that the Peruvians had, and many other peoples have as well, is to distinguish between England and Britain, and I have heard many British Ambassadors explain that they are not the English Ambassador but the British; it is galling for the Scots, Welsh and Irish to be called English. A couple of days before the 'British Day', I received a call from the organisers to say that they did not have a recording of the British National Anthem, which would be needed for the formalities, and could I let them have a copy. I explained that I did not have a recording but that I would ask the embassy for a copy and so I asked the deputy ambassador to bring one with him and, of course, he forgot it... We could not let the organisers down and so I recorded onto a cassette 'Land of Hope and Glory', Elgar's 'Pomp and Circumstance March no. 1', which I have always thought a much better tune and labelled the cassette '*Himno Nacional de Gran Bretaña*', which would be played along with the Peruvian National Anthem and that of Arequipa. I sang along lustily when our 'anthem' was played: nobody complained and I think that nobody noticed we had the wrong music. The British Day was a great success: LABVETSUR was doing great things for the reputation of Britain in Perú.

One of the fascinating features of agricultural shows in Arequipa was that they usually ended in a bulls' fight, not a bull fight between man and bull, although there was a *Plaza de Toros* in the city, but a fight between two bulls. This was a 'sport' unique to Arequipa, which I saw nowhere else in the country nor indeed anywhere else in the world. I was amazed that the spectators were never injured. Basically the two bulls enter a large field (minimum about five acres) from the opposite ends with the spectators milling about in the field, getting out of the way of the animals. On occasions the bulls seem to take no notice of each other for some time and so the spectators shoo them towards each other. Finally, the time comes when one decides that he will see off the opposition and he then charges his opponent and there follows a massive clash of heads. Sometimes they separate and charge again, at other times they stay with locked horns and just shove like a two-bull rugby scrum; eventually one decides that he doesn't want a fight and charges the spectators instead. Some fights can last ten minutes or more, others are quickly over. When one bull has had enough, he turns tail and flees the field. This is a big spectator sport and I suspect that the prime attraction is as a reason for gambling.

The Peruvians, like the Chinese, are great gamblers and will gamble on anything. I was reliably informed that there were regular Sunday fights in Cajamarca between Siamese fighting fish, but this I never saw. However, I did go to the La Joya Cock-Pit one Sunday with my son Richard and later with my father; I felt that, before condemning it, I had to see it. What struck me most was the pit itself as there were Nazi artefacts and swastikas on the walls. The owner was a Peruvian but there was no doubt where his sympathies lay. The room held about a hundred spectators sitting on raised tiers; the arena was a circle of straw bales, with sawdust on the floor. The cocks were kept in large metal cages until it was their turn to perform. The first thing to which I objected was the small sharp blade which was strapped into place on the spur and obviously designed to cause injury, which in view of what happened was rather strange. The cocks were presented to each other in the ring and unlike the bulls immediately took an interest in and an objection to their opponent and the fight was soon enjoined, none lasted for more than a few moments, and it soon became obvious that one was gaining the ascendancy. When that occurred the owner stepped in and stopped the fight by removing his bird before it could be injured, which made the metal spurs quite pointless. As a sport, it leaves a great deal to be desired. If I wanted to gamble, I prefer greyhound or horse racing. And I thought of a poem about poverty and gambling that I had written some years before when I was working in Nigeria:

> We don't have a sewage system in Kaduna,
> But the night soil man visits us of course,
> When we have a little cash,
> Well... we prefer to splash
> And go and put the money on a horse.
> (Kaduna – Africa, 1999)

Despite there being a good number of horses in the department, we were slow to receive equine samples. After the altercation with the army importing horses without an import permit, and their developing Equine Infectious Anaemia (see Chapter 6), the name of LABVETSUR must have spread round the equine community because the horse work increased by leaps and bounds. The big breakthrough came when we were asked to work with the horses belonging to the Jockey Club. Horse racing in Arequipa is arranged along similar lines to the way greyhound racing is organised in Britain. The horses are mostly owned by the Jockey Club as this is a way to prevent corruption, doping and the like. The horses are all stabled at the racetrack and several different trainers each train a group of horses. Percy and Milagro were instrumental in developing work at the stadium. It started with taking serum samples for infectious equine anaemia but soon increased to taking blood samples for biochemical testing and faeces samples for worm eggs. Trust Lucho not to miss a trick, and soon there was the 'LABVETSUR Stakes' in the racing calendar. At the first such race, Maxine and Roxana Lozada presented the winning trainer with his trophy (Plates 44 & 45). The equine samples never looked back.

As described in a previous chapter, the big sport for the rich men of the town was riding *caballos de paso* – the ambling/pacing horse which was of a very similar build to the quarter horses used in the United States for moving cattle. The *caballo de paso* rider has to sit motionless in the saddle and control the horse only with finger movements on the reins, while the horse performs various manoeuvres often at a good speed (Plate 42). The riders in their ponchos, broad-brimmed hats and with their box stirrups are a splendid sight sitting on their perfectly groomed horses waiting to perform as a team. As many as six horses give their simultaneous demonstration of skill and control. In perfect unison the horses will perform their various dressage manoeuvres with the riders appearing to be statues. No display would be complete without the riders lining up their horses facing the audience and then dashing towards them at full tilt with the motionless rider turning their mounts at the very last moment. A well trained *caballo de paso* is a joy to ride and they command very high prices.

As our reputation grew so did our intake of carcasses of dead animals. Following the outbreak of malignant oedema, Lucho had requested the embassy to ask ODA to supply LABVETSUR with an incinerator to prevent the FONGALSUR estate becoming a graveyard for dead animals. The administrators in London sent us photographs and specifications of incinerators that they thought appropriate for us and we selected one of the smaller ones in the brochures and it was just as well that we did because the arrival of the incinerator produced the greatest pantomime scene that I have ever been part of. We were informed by Tony and Mike Flanagan, two Brits of Irish origin, who lived and ran a shipping agency in Mollendo, that the incinerator had arrived and that they would send it up to us. It had been shipped to Perú unpacked and not in a container and so it arrived at the laboratory on the back of an open lorry. The driver was instructed to leave it with us and return to Matarani. How was it to be unloaded? As it weighed several tons it was far too heavy to be lifted even by twenty men, and we could not get twenty men on the lorry to lift the incinerator off. A crane was required. Nobody, including the staff in FONGALSUR, had the faintest idea where to get a crane. The best suggestion was that we contact the council to borrow their *grua* which paraded round the streets of Arequipa lifting and towing away cars and trucks that were incorrectly parked. When it arrived, it was obviously far too small to lift the incinerator. Héctor knew of a building company that might possess a crane, and sure enough they had a mobile crane which would take about an hour to cross the town to get to us. The lorry driver was keen to get back to the coast but had to sit and wait.

The crane finally arrived but it was touch and go whether the crane was heavier than the incinerator. Chains were attached and the crane began to lift. The incinerator was heavier than the crane... and as the chain shortened, the crane's body was lifted off the ground. Another approach was required. The lorry was moved so that when the incinerator slid off it would be in its final position. Planks of wood were borrowed from FONGALSUR to make a ramp; the crane was repositioned and instead of lifting the incinerator it pulled it slowly down the ramp. Inch by inch, the incinerator descended. I was frightened that it would slip off the planks and crash to the ground. Finally it was dragged into its final resting position and the driver was able to set off home. The crane started its journey back across town and we adjourned to my office and Aurora made us all a soothing cup of coffee. In retrospect it was an amusing, indeed ludicrous, episode, but at the time we were all very tense and short-tempered. I was frightened that the incinerator would be dropped and damaged.

There being no mains gas in Arequipa, the incinerator had to be powered by bottled gas and so a safe house had to be built to hold the gas and the necessary piping had to be installed before the first carcass could be burnt, and several weeks elapsed before I could report to the embassy that our incinerator was up and running. However, it proved to be a great boon and many hours of digging were saved.

While we were having fun trying to offload the incinerator the men arrived from Lima to install the radios they had brought with them. Because of the worsening terrorist situation, ODA decided that we had to have a shortwave radio in the Land Rover, and every *posta* where there was a Brit working had to have one. This was in the days before mobile telephones. The main station was installed in my office and a 12m-high antenna was fitted on the roof. Once the technicians had installed it they had no trouble speaking to their office in Lima. The mobile was installed and again they had no trouble speaking to Lima. The next morning they set off for La Joya. I had the base station on all day but heard nothing from the mobile or from La Joya. Eventually they phoned to say that they could not contact us either on the mobile or from La Joya! The reason for the problem was that they had to find a wavelength that would work in the mountains. The following day John took them down to La Joya again and they managed to make it work.

We then had to carry out a series of tests to sort out what was the wavelength that would give us the best results overall. Despite the huge investment, we never managed to make it work up in the Andes, where it was really needed. I suspected that the massive variation in altitude was too great for the system to cope without a much larger aerial.

We took great care to ensure that people working with agriculture knew about the laboratory and its services and we regularly met veterinary representatives of the pharmaceutical industry. Dr Edgar Antonio Aguirre Frisancho worked for a Lima company, but was based in Arequipa. On 25th October 1988, an Aeroperú Fokker F28 Fellowship took off from Inca Manco Cápac International Airport in Puno for a domestic flight to Arequipa, but failed to obtain any substantial height and it seemed to fall out of the air, hit the ground and broke up into several pieces. Of the sixty-five passengers on board, eleven were killed, as well as one crew member. One of the passengers who died was Dr Aguirre: he had been a regular visitor to the laboratory and was a great salesman for our services. He had studied at the Puno Vet School but not at the same time as Milagro. I went to the funeral, which took place in the Apecheta cemetery in Arequipa and I was extremely upset… Dr Aguirre was buried in a cubicle in a 'wall' that held many graves. This is a system widely practised in South America. The service was held in the open by the wall with the coffin on a trolley waiting to be placed in the hole in the third tier and so there was a scaffolding platform for people to stand on. The service was conducted on the ground by a filthy Franciscan monk, and no description of mine could do him justice: he looked as if he had not washed for a month (and stank to prove it). Instead of the customary open sandals, he had on his feet a pair of filthy, what had once been white, tackies; his belt was a piece of grubby string and on his head he wore a Banco Continental sun visor, which he did not remove throughout what passed for a funeral. The only way to describe how he conducted the service was to say that he gabbled: had he been able to read the words faster he would have done so; they came out as if from a machine gun, all he wanted to do was to get through it as quickly as possible and get back to his beer. I felt saddened, Dr Aguirre deserved better; a delightful, friendly young man, cut down in his prime, deserved to go with dignity and solemnity; instead we had this garrulous fool of a priest. When he completed the prayers the priest then squirted the holy water from a squeezy bottle onto the coffin! A couple of workmen lifted the coffin up into its hole in the wall.

But the service was redeemed for me when the priest asked if anyone wished to speak and Edgar's brother was assisted up onto the platform. He had been blinded in an accident and had obviously dearly loved his younger brother and as he spoke I felt the tears welling up in my eyes. I almost invariably cry at a funeral but the priest had left me dry-eyed. I have no real recollection of what was said, but this simple blind man talked about a brother that he loved who had gone and the hole that it left in his life and when he finished and silently placed a rose on the coffin in the wall, the tears were streaming down my cheeks. Others spoke after him, but none so eloquently. While they were speaking two workmen with a concrete slab and a bucket of cement climbed the scaffold and proceeded to close the hole. I left with the feeling that Peruvian workmen and indeed priests had little feeling for the relatives of the dead, but I felt that his brother had given Edgar a decent send-off.

It was not just farmers who wished to use our services as our policy of meeting people in the city began to pay off, and industrialists started asking about using our services. A company at the coast was bottling various types of shellfish – abalone, sea cucumbers, sea anemones, sea urchins, and other varieties that I did not know such as lapas, with the view of exporting them to Japan. The company had obtained a list of the import testing that had to be carried out, and luckily they were written in English. The first requirement was that the work had to be carried out in a government laboratory. This was where our Ministry of Agriculture stamps came in useful, because strictly speaking we were not a government laboratory but a private laboratory in which government work was carried out and the Ministry of Agriculture had an important voice on the board. However, since we considered ourselves to be better than any government or other laboratory in the country, and since I knew we were honest, I felt able to sign that we were a government laboratory. The testing regime was not too arduous as they were basically interested in the sterility of the products. We got the contract, which was a welcome addition to our income; we were dealing with an industrial company as opposed to peasant farmers and so we were able to charge a good price for our work. It is strange how things do not occur in isolation, because, at the same time, a company in the city had decided to put asparagus spears into bottles, also for Japan, but in addition for export to Mexico. The work required was almost identical. This took me back to the time many years previously when I had been working in Kenya and Kenya Breweries wanted our laboratory to examine the water used to make the beer and other samples from the production areas, to ensure that their cleaning techniques were adequate. I checked with Cerveza Arequipeña whether we could be of use to them but they had their own laboratory.

I have described how Dra Rosa Perales had talked the veterinary school of San Marcos University in Lima into allowing her to work in LABVETSUR while maintaining her job in Lima. This had a positive spin-off for both institutes as we were able to forge closer bonds and undertake work for each other. We were visited by the team from San Marcos who were working on camelid problems in the central highlands, and they wanted to share information, to which we readily assented. Dr Rodrigo, who was working on *fiebre de alpaca* thought to be associated with clostridial infection in young camelids and other diseases of Andean livestock, wanted us to collect material for him from our post-mortem examinations and again we were able to help. I made a habit of visiting the vet school on my regular visits to Lima. Dra Norma Noé who worked on Mycoplasma made contact with me as she had heard of my work in Kenya on contagious bovine pleuro-pneumonia, which is a mycoplasmal disease. We became friends and frequently we had lunch together when I was in town. She was a large, friendly woman in her late thirties with a big round face that was regularly wreathed in smiles and she was fun to be with. I can remember her driving me around in her battered old Peugeot 304 and stuck on the dashboard was a notice that read in English 'SINGLE, but still looking'. We went to *cebicherias* and *picanterias* and she took me to a northern goat restaurant where we ate a splendid dish of barbecued goat. I have often wondered whether she ever found anyone, or stopped looking.

During one such visit to the faculty I was asked to visit the bacteriology department who heard about our work on mastitis in dairy herds and they wanted our help.

"Would it be possible for you to come down here and undertake investigations into some dairy herds? We think that several of our bigger herds are suffering from chronic mastitis problems and we have neither the expertise nor the materials for undertaking the work."

I agreed that it would be possible but it would have to be me alone because the embassy would not pay for the flights and accommodation for local staff so far from the project area; this was in the days before the arrival of Keith Haskell as ambassador. I said that I would work out the logistics of the exercise and be in contact with them. We had designed and had made aluminium boxes that could hold almost 200 universal bottles and one of those would be adequate for each farm. I worked it out that if I went down on Friday morning, I could sample one herd on Friday evening, one Saturday morning and evening, and one on Sunday morning and fly back to Arequipa with all the samples on the Sunday evening flight. Herds in Lima were much larger than in Arequipa and I suggested to the team that they select farms with problems that had between fifty and a hundred cows. We would sample all four quarters of each cow but mix the samples in one universal bottle. The vet school staff were to provide me with a vet to help take samples and a couple of technicians to do the recording. The bacteriology department asked for volunteers and the whole department wanted to be involved, despite them having to work at the weekend; it is easy to understand why I enjoyed working in Perú. To give all the volunteers a chance we ended up with a larger team. Three of the four farms selected for examination were around the airport, the fourth was further afield.

I decided to undertake my usual method of work, which was to have a chat with the farmer about the management of his herd and the method of milking. Once we got into the milking shed it was slow work to start with as the staff had to get accustomed to work they had not done before. Unlike working in Leche Gloria plants, speed was not of the essence and the farmers did not object to the milking taking longer than usual; after all they were getting a free health check, courtesy of the British taxpayer.

I showed them the art of wiping off the dust from the udder with an individual paper towel, sterilising the tip of the teat with a cotton wool swab soaked in methylated spirits and then hand milking the teat to take the sample – we collected individual quarter samples but they would be mixed in the laboratory before the cultures were made. Work went with a swing and the staff considered that giving up their weekend was a fair price to pay.

All four farms used milking machines, unlike their southern counterparts. After the last sample was taken we cleaned up and drove back to the veterinary school to deposit the samples in their cold store. I then drove back to the hotel; I had decided to stay in a hotel (Hotel Flamingo) on Avenida Arenales because on Saturday and Sunday mornings I had to be on the farms by 6:00am and on the Saturday we would not finish until almost 8:00pm. After the final sampling on the Sunday morning I spent a few hours relaxing before it was time to go the vet school and pick up the sample boxes and head for the airport.

When the plane landed in Arequipa, Maxine took me straight to the laboratory where I put the boxes in the refrigerator and then home for a nice hot bath, a cold beer and a roast dinner. Monday morning saw the team hard at it: they knew there would be a large number of samples and so all the media had been prepared in advance. As in Arequipa, so in Lima, the cell counts were very high and the problems were caused more by poor udder hygiene and milking machine cleanliness than by any specific mastitis pathogens. We isolated large numbers of enterobacteria (usually of the faecal kind) and not too many cows were infected with *Staphylococci* or *Streptococci* – the classic udder pathogens. Individual farm reports were written and sent to San Marcos. I never found out if they took up the work themselves or whether mastitis investigation was just a one-weekend wonder.

I wanted to expand our services to the southern departments and when I heard that Moquegua was holding an agricultural show I tried unsuccessfully to contact the organisers. Nevertheless, Maxine and I set off after lunch on the Friday for the Moquegua showground where we met the organisers with whom it was agreed that I would give a talk at the show on the Sunday morning at 10.00am. There was not a hotel bed to be had in the city and we had to drive off to Ilo, the port of the department, some sixty miles away where there was a delightful hotel with a vacant room that had a magnificent view of the Pacific Ocean. We occupied the presidential suite which cost the princely sum of £7 for the two of us per night. Ilo is a delightful little town sadly ruined by the copper refinery along the coast. In those days the mine in Toquepala and the refinery in Ilo were owned by Southern Copper, an American company who were able to cause environmental damage that they would not be allowed to get away with in the United States: the income from the copper industry was worth a small fortune to Perú. Where the effluent from the refinery went into the Pacific Ocean, the beautiful deep blue water was bright red for about half a mile off shore. But that was not the worst; the Toquepala mine is high up in the Andes, and the ore when mined is washed before being transported to Ilo on the private railway line owned by the company. The effluent from the mine is taken to the sea by the Rio Plomo (meaning grey). Usually rivers in coastal Perú are surrounded by vegetation; not this one. One afternoon Edilberto and I were returning home from Tacna and since we were in no hurry I suggested to Edilberto that we follow the river to the sea. We passed through an excellent irrigation that was obviously NOT taking its water from the river and as we drove along I noted that the riverbank was coated with a grey/brown sludge, enlivened here and there by splashes of brilliant blue or bright green. I assumed that these were deposits of copper sulphate or copper carbonate. Finally we arrived at a beautiful sandy bay where the river poured its water into the ocean; there was a huge semicircle of brilliant yellow where the river water joined the ocean. The devastation stretched out for about half a mile. I do not know of any copper salts that are bright yellow and so I assumed that it must be salts of chromium that produced that colour. I was sure that there must be better ways of handling the effluent, but I suspect polluting the environment was the cheapest. When we arrived in Perú I purchased a copy of *Documental del Perú – Enciclopedia Nacional Basica*, which has one volume for each department and it would be a wonderful work of reference if each volume had a list of contents or an index; they have neither. The volume on Moquegua has a section on Ilo, which proudly states 'Ilo is the Chimbote of the south.' Chimbote is the most polluted city I have ever visited! (see Chapter 15) The port of Ilo 'is also the centre of a large fishing industry'.

We decided not to go to the show on the Saturday; instead we enjoyed a wonderful rest and spent the day walking along the coast, visiting the excellent market where we bought vast quantities of fruit, which we ate while sitting and reading on the balcony of our room. A very peaceful day. On the Sunday we set off early for Moquegua to be in good time for my talk. The show was a total shambles; in the end I never spoke at all. The *caballo de paso* horses and riders all turned up but there was nowhere for them to perform and so their display was cancelled. There were precious few stands to visit and after seeing the whole show in a few minutes and sitting in the shade drinking warm drinks on a stinking hot day, we decided to return to Arequipa. So much for showing the flag, but we did have a delightful rest.

John Taylor phoned me one morning with the sad news that with his departure the project management would be passed over to the British Council. This was a typical example of political chicanery and was happening throughout the diplomatic service worldwide: the management of all aid projects was to pass to the British Council. This enabled Mrs Thatcher to stand up in Parliament and tell them that she had reduced the civil service by cutting a hundred posts in the diplomatic service. That the British Council had to recruit a further hundred staff to carry out the extra work was not mentioned: the council staff are not civil servants! John asked if I could come down to Lima to discuss the handover to the council and at the same time visit the Ministry of Agriculture to ask them to continue the project. He thought that it would be a good idea if Maxine came with me because the medical adviser was visiting and he thought it a good idea that she should have a session with the doctor about her recent attack of cystitis.

"While you and I are buggering about in the ministry, they can go shopping, or Joan can take her out visiting."

John himself met us at the airport and drove us to his house in the residency.

"I am a bit worried," he said. "I have been looking at the regulations for international projects and apparently 'experts' are not supposed to stay for more than three years. I am sure that you want to stay on?"

"We have barely begun; the service is still in its infancy and we have not even started to develop the field offices. I certainly need to stay on and I am certain my Peruvian colleagues in LABVETSUR want me to stay."

"In Perú there is always a way around the regulations. I can say that we will only renew our support if you are given a new visa and as they will want us to continue the project for the money it brings into the country, I can probably negotiate this myself without involving HE."

I set off early the next morning for a meeting at IICA (the Inter-American Organization for Agricultural Research) to discuss the establishment of a network of veterinary laboratories for Perú; I kept pointing out that you cannot have a network until you have the laboratories! I was banging my head against a brick wall: Peruvian bureaucrats delight in building massive castles in the air – it is so much more fun than working. John and I met for lunch, after which we went to OSPA (the Ministry of Agriculture planning department) and from there to INP (the National Planning Institute) to try and jolly along the renewal of the project (the old one would end in 1989). The charming civil servant pointed out that the law says that experts can only stay for three years!

"However," he said, "exceptions can be made and I am sure that Dr Windsor will have many people in Arequipa who will *demand* that in his case an exception be made. I have heard that Ingeniero Lozada has friends in the senate and so I see no problems."

Within a week we heard that the project would be renewed and that I would be free to stay for a further three years.

After the meeting we retired to John's house nearby for a few soothing beers. That night there was a cocktail party to bid farewell to Mike and Fran Kane (the sergeant assistant to the military attaché) and to welcome his successor. For some reason the food was not up to the usual embassy standard, and the Taylors and Windsors had to find a *chifa* for dinner. John and I were together again the next day when we went to the British Council to discuss the transfer of the management of the project. It all went well and whilst I still had my reservations, I was prepared to reserve judgement and wait to see how it went. The meeting lasted all morning but I managed to see John McGhee in the embassy to find out that the new lease on the house had still not been signed. That afternoon Maxine and I had a meeting with the ODA Medical Adviser out in Perú to see the problems of living in South America at first hand. A pleasant man although he would not agree with Maxine that, living in Arequipa, the altitude was likely to have an effect on her health. He was furious at not being allowed to visit Arequipa because he had been the medical officer on the Majes Project when they were building the dam and tunnels.

A few weeks after our trip to Lima we had a visit from Andrew Moore, the director of the British Council and Justin Gilbert, a member of his staff to see what they were taking on and they certainly enjoyed themselves while they were in Arequipa and impressed the staff of LABVETSUR by their knowledge of, and their enthusiasm for, the project. We had a cocktail party for them on the Friday and it was the best party that we gave in Arequipa. The last guests, Tony Flanagan (the shipping agent from the coast) and Graeme Searles (son of Michi, educated in England) left at 12:45am. One never knows what makes a party go but possibly it went well because nobody sat down. Normally all the women sit themselves down and stay put. It was fun and our house guests returned to Lima the next morning with a good impression of Arequipa.

13

Phantom Laboratories and a Professorial Chair

I was having dinner one evening in the Casa Grande guest house, when in came a tall, thin man in his thirties. Having asked if he could join me he sat down and introduced himself. He was... Sr Guildermeister of the family who had built Casa Grande into a great, profitable farming enterprise. When they had their farm expropriated the family moved to Ica, where they had set up a milling business and produced what was now the largest biscuit maker in the country. Sr Guildermeister was in the north of the country on a selling trip. We talked of the past and the town that had developed on their land and how sad his father had been when the flourishing result of the work of several generations of the family was stolen from them.

"Would you take it back if the government offered it to you?" I asked.

"Under no circumstances," was his immediate reply. "Thirty years of neglect and rape of the farm has destroyed the infrastructure. It would cost millions of dollars to refurbish the extraction plant, the railway line and the laboratory and we would not get permission to bring in vets to run the lab and there is no one in the country. Which is of course why you are here." He gave a wry smile. What a waste: here was a laboratory that in its time had produced vaccines for livestock, which now had to be imported while the laboratory lay inactive and rotting.

Dr Edgar Avila came to LABVETSUR to see me with a very strange story. He was a vet from Puno, and a graduate of the university in that city. His father had been a vet before him and they had a clinical practice in the city, the first I had heard of in southern Perú. His father had been approached by Dr Charles Merrieux, the same man who had been instrumental in persuading the director of veterinary services in Botswana that a new veterinary diagnostic laboratory was required, who said to him that if he built a laboratory in the department of Puno to Merrieux's specification, then his company would take over the Eduardo building to make veterinary vaccines to be sold throughout South America. Dr Avila senior had thought that this would be a great investment for Perú and so sank all his family's wealth into the project and built a beautiful laboratory on the family ranch in Puno. The building had been completed in 1974 and Dr Merrieux was due to travel to Perú to open the laboratory and start the production when members of staff of two pharmaceutical companies were kidnapped in Argentina and despite the companies paying ransom, the men were murdered by the Monteneros, a left-wing guerrilla movement that came to prominence with the departure of Juan Perón. Dr Merrieux removed all his staff from South America and so the laboratory was never opened, or used.

Dr Avila wanted to know if I would be prepared to visit the laboratory and to make suggestions as to what could be done to make the building productive. I immediately agreed to visit his laboratory on my next visit to Puno. The request had come at a particularly good moment because I had been asked by the faculty of veterinary medicine in the city to deliver a course of lectures on diagnostic pathology and the role of veterinary laboratories. There were also reports of a strange disease affecting cattle newly imported into Puno. I was informed that any date that I could make would be acceptable to Dr Avila as it was essential for him to try and capitalise on his father's investment. As it so often seemed to happen in Perú, all the arrangements worked perfectly and I allowed a whole week in Puno. Unfortunately, Maxine was too busy to come with me.

Puno is more than 4,000m above sea level and its climate is affected not only by the altitude but also by Lake Titicaca; luckily the Hotel Sillustani in Puno was centrally heated and so I had no trouble sleeping at the altitude. It is possible to drive to Puno and there was a daily train service but both routes were subject to terrorist interference and so I flew and was met by the dean of the veterinary school who drove me to the hotel where I left my suitcase and I was immediately off to work. I found the students bright and intelligent and keen to learn. Like most veterinary schools in Perú, the students were stuffed with book learning but hardly ever saw a real animal, hence the importance put on the '*tesis*' produced by the students before they qualified. I had insisted that if I was going to teach then I would carry out one practical session for every lecture that I gave and to that end I had brought all my post-mortem gear including materials for taking samples and recording results. At the first examination on a dead goat, I thought that I would be crushed by the students and I had to keep making them stand back so that everyone could see what was going on. It was a real delight to be teaching students who had such hunger for knowledge.

Dr Avila had no need to remind me to bring cold weather clothes because I had had experience of working in the mountains and I did not intend to be cold! We set off in glorious sunshine and drove south towards the Chilean border and then we turned west, more or less following the border through wonderful countryside up on the *altiplano*. In all, we drove for more than four hours before we turned off the road, forded a wide but shallow river and when we turned the corner, there was the laboratory, a rectangular, single-storey building about 40m x 12m built from the local stone with a pitched, tiled roof and beyond it a line of two-storey houses. Before going into the laboratory, I was driven up the hill to view the dam and artificial lake, with its hydroelectric generator, to provide power for both laboratory and houses. After four hours in the car we were on Christian-name terms and Edgar turned a few large taps, the water flowed, he threw a switch and all the lights in the laboratory came on. He switched off the electricity and turned off the flow of water and we drove down to the laboratory.

It was like entering a ghost building when we went in; there was a completely empty, dusty corridor about 2m wide running the length and on each side were laboratories all 5m x 5m. Edgar opened the unlocked door of the first bench-lined room and there were dusty cardboard boxes, most of which had never been opened but which contained microscopes, incubators, centrifuges, electronic balances together with all the assorted small equipment, glassware, media and reagents to set up a vaccine producing and testing laboratory. I was completely gobsmacked. The laboratory, the houses, the power station, the equipment, all the work arranging the building so far from civilisation, the massive capital costs and all undertaken without a written guarantee that Merrieux would use the facilities. We entered each of the laboratories to be confronted by more dusty boxes of equipment. What a wealth of hopes lay there. The houses for the staff were all the same size and had the air of a rather upmarket British council house: two moderately sized reception rooms, three bedrooms, a kitchen with a separate utility room, a single shower room but with a downstairs lavatory. Ghosts everywhere of what might have been, clashing with the present reality of slow degeneration.

What saddened me most was that I was unable to offer Edgar any crumb of comfort. For use as a diagnostic laboratory it ticked all the wrong boxes: ideally a diagnostic laboratory should be in the middle of a town so that an escape of pathogens would not result in the infection of animals; this laboratory could be surrounded by livestock. The town should be at the heart of a livestock industry. Being in a town means the laboratory could have good road communications, postal services, telephone (there were no mobile phones and the Internet was not up and running in those days). Here, there were no postal services and no telephone. Easy access for farmers and veterinary surgeons is essential: this was four hours' drive on an unmade road. There should be good access to technical services such as electricians and plumbers as well as companies to service specialist equipment such as centrifuges and microscopes. It should be easy to communicate with neighbouring laboratories to provide backup services and interchange of personnel, and ideas.

I really could not understand Dr Merrieux's thinking about using this place for a vaccine production laboratory. The only factor in its favour was isolation in an area with a very low livestock population: the terrain was very high (c4,000m), the soil was very poor, the climate was harsh and traditionally the authorities (the Spaniards and their successors) had wanted to keep the border areas free from habitation. In the post-colonial era there had been many border conflicts and several wars between the developing countries, and so the authorities wished to keep the border free for the military. On arrival in Arequipa I had caused great consternation by asking the British Embassy to obtain for me a complete set of maps of the five departments in my patch, namely those of Arequipa, Cuzco, Moquegua, Puno and Tacna. Not long after I had made the request, Maxine received a visit from the police wishing to interview me. Thy called home again that evening and I had to explain to them that if you were trying to control outbreaks of animal disease, it was essential to know the geography of the terrain to determine which way it was likely to spread. They went away duly satisfied and we received our maps, but South American countries have a great sensitivity about their borders and the maps showed almost no detail near to the international borders (Chile and Bolivia). Nevertheless, I could not understand how Dr Merrieux expected staff to be prepared to work anywhere that was four hours' drive from the nearest shop, café, school, or church. Perhaps he thought that the laboratory would develop into its own town with police, post and school as had happened on so many South American farms. In time it would have been possible to produce an airstrip near the laboratory, but that would depend upon whether the military authorities would allow it, and it is no fun trying to take off in a light aircraft at 4,000 metres...

It was a solemn journey back to Puno as I was unable to offer Edgar any possible hope for the family investment. I suggested that he could try and sell the equipment to the Puno Veterinary School: the sooner he did this the better because the most sophisticated items were rapidly becoming obsolete and the reagents and media were probably already beyond use. He thanked me for my time but I could see that he was disappointed that LABVETSUR would not be taking over his laboratory.

The world in general and Perú in particular is littered with objects that were made in the heyday of the British industrial might and Puno has its own magnificent items, the Lake Titicaca Steamships, the first of which was built in London, England in the early 1860s, by the side of the River Thames and then taken apart so that it could be shipped as a kit to Perú, via Arica in Chile and then taken by train up to the Bolivian border. The sections had to be small enough to be carried on mules. A small group of British engineers travelled with the parts and reassembled the boat on the shore of the lake. The *Yavari* was launched on December 25th, 1870. The *Yapura*, which was built in Birmingham, was launched less than fifteen months later in March, 1872. The ships were fitted with small steam engines. The *Coya* was built in Scotland at the end of the nineteenth century, and was still in service when I arrived in Perú. The level of the lake rises and falls by as much as a metre and on one occasion when it was high in 1986 the steamboat had managed to get itself beached, and as the lake receded, there it stayed.

The lake is almost a mythical (mystical?) place and it abounds with strange beliefs and legends: the founder of the Inca people is said to have come forth out of the lake, which is strange because the lake is in the land of the Aymara people. Titicaca also houses the strangest people that I have ever met, the Uros people, who live on artificial islands made from reeds that abound in the lake. These islands are huge and some house ten or more families. The people originally took to living on the islands as a form of defence during the expansion of the Inca Empire, although still owning land where they graze livestock. However, fish provides the main source of their food. The people commute to and from their island by means of reed canoes. The reeds rot and so the islands need constantly to be rebuilt. Luckily there are plenty of reeds round the periphery of the lake. The Uros not only use the reeds for building but they eat the roots and use them for medicine: on my short stay on an island I saw people with the white root bound round their head or arm. I took a tour to the islands for just a few short hours but felt incredibly sad for the people, especially the snotty-nosed children. The Uros people are said not to feel cold but their children certainly suffer from colds. Today their way of life is being influenced by the children attending school on the land, and the increasing number of tourists now that the terrorist problem has been resolved. They intermarry with the Aymara people of Puno and Bolivia and already the Uros language has gone; one wonders for how long this way of life will continue.

Before I set off for Puno I had heard of a problem affecting newly imported heifers. An attempt was being made to improve the quality of the few dairy herds in the region and a group of heifers had been imported. Half were Holstein and the other half were Brown Swiss; seemingly only the former were affected. An animal died during my stay in the city and the farmer agreed to bring it to the faculty for us to carry out a post-mortem examination. Before the examination was half done I knew what was the problem. When we removed the skin there was marked oedema in the subcutaneous tissues – there was fluid everywhere, particularly over the chest, which gives the disease its common name: 'brisket disease'. On opening the chest the lungs were awash with fluid and the heart was massively enlarged, particularly the right side. A detailed examination of all the tissues confirmed that the animal had died from altitude sickness. And the only answer was to get the remaining Holstein cattle down to a lower altitude. The Brown Swiss animals, originating from the mountains in Switzerland, are accustomed to living at high altitude and so they were not affected. As you go higher up the mountain the air pressure decreases which means there is less oxygen available for an animal to breathe. To compensate, the animal's heart works harder to pump more blood to all the organs and so the heart muscle increases and the blood pressure goes up. As the pressure increases so the liquid of the blood is forced out of the blood vessels and into the tissues, which become waterlogged. The blood, having lost liquid, becomes much thicker and so harder for the heart to pump and the vicious circle goes on until finally the heart gives up and the animal dies. The only answer is to get the animals back down to a much lower altitude and there let them acclimatise in the same way that mountaineers do when climbing Everest: they slowly move up the mountain over a period of weeks. Future batches of Holsteins would have to be introduced slowly to their new mountain home.

My surprises had not come to an end as I was asked if I would care to go to the potato market on the Friday afternoon. I was not prepared for what I saw: I did not realise that there were so many varieties of potato in the world from black to white with reds, blues yellows and brown in between, from huge to small. But not just ordinary potatoes, *chuños*, the Andean freeze-dried potato that is prepared by the local people, by soaking the potato in cold water and then placing them on the roof of the house at night to freeze and then in the day the water evaporates off (lyophilises) leaving a small, wrinkled potato that can be stored almost indefinitely and restored to use by soaking before cooking. I later found that they made a tasty addition to a stew.

On arrival home I was asked by the British Council in Lima if I could assist the chemistry department of the University of San Agustin. When I visited the chemistry department, I found yet another problem of historical proportions! Following the Communist coup of Juan Velasco Alvarado, who became president of Perú in 1968, the Hungarian Government had presented the University with a large amount of equipment of which the biggest and most expensive was an atomic absorption spectrophotometer. Like the equipment in Puno it was still in its box, unopened and unused almost twenty years later. The reason for this was that the instructions were written in Cyrillic script. They had taken the instructions to a Russian speaker who informed them that the language was not Russian and they had done nothing more for well-nigh twenty years. My arrival had stimulated them to activity and so they had contacted the British Council. I took away the instructions and gave them to a friend who spoke Russian, who informed me that they were written in Spanish but for some reason the Cyrillic script was used. I returned the instructions to the university together with a copy of the Cyrillic alphabet for them to transliterate. I suspected that they never would do it and that the equipment would remain in its wrappings until it was put in a museum.

The increasing reputation of LABVETSUR resulted in my receiving more and more requests for laboratory personnel to help elsewhere and where it was possible we accepted these appeals. Where air travel was involved it had to be me, because the embassy would not pay the airfares for the Peruvians. Staff in Pucallpa, a jungle port on the River Ucavali, a major tributary of the Amazon, wanted my assistance. The Ministry of Agriculture of the region was arranging a course of training on diagnosis of disease for its staff and they asked the ambassador if I could be spared to assist them. The embassy was fairly cagey, because the region was regularly subjected to *Sendero Luminoso* attacks. Keith Haskell phoned me to ask my opinion. I was very keen to go because I had only made a few forays into the Peruvian jungle. It was agreed that I should go providing that I did not travel outside the town boundary (this could not be observed because part of the workshop programme included visits to local farms).

I flew to Pucallpa and found it to be a bustling if not very attractive town. The odd, or should it be worrying, feature was that there were vultures everywhere, sitting in the treetops and on the roofs of many of the town buildings. I later found when we went to the abattoir for my post-mortem examination demonstration, that this was their epicentre and there they sat waiting patiently for the by-products of the slaughterhouse work: it was cheaper to feed the vultures than to incinerate the waste. It had been arranged for me to stay in the *Turistas* Hotel which was in the centre of the town and it was very comfortable, with a delightful staff, a far cry from many of the other *Turistas* hotels. From the hotel I was driven to the Ministry of Agriculture offices. The veterinary officer in charge of the region explained to me what he wanted from me and I pointed out that I was not supposed to leave the town boundary.

"There is no terrorist trouble here during the day, and what little we see here is only during the night: the problems are greatly magnified by the local politicos as a way of getting more central government finance," said the director. I agreed to take part in the farm visits.

The meeting opened after lunch with all the usual fluff and hyperbole that accompanies Peruvian openings. I was amazed to see that there were between thirty and forty participants. Once the meeting was underway, the Director explained the purpose of the workshop which was to capitalise on the presence of 'an international expert pathologist' who would give them 'the benefit of his experience in many different countries in the world'. At the close of the session I returned to the *Turistas* with several of the local vets and we sampled the San Juan beer, said to be the only beer brewed with water from the Amazon. It was a pleasant, light beer, if a little sweet, but perhaps that is a good thing in a hot climate. While we were sitting in the bar, from which there was a good view of the main street, night fell; as soon as it was dark a large open lorry drew up at the entrance of the hotel, and several soldiers, at least I hoped they were soldiers, because they were not wearing uniforms, descended from the back, all carrying rifles and all wearing black balaclavas. At first I felt nervous. If they were the goodies, why were they covering their faces? It was later explained to me that they were all local boys and they did not want any terrorist, with whom they might come into contact, to recognise them and so make their families a target.

Dinner was a huge surprise: the waiter suggested that I try the local speciality, spicy pork sausages, served with chips made from plantains and a dish of chopped onions in vinegar. It was delicious, in fact it was so good that I had the same dish on each of the three nights I spent in Pucallpa. I never saw this meal anywhere else in Perú. I brought some of the sausages back to Arequipa, but they were not the same without the plantain chips and the spiced onions.

The next morning I delivered my talk on the importance of carrying out a proper post-mortem examination and checking every organ and tissue. We then adjourned to the local abattoir where I was able to put my principles into practice. Not surprisingly I was offered pigs for the examination: I saw more pigs in Pucallpa than anywhere else in Perú. The slaughterhouse was large, airy and relatively clean; water was no problem since the river was nearby. It was more a covered yard than a building with cradles for butchering the animals. As I always experienced in Perú there was a reticence on the part of the local vets to get their hands dirty: the old Spanish customs die hard, and professional gentlemen do not dirty their hands. I had brought a box of disposable rubber gloves with me and, by the end of the session, most of them had at least handled a few organs.

We were very lucky that one of the animals to examine was a dead pregnant sow. I went through the routine examination but when we got to look at the pregnant uterus, it was obvious that had she not died she would have aborted because she was infected with what I believed to be *Brucella suis* as all the piglets had the typical lesions of the infection – large necrotic lesions in various of their organs. This aroused great interest because most of the participants had never seen the condition before. (I assumed that this was because they had never looked!) Large numbers of samples for examination were taken although they would not be examined as I would be staying in the residency on the way back and I had not come equipped to transport pathological samples.

Farm visits were planned for the afternoon and they were a real eye-opener for me as I had never before visited a jungle farm. I was not sure what my role was supposed to be on these visits, as having no experience of managing livestock in a jungle I did not know what would work. But it was fascinating; the livestock comprised pigs, goats, poultry and a few cows. It was the forest that was most interesting: for the first time in my life I saw cocoa growing, with their small rugby-ball shaped fruits. Brazil nuts growing in their pods showed why the nuts resemble orange segments because that is how they grow. I also saw the quinine tree (*Cinchona*) from whose bark comes the malaria cure and the coca bush from which they produce cocaine. This bush did not grow well here, I was informed: too hot. They grew better in the '*seja de selva*', the 'eyebrows' of the jungle, halfway up the mountain, whereas Pucallpa was right down in the jungle proper. Mangoes, avocados, pawpaw, bananas, plantains, breadfruit... it seemed that anything could grow here but you could not farm it: the moment a plantation was developed then the parasites multiplied faster than the hosts and disaster ensued. It had to be one Brazil nut tree, one rubber plant, one cacao tree and all well spaced. It was only this that saved the area from being devoted to monoculture oil palm production.

During the meeting I heard about a veterinary diagnostic laboratory in the town which had been started by the Dutch Government some years before. I was asked if I could have a look at it and make some recommendations. The closing ceremony was almost a repetition of the opening, with the organisers patting themselves on the back for a very valuable workshop, and the participants, one by one, thanking the organisers. The 'great international expert' was again thanked for coming and then we all dispersed and I was taken to the Dutch laboratory and what an eye-opener it was. The single-storey building was smaller than that in Cajamarca but larger than LABVETSUR. There was a reception office and several medium-sized laboratories all beautifully equipped with microscopes, incubators, pH meters and some simple photometers. The benches had been well made with impervious work surfaces. The preparation room had large sinks, balances, autoclaves and boxes of glass petri-dishes, each dish still in its paper wrapping.

It was a similar story to the laboratory in Puno. Twenty years previously the Dutch Government had built and paid for the laboratory and fully equipped it with everything necessary for a diagnostic laboratory, and two Dutch vets and a laboratory technician had come out to set up a service. Within months there had been a terrorist attack in Pucallpa (well before the days of the *Sendero Luminoso)*; the Dutch Government recalled their staff and closed down the project, since which time the building had been inactive although the Ministry of Agriculture maintained a vet on the premises; apparently he did nothing. The outlook for the Pucallpa laboratory was different to that in Puno, as it was based in a town at the centre of all local communications with reasonable access to farms within 40kms. The penny dropped: this was the real reason that I had been invited to the workshop. They wanted the British Government to take over where the Dutch had left off. This was not going to happen but I was able to offer help. It seemed such a waste to have all these facilities and for them not to be used. I offered to train veterinary and technical staff in LABVETSUR and I thought that once they were up and running we would be able to send some of our Peruvian staff to give them a hand. I pointed out to them their major problem – how was the laboratory to be financed? Without a large flourishing livestock industry, the laboratory would never pay its way. There were no big livestock or poultry farmers in the area, everything was small-scale. However, if the veterinary department were to base its field operations in the laboratory and if the work carried out were restricted to simple basic testing then it might prove viable. I left the laboratory having given the people there a little hope.

I returned to the *Turistas* Hotel for my final portion of *salchichas, platanos fritos y cebolla* washed down with San Juan. I liked Pucallpa. Casa Grande, Puno, Pucallpa, all dying; what other unused laboratories littered the country? What hopes, dreams and money had been invested in these laboratories that sat idle while their equipment slowly turned to dust?

Twice-yearly visits to Puno were arranged and on one of the trips Maxine was able to come with me. This visit can be precisely dated, because we were listening to the World Service of the BBC when it was announced on 28th November 1990 that John Major had been elected to replace Margaret Thatcher as leader of the Conservative Party and hence prime minister: neither Maxine nor I had heard of John Major, although news of Mrs Thatcher's downfall had reached us in Arequipa.

The reason for this particular visit was to take part in the graduation celebrations of the Puno Veterinary School. I had been invited by the students 'for a very special reason' although I was not told what it was. On this occasion I was part of the audience and not on the top table and it being a glorious sunny day the whole proceedings took place outside in the grounds. It was a strange experience, rather like being back at school as we sat not on chairs but at desks – real secondary school desks – being a combination seat with an attached worktop which lifted up to provide a storage compartment for your personal effects. I have a very clear memory of this desk, because there was a nail that protruded through the front that wore a hole in my suit trousers! The dean talked about the students and how they were all setting off on their careers and how he looked forward to reading their theses and confirming their degrees. He then turned to the 'distinguished international veterinary surgeon' (Peruvian professionals were very good for my morale!), who had given up his time to come to Puno and had done so much to assist with the teaching of the students. The board of the faculty had decided that as a thank you to me for my efforts I was to be appointed an honorary professor of pathology and would I come forward to receive my medal confirming the honour. As I rose to collect my medal, the nail did its business, leaving a small gash in my trouser leg. The medal was placed round my neck, hands were shaken, and photographs were taken and then the party began.

One thing can definitely be said for the Peruvians: they certainly know how to throw a party, and I do not think that it is just the pisco sours, although they certainly help. Despite the poverty of the country and many of the people, they are all very hospitable and it was a cocktail and lunch party all in one. I remember that Maxine and I were surrounded by students, all happy and excited, and once the music started the dancing began. For me it was hard-going at 4,000m above sea level but for Maxine it was much worse and the experience is seared into her memory as she found it almost impossible to cope with the altitude, shoes with heels and dancing on grass. We stayed until exhaustion overtook us and we retired to the Sillustani Hotel and collapsed onto our bed. It was then that we learnt that Michael Heseltine had been defeated and that our new prime minister was John Major.

The next day was heavy cloud and non-stop rain and so we decided not to visit the Uros on their reed islands but to restrict our activities to the town, including a visit to the potato market, and the following morning we flew back to Arequipa. It had been one of my early ambitions to be a professor, and I had actually done it, even if it was only an honorary one, but I still have the medal to prove it.

14

Journeys High and Low

Machu Picchu is undoubtedly one of the world's magic places; an Inca stronghold in the high central Andes, it was hidden from the world for several centuries (Plate 46). When the *conquistadores* arrived in what today is Perú, they set about destroying the people and their culture, and they almost succeeded; luckily, they never found Machu Picchu. When we arrived in the country in 1986 the population had only just returned to the pre-colonial level. In order to wipe out the people the Spaniards destroyed the terraces that made agriculture in the mountains possible. As the population decreased so the habitations were deserted and the jungle took over. There is a theory that the village of Machu Picchu was deserted before the arrival of the Spaniards, which would explain why it is not mentioned in any of the ancient texts. It was totally unknown until the arrival of the American, Hiram Bingham, in 1911; it is thought that he stumbled upon it by accident while looking for the Inca capital of Vilcabamba. He returned later with a bigger team and basically cleared the jungle from the site but it was not until the 1930s when Peruvian archaeologists started work that the place became accessible to the public.

The town is set on a mountain in the Sacred Valley with that great sugarloaf mountain, Huayna Picchu, guarding it to the north, and is roughly divided into an urban sector and an agricultural sector, and into an upper town and a lower town separated by what is now a huge turfed open space – the plaza. Water comes from mountain springs that could not be cut off by an enemy. Extensive terraces were used for agriculture and sophisticated channelling systems provided irrigation for the fields. It is thought that the fields were more than adequate to feed twice the population. The architecture is adapted to the mountains: approximately 200 buildings are arranged on wide parallel terraces around the vast open plaza that is oriented north-west to south-east. The various compounds are long and narrow in order to exploit the contours. The temples are in the upper town on the south-west, the warehouses in the lower. The north-eastern section of the city appears to be residential. The western sector, separated by the plaza, was for religious and ceremonial purposes.

Even with the terrorist problem at its height, Machu Picchu remained a place to visit, and we made several family trips to the ruins. There was no road to the place and there were only two routes in, one was to walk the Inca Trail, which was a journey of two to three days carrying your food and tents (which we never did) and the other was the usual tourist approach, by train from Cuzco. There was a standard daily tour by which you left at 7:00am for the four-hour train journey and returned at 4:00pm. There were also trains during the day that went beyond Machu Picchu into the jungle town of Quillabamba. Machu Picchu is in the 'seja de selva', on the Atlantic side of the watershed, 1,000 metres lower than the city of Cuzco. The train journey is a delight in itself, as it follows the valley of the Urubanba River (the Sacred river). To get out of the valley, there is a hairpin rail track: the train drives beyond the hairpin and stops; the driver gets out and changes the points and reverses the train to the next hairpin where the process is repeated and then again and again until the train gets out of the valley. It is some feat of engineering to get a train down to Cuzco and I wondered how the British engineers managed the feat.

On arrival at Machu Picchu Station you have to take the bus that rounds more hairpin bends as it grinds its way ever upwards to the ruins. From the very moment when I entered, I was enchanted. Those who believe in them say that ley lines pass through this magical place. Through the whole town runs the long, wide strip of turf, the plaza, and it was thought that here, the Inca paraded his army. Above and below this are the stone buildings that formed the dwellings and temples, offices and cemeteries of the people. We had to thank the terrorists for the paucity of tourists in Machu Picchu, but as I stretched out on the turf under the crystal-blue winter sky, I felt as if I was in heaven; there was peace, perfect peace, broken only by the soft sounds of an alpaca that was grazing nearby, gently lowing. I never once went to Machu Picchu without sampling this peace. But we were there for tourism and the children wanted to see the sights and be amazed by the wonderful craftsmanship of the Incas, building their houses from stone without mortar. They were a pre-Iron Age society and had no metal with which to cut the stone and so a harder stone was used to make cracks in the stone and in winter, water put into the cracks would freeze and split the rock. Failing that the stones were heated and water was used to crack them. Walls were built that were like jigsaw puzzles as the stones were fitted together. Stone tools were used to cut the wood for roof timbers. The most significant building in the town is the Temple of the Sun, which contains the Inti Watana, which like our own Stonehenge is thought to be of astrological significance, as during the winter solstice it points directly towards the sun.

On one journey to Machu Picchu, I went with Richard and his school friend Andrew Cranch: we did not go on the tourist train because we were going on to Quillabamba. We got off the train at Aguas Calientes and checked into the Hostal Las Caminantes ($1.25 per night) and the boys grabbed the room which had a private bathroom, which because of the hot springs had hot water. We left the bags in the room and walked along the line to Machu Picchu where we took the bus up to the ruins. On the journey, I sat next to a Chilean botanist who had been born in Machu Picchu. Both his Chilean parents were botanists and they were studying the orchids of the area; he arrived rather early and his mother gave birth in the hostel in Aguas Calientes. What an interesting man he was and what a fountain of knowledge. He informed me that his parents had found more than fifty species of orchid growing on the hill leading to the ruins and on our journey, he pointed out more than a dozen varieties in flower at the time. On that trip, I left the boys to explore on their own while I communed with nature on the turf of the plaza. We were lucky because it was just after Christmas and despite being the rainy season, we had glorious weather. The journey in the bus down to the railway station was, as always, a delight. We were met at the bus by some early teenage urchins dressed as Red Indians with feathers in their hair. As the bus took off they waved us goodbye, but by the time we arrived at the first hairpin bend, they were there to greet us: they had taken the direct route down the hill. With each bend, there was our band of well-wishers. They beat us to the bottom and were there waiting with their hands outstretched, expecting a well-earned tip.

We walked back along the railway line to Aguas Calientes, took our towels and swimming costumes from the room and went to see whether the name of the village – Hot Waters – was justified. There was no swimming pool but several circular concrete tubs about three metres in diameter constructed on a lawn; it was delightful to lounge in the glorious hot water in the evening sunshine with a beer in hand and talk about the ups and downs of the day. We had been warned about thieves on the local train and despite going through several long tunnels through the hills, there was no illumination on the train (the tourist trains were different). After we came out of one tunnel, Richard noticed that my video camera, which I had placed in the overhead luggage rack, had gone. Richard went one way down the train and Andrew the other, and as there is no safe way to get off a moving train, the thief was cornered by Andrew, who sat on him until a railway employee arrived. At the next station there were police to greet us and they escorted the miscreant away and I suspect he was given a good kicking before being turned loose to make his own way home. I think that this episode made a bigger impression on the boys than the ruins...

The hostel café, it could not be called a restaurant, served a perfectly acceptable chicken and chips for the boys while I had fresh bream from the river. Luckily, we had sleeping bags with us because the rooms were far from clean and I was not sure who had slept in the bed before. We placed plastic sheets over the beds before unrolling the bags, to prevent the bugs from transferring. When I awoke in the night to go for a pee my torch picked out for me the largest cockroaches that I have ever seen; some were longer than the span of my hand (nine inches), but they seemed harmless patrolling the walls of the room and I was able to return to sleep.

The boys had wanted to climb Huayna Picchu; in those days, it could only be attempted in the early morning, which would mean that we would not be able to catch the train to Quillabamba until the following day. In summer, there was danger of rain which would make the ascent treacherous, despite the rope handrail all the way to the summit. James Blount, a young, fit diplomat working in the British Embassy, who had seen service in Afghanistan during the Russian invasion, had climbed Huayna Picchu when his younger brother was out visiting. Despite being keen mountaineers, they had both found the ascent hard-going, and were astounded when they reached the summit to find a little old Indian woman sitting on the top with her traditional red beret, selling rather expensive bottles of Coca-Cola.

The two-hour journey by train was delightful, with no more attempted thefts on the way. The train continues to follow the course of the Urubamba River as it makes its way down the eastern or Atlantic side of the Andes to the jungle town of Quillabamba, which is at an altitude of less than 1,000 metres above sea level, and where the climate was definitely equatorial. Having read in the guidebook about the steps up to the town (more than 150 of them) we took the taxi into town and asked the driver to take us to the best hotel and he took us to the Hostal Quillabamba, which was a very different place to where we had stayed the night before. Despite it being New Year's Eve, we were able to get accommodation. I changed into shorts (I normally wore long trousers in Perú to accord with the local custom) and set off for a walk in the country. It was glorious as we followed a tributary of the Urubamba upstream in the afternoon sunshine; what struck me most of all were the butterflies, some small, some large and some absolutely enormous but all wonderful colours of the rainbow, a truly beautiful living work of art as they looked for food on the margins of the stream. The further we walked, the more the trees, until we were in total canopy, with dappled light showing through. We came to a large house and in the garden was the biggest mango tree that I had ever seen in full fruit with the bright orange treats throughout.

"Let's see if the farmer will sell us any," I said to the boys who were in immediate agreement. I knocked and a tall, elegant Spaniard came to the door. I asked if we could buy some mangoes and in a trice his two young sons were up the tree throwing them down for us to catch. We filled my shoulder bag with the fruit – more than enough to get us back to Cuzco – but when I offered to pay, the farmer declined; however, I insisted that he take the money, if only to give to his sons, and he graciously accepted a note for 50,000 intis (about two dollars in those days). We continued on our way eating mangoes and tossing the skins and stones into the bushes.

On our return to the hotel we noted the presence of Seventh Day Adventist missionaries everywhere: they are unmistakable in their dark grey suits and their crisp white shirts, bearing a large name badge. How they survived in the jungle I do not know and I am certain they would have made very few converts in this quintessential Catholic country. We decided to sample the hotel dance but the band was atrocious: Richard reckoned that they could only play four notes. The local mayor with his sharp suit and Che Guevera moustache was a dead ringer for a *narco-traficante* (one who deals in coca leaves or cocaine). The boys wanted more action and soon took off for the local disco. I also wanted something more interesting and more Peruvian and was directed to a bar where Andean folk groups played and sang. I spent a very pleasant evening with a group of Colombian tourists while we drank Cuzqueña beer and saw in the New Year.

We had a later start the following day and after breakfast we found the market where we bought a chain and padlock to secure our suitcases and video camera for the return journey. I chanced to see some Tramontina knives on sale. The steak knives we used at home, which we called Massé knives after Carlos Massé from Salta, Argentina, who owned the hardware shop where they were bought, were made by the Brazilian company, Tramontina, and have proved to be the best knives ever, and so I bought one large and two small carving knives, which we have to this day and they are still brilliant.

There being little of interest in the town we decided to explore more of the jungle scenery. We purchased some rolls and a tin of ham and some tomatoes and with the mangoes we set off for a memorable if uneventful trip. It was early to bed for an early start to catch the train to Cuzco. The train journey was anything but uneventful... At one of the stations on the way to Machu Picchu a group of young men boarded the train with half a dozen enormous sacks (standing six-foot or more high). It transpired that the sacks were full of coca leaves bound for an illicit cocaine factory near Cuzco. Unfortunately for the men, but great for our amusement, the police had heard about the movement and boarded the train to look for the sacks. This was the signal for several men to clamber out of the window and onto the roof of the train and for the sacks to be passed up to them. The train was searched from end to end but no trace of the coca leaves were found. The police left at the next station – this was a slow train stopping at all stations – and the sacks made their reappearance through the windows. This was repeated as more police boarded the train at the following station and the disappearing trick was repeated. I felt certain that the police had to be in on the deal as they must have known or guessed what was going on. The last stop on the journey was Porroy, a village at the top of the escarpment before the descent into the valley. It acquired its name from Pizarro's *conquistadores* who made their camp there before descending into the valley to deal with the Inca. The story goes that when Pizarro arrived at the edge of the valley he looked down on the city of Cuzco and said:

"*Bastante por hoy.*" (Enough for today.) The name Porroy has stuck. I have always been fascinated by place names with meaning and I thought back to that platinum mine in the northern Cape of South Africa called Otazell: the reason for the name is that the daily temperature is often in excess of 40° C, in other words it's as 'ot as 'ell. But perhaps the best of all is the old airport in Nairobi which was at a place called Embakasi. When the Uganda railway was built in the nineteenth century, they arrived in Nairobi and there the work stopped for more than a year as the engineers looked for a way to take the line down the Rift Valley wall. This is why Nairobi exists (it is the Maasai word for swamp). Hunters or others wishing to hire porters to travel up country had to take them from the head of the railway, where there was an old Scotsman in charge of allocation. When addressing the locals, he preceded all statements with:

"You buggers – come on, you buggers – I want ten of you buggers..."

For the Maasai the rail head became 'the place of the buggers' or Em Buggersi – shortened to Embakasi. I think that *conquistadores* felt the same when they climbed the valley wall to continue their journey east and looked down into the valley: I can imagine the leader taking one look and saying:

"*Maaaaadre de Dios*!" Moooooother of God, what is this place! And that is the name of the department that adjoins Cuzco.

We arrived in Cuzco, unlocked our possession from the overhead rack and made our way to the hotel. Cuzco, being the take-off point for Machu Picchu, is a real tourist town but there is much more to see than the ruins. The town and its close environs are full of wonderful places and buildings. It was the centre of the Inca Empire and legend has it that the first Inca, Manco Capac, said to be the son of the sun (hence the Sun God), appeared in the twelfth century. He arrived in the heart of Aymara territory when he was born in Lake Titicaca. It is said that he travelled widely with a gold rod, which from time to time he plunged into the earth; on his arrival in what is now Cuzco the rod disappeared completely into the ground, which persuaded Manco Capac that he had found the centre of the earth, which was the place to build his capital. It was not until Inca Pachacutec in the fifteenth century that the great Inca expansion occurred, which continued until the arrival of the Spaniards. He moved south towards Lake Titicaca but more importantly to the north to Cajamarca, Trujillo and beyond into Ecuador. It seemed to be a tradition among South American tribes that each leader had to build his own palace and not move into the one of his predecessor. As we walked uphill from the Plaza de Armas we saw the remains of several palaces. The *conquistadores* demolished the last palace, which stood on the site of the present day Plaza de Armas, to make way for the building of their cathedral. The Spaniards made a habit of this as they destroyed the Aztec temple in what is now Mexico City to build their cathedral. For me the only thing of interest in the cathedral in Cuzco is the painting of the Last Supper: Christ and his disciples are eating guinea pig! Like many Catholic cathedrals it is very dark inside and there is little of interest other than for aficionados of sixteenth- and seventeenth-century religious paintings: the Windsor family members are not among them.

There are few Inca buildings left in Cuzco, most were pulled down for building materials or for redevelopment. What does remain, however, are many Inca exterior walls that were incorporated in new buildings, including the famous seven-sided stone: the masons would have made wonderful jigsaw-puzzle solvers. Around Cuzco, it is another story as there are Inca remains everywhere in the Sacred Valley of the Urubamba River.

For our earliest trips to Cuzco, on the recommendation of LABVETSUR staff, we stayed in the Hotel Garcilaso where you were greeted with a cup of coca tea, in their friendly attempt to prevent their guests from suffering from altitude sickness. The rooms were clean, cheap and they had constant hot water. However, once the Hotel Internacional San Agustin had been renovated we moved our custom there: it was more expensive, but centrally heated and with very comfortable rooms and a decent restaurant. It also made, according to Maxine, the best Bloody Mary in the world. The only problem was that it took the barman ten minutes to prepare it, which was fine when they were not busy... On arrival at the hotel, the first thing to do was to book the train to Machu Picchu, to ensure that you could get a seat. On our first visit to Cuzco on the first afternoon we booked for a guided tour of Sacsayhuaman, the Inca fort that overlooks and protects the city. The present-day ruin is only a small percentage of the original fort as the Spaniards tore down the walls to build their houses. The Incas had built the city of Cuzco in the shape of a mountain lion with the fort of Sacsayhuaman at its head and the zigzig fortification walls were the teeth, and these remain to this day because some of the stones are so huge that the Spaniards could not carry them away.

As in Machu Picchu, so in Sacsayhuaman there is a large parade ground, which today is still used for ceremonial purposes, particularly the Inti Raymi ceremony held in midwinter, asking the sun to return. This fort was the last redoubt of the Inca Empire and when it fell, it marked the end of the Inca fight against the *conquistadores*. It is no wonder that the Spaniards tried to destroy the fort. We did not take the tour bus back to the city but walked down the hill and what a delight it was: the track had grassy banks on either side and there were alpaca and llama herds grazing, mostly tended by women in their brightly coloured outfits. The cochineal beetle is a parasite on the Opuntia cacti, which grow everywhere on the Andes, and from this they produce the dye for their clothes. Even the men wear red shawls. However, the women have a very different headgear from the Collagua women; they wear a broad-brimmed woven red beret, although some bowler hats can still be seen.

We did not tour the Sacred Valley until Claire brought her school friend Louise Wattam for a holiday. Despite giving her time to acclimatise to the altitude, Louise suffered from *soroche* (altitude sickness) when we went to Cuzco and so we did not go up to Sacsayhuaman that Saturday afternoon but pottered about the Plaza de Armas, being pestered by urchins trying to sell us everything from postcards and guidebooks to watercolours of the city. We planned a tour of the Sacred Valley for the Sunday and we set off by coach for the colonial town of Pisac in high spirits, to visit the Sunday market and the Inca ruins. It was total alert for your possessions when we entered the market, which was heaving with people, mostly locals in their colourful clothes, but also many tourists come to savour the atmosphere and purchase the weavings, carvings and delightful decorated pottery made by the locals. Several bands filled the air with music of guitar, *flauta, tambor* y *caña* (recorder, drum and pan-pipes) as they laboured to sell their CDs. The coach then drove us on the new road, which is several miles long, to the Inca ruins, which can be reached from the colonial town by a short but very steep climb! The land terracing was amongst the most impressive carried out by the Incas and having been restored is still used for agriculture today. The ruins themselves are magnificent with huge great rocks woven into walls with gigantic doorways making them a serious defender of the Urabamba valley. We then drove on to Ollantaytambo for lunch where we had to queue standing outside the restaurant, and this was the final straw for poor Louise, who passed out and was caught by Maxine who lowered her to the ground. Luckily near us in the queue there was a Brazilian who rushed to our rescue; he stated that he was a doctor and proceeded to examine Louise. She had just passed out from altitude sickness, and he administered a few drops of 'Coramine', a respiratory stimulant, and within seconds Louise was sitting up and seemingly back to normal. We thanked the doctor for his services and he told us that he never travelled anywhere at altitude without his 'Coramine'. Luckily the restaurant soon emptied from the first sitting and we were able to find a table so that Louise could sit down.

Poor Louise suffered from *soroche* in the Andes and from heat exhaustion when we took her to the jungle. Maxine and I thought that this would be a good opportunity to get into the Peruvian jungle to see how it compared with the African bush. Maria-Angelica, our friendly travel agent, suggested that we book into the Explorer's Inn in Puerto Maldonado: not really in the city but a four-hour boat trip from it on the Tambopata River. The package included transport to the lodge from the airport by taxi (which turned out to be the back of a truck) and the launch on the river to the lodge which had wooden seats, for a four-hour ride! Accommodation was in three separate chalets (shacks?) and all meals and tours were included. We flew to Cuzco and then to Puerto Maldonado without a problem and we were met at the airport by a hotel representative who had hired the truck to take us to the launch and we piled onto the back and sat on our cases for the journey of three or four miles. The best thing that can be said about the launch is that it had a canopy to protect us from the fierce afternoon sun. It was a pleasant if uncomfortable four hours and we arrived at the lodge at dusk. We were well prepared for the discomfort to come as it was the most uncomfortable hotel in which I have ever stayed! There was not a comfortable seat in the whole place as the chairs had all been hewn from tree trunks: they were also very heavy to move (Plate 47). The beds were at least clean but lumpy and I believe the mattresses were filled with straw. The most comfortable receptacles for a body were the hammocks strewn round the lovely wild gardens.

Dinner was most interesting as we were presented with a section of bamboo about a foot long and four inches in diameter with a banana palm leaf tied with string closing both ends. This was our main course and was tasty – meat and vegetables which were mixed together and cooked in the bamboo container. Fresh fruit and the usual execrable coffee concluded the meal. We were all exhausted and we had a whole-day trip to experience the next day and so we went almost directly from the dining room to the bedroom.

A fascinating feature of the Tambopata and Madre de Dios rivers is that, although at one point they are separated by only a few miles and both join the Amazon River, they flow in opposite directions and join the Amazon more than a thousand miles apart. This fact was pointed out to us early the next morning by our guide on the tour. We started off the tour on a tributary of the Tambopata River and our first stop was when we got to the rusting hulk of a large river launch and this was when we heard the story of the divergent rivers. A British missionary doctor had decided in the 1920s that he needed a launch to reach his native patients and had ordered one from a British yard. The boat was duly despatched by steamer to Brazil where it was floated on the Amazon and set off on its journey to Puerto Maldonado. Unfortunately, they took the wrong tributary and ended up on the wrong river on the wrong side of Puerto Maldonado. The boat had to be dismantled and carried over the hill and rebuilt four miles away on the Tambopata River. For many years the doctor used the boat for plying up and down the river; during one year of particularly good rainfall the doctor had been able to travel further upstream than ever before, but while he was in the jungle the river went down and on his return to the launch he found it beached in the mud. All attempts to get it back into the water failed and there it remained and there it will stay until the rust crumbles it away and it finally disappears. We left the boat and went on foot into the jungle and in the middle of a clearing we stopped and with his machete the guide cut down a small palm tree and cut off the outer coat so that we could eat the palm heart. I had often had the canned variety before but this was the first time to taste the real thing and it was delicious and so refreshing. Later on our travels we were able to taste the fruit used to flavour the popular Peruvian drink 'Inka Kola', which because of its yellow colour and disgusting taste I named *orina* (urine) cola!

Lunch was taken on board the boat and consisted of Spam (?) sandwiches – some sort of canned meat in a rather pleasant home-made bread. Local fruits and the usual disgusting coffee completed the meal. I could never accustom myself to the fact that Perú produced the trees from which a delectable drink could be made and yet what was served up was usually execrable. It was the method of preparation that caused the problem.

The afternoon was spent on the launch watching the antics of the giant otters (*Pternonura brasiliensis*) playing in the river, or trying to see through the binoculars the blue and yellow macaws as packs of them flew overhead. The Amazon jungle is home to many species of birds but because of the dense canopy of the forest it is very difficult to see them. When we lived in Africa (between 1965 and 1986) it was much easier to see a great variety of birds; with the massive expansion of populations in Africa and the consequent destruction of the bush, the birds have flown. In 1965 on a journey from Nairobi to Naivasha, once you had descended into the Rift Valley you could see a bird of prey resting on almost every telegraph pole – augur buzzards, black kites, black-crested hawk eagles – in the noughties when travelling the same road, I did not see one!

We returned to the lodge in mid-afternoon after a fascinating day in the Amazon jungle. There was no swimming pool in which to wash away the efforts of the day and so we clambered into hammocks and drank cold drinks and chatted and dozed until it was time to shower and change for dinner. We were greeted with a dish called *patarashca* with the food cooked inside the leaf of what I thought was a banana palm, and the major constituent was small fish from the river.

The following day was a repetition of the first, with a different guide and different places along the river. I was disappointed that we were not taken to an Indian village and we saw neither of the two species of cat: the small ocelot (the size of a large domestic cat and once hunted almost to extinction for its skin) and the jaguar, the third-largest cat after the tiger and the lion and one of the few cats that enjoys swimming, fish being among its diet. Our guide said we should keep a lookout for a jaguar but the only mammals we saw were more of the giant otters. When walking through the jungle we were shown Brazil nut trees bearing fruit – like a large orange and the nuts are arranged in two hemispheres resembling segments in an orange (hence the shape of the individual nut). We were shown cacao trees with their chocolate fruits, custard apple trees, mahogany trees and many other varieties whose names I have forgotten. The sad thing about the Amazon jungle and perhaps its saviour, is that all attempts to put the different trees in plantations have failed. Growing rubber, mahogany or Brazil nut trees under forestry conditions, where the trees could be managed and the produce harvested economically, have all failed. Evolution occurs so quickly in the jungle that where large numbers of a single species are grown together, parasites, be they protozoa, bacteria, fungi, viruses or insects, quickly multiply and destroy the crop.

On our return to the lodge we were warned that Aeroperú would be on strike the next day (the one before our departure). Strikes were a prominent feature of the reign of Alan Garcìa: the national airline, the farmers, the bus drivers and many other occupations were regularly stopping work on some pretext or other. We were due to take the launch back to Puerto Maldonado after lunch and so we spent the morning in the grounds of the lodge looking for birds and butterflies although I think that the children spent most of the morning reading. The trip back was as uncomfortable as the journey out (Plate 48). It was early evening when we checked into the *Turistas* Hotel and after a shower and change of clothes we went to the restaurant for dinner. The menu consisted of chicken and chips or freshwater fish and chips and we all ordered the chicken, and we waited. And we waited. Other diners came and were served but the Windsor family remained hungry. Eventually I could take no more and I stormed into the kitchen and asked what was going on: it was easier for them to prepare the food for two than the food for six! I stood there and supervised the cooking of our meal and finally we ate.

The hotel receptionist informed us that the Aeroperú strike was off and that we should get to the airport early next morning as all the people from today's flight would be wanting to fly tomorrow, and the plane was always full. We were up early and after our *huevos revueltos con jamón* – the chef did not delay our breakfast – and after a cup of lukewarm, awful coffee, we were on the back of the truck and off to the airport. What a pantomime! The airport was solid with people all wanting to get on the plane to Cuzco. For once I was grateful that we were 'gringos'; because foreigners paid more for their flights than local people, we were told that we would be given priority. As the flight was so overbooked they were not allocating seats on the plane. We checked in, our luggage was taken and we made our way to the departure lounge. This was in the days before the international terrorists ruled the world and airports became giant metal detectors, staffed with mini-Hitlers who revelled in making old men remove their shoes and stealing women's deodorant. Nevertheless, because the state wanted to know what their citizens were doing, there were pre-flight checks of documents, and customs checked that we were not carrying illicit goods from the jungle such as animal skins or drugs.

The plane arrived from Cuzco and we were allowed to go to the gate, which was of expanding metal, such as you see in old-time lifts. Being gringos, we were moved to the very front so that we could board the plane first. The children were told to sprint to the plane and 'bag' a complete row of six seats, while Maxine and I moved at a more gentle jog with all the hand luggage. On the plane it was sheer pandemonium as people jostled for seats. Finally the hostesses got everyone seated and saw that we were all strapped in and we were off. As soon as the 'Fasten Seatbelts' sign was switched off almost the entire plane lit up and were puffing away despite the 'No Smoking' signs. This was a regular feature of Aeroperú flights, as was the applause once the plane had landed. The flight from Cuzco to Arequipa was much more demure. Louise was much happier once we were home and we decided that she had had enough excitement for one holiday and so no more long trips away from Arequipa were undertaken.

That was the only family trip that we made into the Peruvian jungle and the Windsor family never travelled in the vast bulk (80%) of the country. Our journeys were made either to the *costa* (the strip of land between the Andes and the sea) or the *sierra*. The country is so vast, the terrain so difficult, that it would be almost impossible to explore the whole country in a lifetime. The children made several more trips to Machu Picchu on their own, and Maxine took her mother. The majority of our guests made the journey to Inca country on their own. My godson, William Crouch, and his Bancroftian school friend Alex, walked the Inca Trail to Machu Picchu, as did Daniel Auber and his friend. The Halls, Potters and other guests flew to Cuzco.

15

Holidays on Land and at Sea

Lt Dr Hector Apergis

Maxine's father, Dr Hector Apergis, was born in the Victorian era, the son of a Greek cavalry officer and an English mother and the family moved to England early in the twentieth century. After schooling at Dulwich College he qualified as a doctor at Guy's Hospital in London and took part in the last cavalry charge of the British Army in 1917 in Huj, Palestine, when serving as a medical officer with the XXI Corps. On his demob he went into general practice with Dr Greenwood in Crouch End and took over his practice when Dr Greenwood moved to Kenya.

Maxine and I met Dr Greenwood when we were living in Kabete. The doctor's practice expanded when he took a surgery in Harley Street. At the start of the National Health Service the doctor felt too old to change his ways and remained in private practice. As he aged, the colour of his patients darkened as many Indian and West Indian patients considered that a private doctor had more time to listen to them. Right to the end, Dr Apergis looked after his patients and he was seeing people well into his nineties. We were in Arequipa when he died in 1987 and Maxine felt that she could do little by going home for the funeral as she had two sisters to assist with the arrangements and that it would be much better for her mother to come to us as soon as she could free herself of the bureaucratic problems caused by death.

Twice during our time in Perú, Maxine's mother came to us for a holiday and they did wonders for her health: the clean, dry air was great for a woman who suffered from chronic asthma and even when taken to the heights of Aguada Blanca (13,000ft) she was able to breathe freely. I always called her Ma and was genuinely fond of her. On her first arrival Maxine flew to Lima to bring her south and she was able to sit under the shade on the garden swing and gently recover from the journey. She was a wonderful house guest to have, as she enjoyed everything we did and every place we visited. She had a special affection for the old watermill at Sabandía and the *picantería* at Selva Alegre with its different view looking into the gorge caused by the Rio Chili; although, like all of us, she did not like to see the majestic condor in his tiny, lonely aviary; you put up with it because the food was so good. I was having a busy time in the laboratory and so Maxine took her mother to Cuzco and Machu Picchu. On their return Ma was full of the wonders of the Inca ruins and the incredible way they constructed their buildings.

Clever planning was required because I had to go up to Cajamarca and it seemed a great opportunity to take Ma and the family to see this lovely northern town. I flew up with the usual stopover in Lima in order to get all the work out of the way so that I could be free to show them the tourist sights of that beautiful valley. Maxine and her mother would drive up in the Land Rover with a stop in Nazca to arrive in Lima to collect the children arriving from England for their summer holidays. Maxine and Ma had an uneventful journey to Lima where they stayed the night with John and Joan Taylor. Early the next morning the children were collected from the Amsterdam flight and much to their dismay the Land Rover set off for the north instead of driving south. We could understand their disappointment at not going directly home from school but I felt that they should see the north of the country when the opportunity presented itself. The cost of five flights from Arequipa to Cajamarca would be several hundred pounds but because I was working in the north we could use the Land Rover for the journey. It was also a wonderful opportunity to show Ma the Peruvian coastal scenery, which in part is truly majestic with the road looking down into the deep blue Pacific from 3,000ft above.

The journey north from Lima is very different from that to the south as the road follows the low-lying hills close to the sea which in winter were usually clouded in fog. The further north you travelled the flatter and straighter the road and the family party made good time to Trujillo where they were staying the night in the *Turistas* Hotel. En route they passed Chimbote, perhaps the most unpleasant town in Perú; until I drove through Chimbote I did not realise that there were so many different colours of smoke; in Chimbote you could see them all, blue, green, yellow, orange, red, deep purple, they had them all belching from the various factories and smelters. Were that not enough, the town was also a port where the boats landed their fish, the majority of which were turned into fish meal, and so if you were not being choked by the smoke you were nauseated by the smell. What one could regularly see in the north were houses with their own cable hooked over the power lines, extracting free electricity for the house.

The night in the hotel was uneventful but the next morning was not. There was no water for a shower or even a wash. Maxine went and complained and they had breakfast while the problem was resolved. However, on returning to their rooms they found them to be under water as the children had not turned off the showers when the water refused to come. Half-empty suitcases were floating on the pond and as Richard had strewn his clothes over the floor they were all soaking. They finally managed to put all the dry clothes into a couple of dry cases and continue on their journey. I was saddened that the children never really appreciated the wonderful road up the inter-Andean valley to Cajamarca with its ever changing scenery and plant life. Even in winter there was an abundance of flowers in bloom in every new side valley. Once away from the coastal mist the sky was clear and the sun shone lighting up the flowers. They can be forgiven for ignoring the villages because one Andean market town is very similar to another unless you are looking for the differences. Finally, the torment was over and there was Dad waiting to greet them in the *Turistas* Hotel in Cajamarca and after a quick unpacking of the sodden luggage and a cold Coke it was off to the Baños de Los Incas for a swim in their glorious warm pool, while Granny sat and snoozed on a lounger under the sun-shade and the younger members of the party worked off their energy after being cooped up in the Land Rover.

Dinner that night was in Salas; fine dining would be later in the week but the succulent steaks and chips made up in part to the children for not being in Arequipa. The next few days were a mixture of visiting tourist sights and lounging by the pool. The children were amazed to see the 'gold room' *El Cuarto de Rescate*, to which the Incas brought their gold and silver to pay for the ransom of their king, Atahualpa (Plate 49). This is the only remaining Inca building in Cajamarca and compared to those in Cuzco it is not much to see. From all over their kingdom they collected an estimated 6,000kg of gold and 12,000kg of silver, which was melted down for bullion to be shipped back to Spain; it was probably worth getting on for £100 million at today's prices. All in vain: instead of returning the Inca to his palace in Quito, they burnt him; however, as he had converted to Catholicism, they garrotted him first.

Of course the family wanted to visit the Ventanillas de Otusco, the pre-Inca burial ground, where the mummies can be seen in their niches cut into the hillside. They are an amazing sight and remain undefiled: perhaps the local people are frightened of their ghosts. What is it about mummification that it was practised by many ancient societies? Every time I visited Otusco I thought about this question: was it only in dry countries that this process was carried out? The boys revelled in seeing all the dead bodies particularly where the bodies had not been mummified and erosion had brought the skeleton to the surface. The locals must have passed these graveyards but it seems the dead were never touched.

We took the family to try out the basket on a hawser river crossing, which they came to enjoy, although we could not persuade Granny to have a go (Plate 34). During these visits, Marcos Chávarry was invaluable acting as guide and facilitator and showing us artefacts not mentioned in the guidebooks, including the ancient burial site which so impressed the boys, where the bodies were buried not mummified and where erosion had brought the skeletons to the surface (Plate 50).

On the last afternoon of the holiday we visited the ranch of Ing Agusto Zingg, one of the largest and best farmers in the area. We visited the dairy, saw how the fields were irrigated and ended up in the stables where we all had a ride on his *caballos de paso*, which was a novel venture for my daughter, Claire, who was a keen horsewoman but had never ridden a horse that did not trot; she found the experience to her liking (Plate 51). Granny entertained us all to dinner at La Cajamarques, probably the best restaurant in the city and certainly the most elegant. This was our last night in Cajamarca and Marcos and Enrique Lopez were included in the invitation. Marcos and Enrique were at the hotel to see us off the next morning on the short hop to Trujillo where we would spend the night in the same *Turistas* Hotel where they had had the flood. We checked in soon after lunch and then spent the afternoon in the Chimu ruined city of Chan Chan, undoubtedly the largest adobe city in the world being almost fifteen square miles in area, which, at its greatest, was said to house 50,000 people. The Chimu kings each built their own palace and so there are nine royal palaces, of which only one has been properly excavated; the remainder lie buried under the desert sand (Plate 52 & 53, for detail see Plate 35). It is the sand together with the fact that it rarely rains that has preserved the buildings. Whenever the warm current *el Niño* runs, then it can rain, which affects the adobe structures, particularly damaging to the friezes. The buildings were at one time decorated with precious metals, but looters, commencing with the *conquistadores*, have removed it all and only the friezes remain. As with the metals so with the contents of the buildings – all gone. The kings were buried in their palaces and that was similar to the Egyptians; how can two cultures so far apart have so many similarities? As with the Egyptians, so with the Chimu: the kings were buried with their possessions. The Egyptians did it because they thought their kings would need these things in the afterlife. Did the Peruvians think the same?

Not only did we visit the Chimu palace but we went to see the pyramids (yet another similarity!). The Temples of the Sun and Moon belong to an earlier civilisation to the Chimu, seven centuries earlier is what the archaeologists say. The Temple of the Sun is built on the banks of the *Rio* Moche and is the largest adobe structure ever built. The base of the pyramid is about 400 yards square and it is about 150 feet high and it has been calculated to be constructed from more than 50 million adobe bricks. Like the pyramids in Giza it is a solid structure but no burial chambers have been found, unlike its neighbour, the Temple of the Moon, which contains many burial chambers. The *conquistadores* are reputed to have attempted to destroy the Temple of the Sun by diverting the Moche River but only succeeded in washing away a corner; however, it is possible that *el Niño* was the culprit. Even the children marvelled at the grandeur of this structure.

We found a hamburger bar for dinner that night and it was early to bed for an early start the next day as we were planning to drive to Nazca so that we could be home in two more days. There was no stopping for the tourist sites as Maxine and I shared the driving and by mid-afternoon we checked into the *Turistas* Hotel in Nazca. It had been a long drive but a relatively straightforward journey; the hairpin bends were for the following day. We had a swim and then Richard and I played a set or two of *fronton*, a Peruvian game similar to squash or racquets but played with a bat and tennis ball. I left Richard and Guy playing while Maxine, Ma and I adjourned to a small lecture room to listen to Dr Maria Reiche talk about the 'Nazca Lines', the origin of which had eluded people for years. Dr Reiche had been studying these marks in the desert for almost fifty years and was the world's leading authority on the subject. She lived as a resident in the hotel and in return spoke each afternoon to the hotel's guests. We were lucky to hear the great lady speak as Dr Reiche was nearing the end of her life and often her talk was delivered by her sister Renati. This was enough to enthuse Ma to want to see the lines. It would not be possible during this journey because the children were eager to get to Arequipa to see their friends. However, we decided that we would bring Ma back to Nazca during her return trip to Britain and allow time for us to spend a morning looking at the lines.

We showered and dressed and were relaxing in the bar for a pre-dinner drink. Ma, who was normally a sherry drinker, was persuaded to take a gin and tonic and so I ordered a white wine for Maxine, fresh orange for Claire, Coke for the boys and gin for Ma and myself. I thought it strange when the barman arrived with the tonic already dispensed. It was even stranger when

I took a sip and could taste no gin. Ma concurred. I took the glasses back to the bar and complained and the barman dispensed more gin into the glass. On my return we were still unable to taste the gin. Desperate remedies were called for and so, saying nothing to the barman, I left the bar and made my way to the office and took my complaint to the manager. Whether he was involved with the racket or not we never found out but he certainly took action. When we tasted the 'gin' straight from the bottle it was water, which the manager poured down the sink. A fresh bottle was opened and we were able to enjoy our gin, for which we were not charged. While we were having our drinks a small dark-haired man entered the bar and as he was alone and obviously seemed to be English we asked him to join us. Walter Yager, a Peruvian of British descent, had a small farm in Nazca and was growing asparagus for the English market; he asked if we would care to try some, to which we replied, "Of course."

"In that case I will leave some for you at the hotel reception tomorrow morning."

He was as good as his word and the next morning there was a large box of asparagus waiting for us at the reception; we took it home and it was delicious. To this day we always look out for Peruvian asparagus in the supermarket. The chances are that it was produced by that small man who gave us a basketful to try. Although today it is a large international company.

The journey home was uneventful. Maxine took us to the 'rabbit hole' tunnel, I did the leg through Cerro de Arena to Camaná. Having driven the route on several occasions, I was confident enough to drive at a normal speed and we arrived home with Maxine at the wheel as dusk was falling. The children were on the phone immediately. By now they had a large bunch of local friends, which did not include any of the children from 'good' British families (Plate 18). Guy was a great collector of people, a trait he had inherited from his maternal grandfather. He and Claire would go off to town on a Saturday afternoon to meet friends and often the phone would ring and it would be Guy to ask,

"Mum, would dinner stretch to two more as I have found these friends in the town?" or,

"Mum, I have met these two English girls in the town, could we put them up for a couple of nights?"

The answer was always yes. Richard got a shock the first time he invited a young Peruvian girl to go with him to the cinema. He had met a young secretary in FONGALSUR, Rocio, the assistant to Milagros, and she had agreed to go with him to see *Dirty Dancing* and they agreed to meet in Manolo's, the best coffee bar/café in Arequipa. Not only was Rocio in Manolo's, she had brought along her cousin as a chaperone! The friendship did not flourish! Some years later we were invited to Rocio's wedding and the reception was held in the Jockey Club headquarters in the city. We arrived at the club while the newlyweds were doing their visit to their old schools before the reception, but we could not stay even to await the arrival of bride and groom as the music was played at such a volume that my whole body was vibrating with the sound. We had to leave...

The holidays were always too short and no sooner had they arrived than they were gone. It was always a sad time when they went. Richard never accepted being sent away to school although it did wonders for his academic achievement. Claire on the other hand loved it: it enabled her to live *Malory Towers*. She missed home and in particular her mother but she loved the camaraderie of the girls. Guy was very unhappy during those first weeks at Orwell Park; a week after he started my mother received a letter from him which said,

"I hate this place, please come and take me away."

I think that he grew to enjoy his schooldays, he certainly made many friends. I found it hard to be in a foreign country as the children progressed through school, as we were unable to take part in so many activities: Richard singing in the choir when it performed in the Royal Albert Hall, or playing hockey, Guy fencing for the school or playing in the Oakham School Big Band, Claire performing on the stage or the piano. These we missed. I thought back to my schooldays and how supportive my parents were; I do not think my father ever missed an inter-school rugby match in which I played. Even on a Wednesday afternoon he would come down to West Grove to watch me play in the Colts' Fifteen and after the match all eight of the scrum would pile into his old Austin 12 and he would drive us back to school for the after-match tea. The opposition would return to school in their coach, while the home team had to walk the mile and a half. I missed giving my children this support. However, it was a sort of *Catch 22* situation – I had to work overseas to pay the school fees and the children had to go to boarding school in England because we were overseas.

The children had returned to school and all too soon it was time to take Ma back to Lima for her flight home. As we had promised her, we allowed time in Nazca to see 'The Lines'. We left early in the morning and arrived at the *Turistas* Hotel in good time to spend the late afternoon driving round in the desert. Naturally we had to stick to the tracks and not drive anywhere near the lines, but very tall viewing platforms had been erected in order for tourists to see the various designs engraved on the earth's face. Places to park the car were clearly marked and from there you could walk to a viewing platform, climb the steep stairs and look down on the primitive designs of animals and birds, of which the monkey, the dog, the spider and the humming bird are probably the most famous (Plate 54). These creatures, some of which are huge, form only a very small part of 'The Lines' as there are hundreds of lines and mathematical designs, rhomboids, triangles, quadrangles and hexagons. We viewed the monkey and the spider before returning to the hotel to book our flight for the next morning and to attend the talk.

The monkey – note the many lines

Only the sister Renati was there that evening but the book that we purchased was signed by both sisters. Some of the lines are 30cms deep and they were made many centuries ago by removing the top dark layer of the desert floor to reveal the pale sand beneath. Some of the lines are more than a kilometre in length and perfectly straight. Who did it, how did they do it and why did they do it? These are the common questions. Dr Reiche came to Perú to teach mathematics but soon became fascinated with the enigma of 'The Lines', properly called geoglyphs. She believed that they were created by the Nazca people between 1500 and 2000 years ago and like our Stonehenge are of astrological and possibly religious significance.

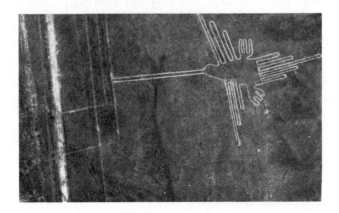

The hummingbird

Many other theories have been propounded and perhaps the most outlandish was that of Erich von Daniken who suggested that it was a sort of inter-planetary space station for extra-terrestrial space ships to land. Since the death of Dr Reiche, a German–Peruvian team of archaeologists have been investigating the mystery and perhaps they have produced the most rational explanation, which is that the Nazca people realised that in a hot, dry country water in rivers evaporated before it could be used, but if it was brought underground then they would lose less. The lines marked the route of the water. This does not explain the geometric figures nor the animals. It is thought that the latter could be doodles: the workmen, tired of producing straight lines, decided to have some fun during their tea breaks. I have found no better source of information on the present work than that of Stephen R Hall, in the *National Geographic* magazine of March 2010 and the following extracts are quoted with permission:

The coastal region of southern Peru and northern Chile is one of the driest places on Earth. In the small, protected basin where the Nasca culture arose, ten rivers descend from the Andes, to the east, most of them dry at least part of the year. These ten fragile ribbons of green, surrounded by a thousand shades of brown, offered a fertile hot spot for the emergence of an early civilization, much as the Nile Delta or the rivers of Mesopotamia did. "It was the perfect place for human settlement, because it had water," says geographer Bernhard Eitel, a member of the Nasca-Palpa Project. "But it was a high-risk environment—a very high-risk environment." ...

...In their 2003 book on Nasca irrigation systems, archaeologist Katharina Schreiber of the University of California, Santa Barbara, and Josué Lancho Rojas, a local schoolmaster and historian, point out that the Nasca River, which goes underground about nine miles to the east, resurfaces like a spring on the doorstep of Cahuachi. "The emergence of water at this point," they write, "was almost certainly regarded as sacred in prehistoric times."...

...The Peru-German archaeological initiative has explored the region from the Pacific coast to altitudes of nearly 15,000 feet in the Andean highlands. Almost everywhere they have looked they have found evidence of Nasca villages—"like pearls in the valley margins," says Reindel. "And near every settlement we find geoglyphs."...

...These new findings make an important point about the Nasca lines: They were not made at one time, in one place, for one purpose. Many have been superimposed on older ones, with erasures and overwritings complicating their interpretation; archaeologist Helaine Silverman once likened them to "the scribbling on a blackboard."...

...There is little question that water—or more precisely, its absence—had assumed paramount importance by the endgame of the Nasca culture, roughly between A.D. 500 and 600. In the Palpa area, geophysicists have traced the creep of the eastern margin of the desert about 12 miles up the valleys between 200 B.C. and A.D. 600, reaching an altitude of some 6,500 feet. Similarly, the population centers in the river oases around Palpa moved farther up the valleys, as if they were trying to outrun the arid conditions...

© National Geographic

We were up early the next morning to take the ancient old monoplane that rattled down the runway and finally managed to clamber up into the sky. It was a four-seater plane and Ma was in the co-pilot's seat with Maxine and me squashed in the back. Despite being spring there was no mist and we had a wonderful view of the lines. My favourites are the monkey and the hummingbird, as there is no mistaking what they are. One of the advantages of being in an old, small plane is that it flies very slowly and so we were able to have a really good look at the various animals. A disadvantage is that it shakes and rattles and both ladies became queasy; having much greater experience of small planes, the vibrations had less effect upon me. All three, having enjoyed the flight, were not unhappy about being back on the ground. After a late breakfast we were on the road for what now seemed a short journey to Lima and a long discussion about the geoglyphs and their meaning. There was a wonderful *cebicheria* not far from the Taylors' house and we took our hosts and Ma for a farewell *cebiche mixto* and the next morning we drove her to the airport for the plane to Amsterdam and then to London and by mid-afternoon we had returned to Nazca and the next day to Arequipa and an empty house.

Jumping ahead to our last Christmas holiday in Perú, the Windsor family were invited to the residency for the New Year celebrations so that all the children could be together. We decided to drive up and take the opportunity to explore the coast on our way home. The embassy party was traditionally a fancy dress party and this year the theme was 'shipwrecks' so between Christmas and the New Year the family spent the time making their costumes and ended up very much the best-dressed family. I felt that Claire and Maxine as Prospero and Caliban should have won the prize as Claire looked every inch the part with her flowing hair and false beard and moustache, and Maxine made a wonderful cowering slave. Richard as a pirate, Guy, Saving the Whales for Green Peace, and Roger as King Neptune could not compete (Plates 55 and 56). However, the prize for the best costume went to Long John Silver who spent the evening with his leg doubled up behind him in a peg leg and a real parrot on his shoulder. It was a great party with wonderful food and dancing by the pool, and being mid-summer in Perú, the climate was balmy.

Once the New Year had been safely seen in, the young ones decided to take off in search of greater excitement. They certainly found it. Richard by then was at university in Edinburgh and so had heard of the concept of 'first footing', which is an old Scottish custom. Once the bells had rung in the new, you went in search of strangers, bearing gifts of coal or peat, some shortbread and, of course, whisky, and you went out to share them. I do not think that the children went out with these traditional gifts but together with the sons of the Dutch and Indian Ambassadors, they went looking for a party. They walked down the long hill from the residency and out into the main road, having decided to stop at the first house where they heard the sounds of music or laughter. It was not long before they found one. They knocked on the door and were welcomed into the house, which to their dismay was decorated with swastikas and Nazi memorabilia and their hosts were wearing military uniforms. However, they felt that having gone in, they should at least have a drink before taking their leave, explaining that the idea was to visit many different parties. Having left the house they ran away as fast as possible and decided to return up the long road to the residency. I had gone to bed but Maxine had decided to wait up for them, and when the children returned they found her fast asleep, curled up on the sofa, clutching an empty champagne bottle.

On New Year's Day the adults went to a lunch party at the house of the military attaché in a very smart suburb by the Los Incas Golf Course. The ice was broken by a game that was played. On arrival a glass of champagne was placed in the hand and a name was pinned to the back. The idea was to find out who you were by asking questions to which the respondent was only allowed to say "yes" or "no". I was the new Peruvian Secretary General to the United Nations – Javier Pérez de Cuellar – and by the time I had made the identification I had spoken to everyone present and finished my second glass of champagne. After the party we visited the Gold Museum, which was also in Surco, housed at the foot of the hill up which you ascended to the residency. The artefacts were collected by a Peruvian businessman, Miguel Mujica Gallo, who wanted to display the wealth and history of Perú to give the nation pride and he had assembled a fine collection of mostly pre-Inca gold artefacts which he gave to the nation. He not only collected gold, but weapons from around the world and across the centuries, suits of armour, pistols, rifles, machine guns, small canon, and spears, swords and knives from the knightly era up to the present day. In his collection was the carbine used by President Juan Perón of the Argentine. What I found most interesting were the Nazi daggers: apparently a set of special daggers had been made for Hitler, Goebbels, Goering, Himmler and Hess. The only one not in the collection is the one that belonged to Hitler. It struck me as most odd that a man who collected items of such beauty as the Tumi, a ceremonial knife of gold and turquoise, or the ceremonial vase in gold and crysocola, both from the Sican culture in the third century AD from northern Perú, could also be a collector of items of death.

The Windsor and Haskell children, together with Limeño friends of the Haskells including the sons of the Dutch and Indian Ambassadors, had great fun visiting the night spots of Lima. A member of the family would take them into the city and they would either take a taxi home or walk. Their exploits caught the eye of *Gente* magazine which was a sort of *Today*, or *Hello* magazine combined with *Tatler*.

The caption was 'An explosion of happiness and youth'. There might have been a different story had the press heard what happened after one ambassadorial party when they were walking back home and one had had too much to drink. The police passed by as the young man was vomiting in the gutter and stopped, sensing the opportunity to extort a bribe. In Perú you always carry your identification documents and they were able to show that the family had diplomatic status and so they got back unmolested.

• **Explosión de alegría y juventud; Claire Windsor, Iván Díaz Rainey, Jonathan Haskell, su linda mamá María Luisa, y Guy Windsor.**

One fascinating feature about staying in the residency is that it had been designed for members of the Royal Family to stay. Although the guest wing was within the main building it could be closed off by lockable doors so that it could be made completely private. Really it was more the thought of occupying the same bed, but the beds were single!

The return journey started with a stop at Pachacamac, the only archaeological remains around Lima and actually on the road south. The children found them fairly boring and so we did not spend too long. It had been an important Inca site but its origins were much older and of adobe rather than stone. Before being taken over by the Incas it must have been of religious importance as there were the remains of several pyramids to be seen; some you can climb to the top, but we did not. The most interesting

Inca construction was the restored 'Room of the Chosen Women', although we did not find out what they were chosen for. After lunch in the café we set off for Paracas, 150 miles south along the good part of the Pan-American Highway, where we were booked into the Paracas Hotel. We arrived in time for a swim in the pool. We were staying there for the night to take the boat the next morning to the Ballestas Islands. It was early to bed as we had to be on the boat at 7:00am the next morning.

Poor Guy suffered dreadfully from motion sickness and despite a pill, he did not enjoy the hour and a half boat trip to the islands and before we had left the bay, he was feeling nauseous. It was a most fascinating journey as we left the harbour. Pisco, the main town near Paracas, as well as being the home of the spirit, is a military centre and the bay was a repository for all the old Peruvian navy ships that were in various stages of rusty decomposition and as we left the bay there on the hill to our right was this massive candelabra in the sand. It was a geoglyph like the Nazca lines and has been there since time immemorial; the origin is unknown as was the reason why it is there. Once we left the bay, the journey to the islands was uneventful, if not to say rather boring, enlivened by the rough sea and the birds, particularly the boobies, which would be flying along and suddenly they would fold their wings and drop like a stone, hoping to come up with a fish in their claws. Flights of pelicans went past looking like pterodactyls in their gaucheness.

The main island was alive with birds and sea lions. None of the islands off the coast of Perú is inhabited and it is forbidden to land on the islands other than for the collection of guano. This was a massive industry in the nineteenth century and boats left the Peruvian ports laden with guano for delivery to Britain. The boats needed ballast for the return journey, as a result most of the small habitations along the Peruvian coast are built of timber from Britain, and Arequipa is paved with York stone. It is little wonder that more than a hundred years later they are still harvesting guano as there must be millions of birds living along the Pacific coast. The waters are cold from the Humboldt Current coming from the Antarctic and as a result are alive with fish of which the most common is the *anchoveta*, which forms the basis of the fishmeal industry as well as the avian diet. The sea was very rough and the helmsman had difficulty in holding the boat still so that we could watch the antics of the thousands of sea lions, the waddling of the Humboldt penguins or the pelicans swimming majestically by. The movement of the boat made taking photos a difficult business, and did not help Guy to enjoy the trip.

We saw more wildlife on that boat trip to the Ballestas Islands than anywhere else in Perú; it is a memory that will long remain in my mind's eye. Not even the wildebeest migrations in the Serengeti compare with those islands for numbers of birds and animals but I do not think that any of my children appreciated the huge concentration of nature on one small spot. It brought home to me, the massive numbers of fish that there must be in the sea to feed all these birds and animals. I thought back to my practice days in Malton, Yorkshire, where one of the more interesting clients was Flamingo Park Zoo, which had just opened up in Kirby Misperton under the direction of Reg Bloom who had come there from Windsor Safari Park after working as a game trapper in Kenya. The zoo was constantly acquiring new animals, including a pair of elephant seals which had just arrived from South Georgia; they had travelled each in a large open wooden crate and for the many weeks on board ship they had not eaten. We tried them on some herrings, and one had eaten greedily, the second showed no interest in food. We released the one that was feeding into the newly constructed pool, and I worked out a diet sheet, to slowly build up the fish intake. I was at a loss to know what to do with the recalcitrant seal, and I finally decided to gave a large dose of mixed vitamins by mouth, to stimulate its appetite; I stood on the wooden case then tickled the mouth of the seal with a small stick; he responded by opening his mouth to grab the stick and as he did so I poured the medicine down his throat – a primitive but effective technique. It produced a very rapid result and not the one I was expecting: within a few moments the seal started vomiting and out poured a bucketful of intestinal nematode worms! The seal was released into the pool. This had taken place on a Friday afternoon and I suggested that they feed the seal with one fish that evening, A second fish was to be given the next morning and two more were to be given at midday, and so the quantity was to be built up slowly over the following week. I was at a dinner party that Saturday night when the phone went. Our hosts answered it, and indicated that the call was for me. It was Reg Bloom, and he was very worried:

"Can you get here straight away? That elephant seal you treated is bleeding to death."

"I will be with you in about half an hour: can you make sure that there are two or three people to help?"

I had no idea what to expect or what I would need to do. I always carried chloral hydrate, which, in those days, was a useful general anaesthetic for large animals (the new anaesthetic agents were still not available for vets). I arrived at the zoo to find at least a dozen helpers round the pool and the seals swimming round in what appeared to be blackcurrant juice; the one who had refused to eat was obviously in some trouble as it was thrashing about and it had damaged its flippers on the concrete of the pool.

"Tell me what has happened, it seems to me that one of the seals is suffering from severe colic."

Reg Bloom pushed forward a young girl who was almost in tears.

"I fed the seal this morning and gave it two fish as you instructed. I fed him again at lunchtime and gave it three as you instructed, but he looked so mournful that I gave him some more, and in the end I gave him the whole bucketful."

"Well, now we know the problem we can go about sorting it out. But remember it takes a long time to starve an animal to death but overfeeding can kill in hours. Can you drain the pool?" I said to Reg. Once we had drained the pool a couple of the workers roped the colicking half-ton beast, and for the first and only time in my life I gave an intravenous injection to a seal and as the choral hydrate went in I could see the seal relaxing. Once the animal was anaesthetised, I was able to give it a detailed examination. Both front flippers had multiple abrasions, which I cleaned with a mild disinfectant solution. I told Reg not to refill the pool until the animal had recovered and the young lady to stick to the diet. I washed up and left. The seal made a complete recovery. I returned to the dinner party, smelling of disinfectant, but with a good story to tell. Just seeing what one elephant seal could eat in a day and there before my eyes on one small island were thousands of sea lions and hundreds of thousands of sea birds and there were thousands of such islands along the Pacific coast of South America. What a repository of food are the oceans of the world and all the while the boobies were trying to deplete them.

That night we stopped in the *Turistas* Hotel in Nazca and returned to Arequipa the next day. Arequipa in summer was a different city to what it was the rest of the year. From December onwards the rich and not-so-rich Arequipeños disappear. They remain or return for the Christmas celebrations but by the second of January they have all gone. Where to? Mejia is the answer. Every Arequipeño owns or aspires to own a house in Mejia by the sea. Why, I could never understand. The sun is so hot in summer that in the middle of the day you cannot go out in it. The sea is always rough and very cold, you cannot stay in it for long, and what passes for sand is grey and gritty and impossible to walk on barefoot as it gets so hot. And yet everyone in Arequipa wishes to be seen on the beach in summer. There is no point in going to the beach before eleven o'clock in the morning, because there is nobody there. But on the stroke of eleven, you can almost set your watch by it, the ladies appear and parade along the beach in the latest swimwear although the swimsuits never touch the seawater. They appear in their droves and small groups of them can be seen everywhere. By one o'clock, it is too hot and they have all gone, many to the Mejia Club for lunch, not to reappear until the cool of the evening. These women are invariably unaccompanied by men unless it happens to be the weekend. For the women spend much of their summer at the beach while their menfolk remain working in Arequipa. The road to the coast is packed on a Friday evening as husbands rejoin their families for the weekend. No social activities occur in Arequipa in January or February but I suspect that does not go for sexual activity as the men have a free hand to visit their mistresses while they are off the leash.

We did not possess a summer house at the coast nor did we need to rent one, as we had many friends who did, and at various times we stayed with the Flanagans or Marjorie Michell who had houses in Mollendo rather than ten miles down the coast at Mejia. The Roberts had a house in Mejia in which we were able to stay during the week as Evelyn, being American, was not too keen to be one of the Mejia girls, and preferred to stay in Arequipa with Reggie. The Hallenbecks had a house near that of the Roberts. David Hallenbeck was an American astronomer/engineer and ran the NASA radio-telescope in Perú. His wife, Sonia, who was Peruvian, became a friend of Maxine's, and Charlie, the oldest of their three boys, became a firm friend of Guy's. The water was almost too cold to swim in but it was great fun to go macha hunting. Machas (*Mesodesma donacium*) are a type of clam or bivalve and the shell seems to be a cross between that of a mussel and an oyster. They are native to the Pacific in Chile and Perú and they can be found in the shallow water above the low-tide mark. They live just below the surface of the sand and you wade in the shallow water at low tide and search the seabed with your toes for hard objects and when you find something you bend down and scoop up the mollusc. They are usually cooked and served in the half shell with onions and chillies, or at least they were: apparently some disaster has overtaken them and they have all gone.

Early in the new year we were invited by the Hallenbecks to spend a weekend at their summer house. This fitted in nicely with an official visit to Mollendo on the Monday morning. Saturday evening we went to a show in the Mejia Club which did not start until 11:00pm and consisted of one rather indifferent group – keyboard, guitar and drums together with a reasonable singer who unfortunately only seemed able to sing one type of song. This went on without interval until 1:00am by which time I could hardly keep my eyes open. Sonia was all for taking part in the disco that followed, however, Max and I persuaded her that we could not stand let alone dance. The next morning we did not wake until 10:00am and it was a miserable day; the mist hardly lifted and the sun never appeared all day. We spent some time on the beach but I did not go into the sea. We had lunch at the club and then Max and I went to Mollendo to meet the lab team who had come down for the *Brucella* testing the following morning, and then we went to pay a courtesy call on Marjorie Michell before returning to Mejia. I spent the next morning driving between Mejia and Mollendo visiting the laboratory team and poultry farms, where I was trying, fairly unsuccessfully, to drum up trade. I thought that they were all breeding farms whereas only one actually bred chickens, the others all sold eggs. I also visited the cheese plant, which we had not been testing, and as a result of that visit Edilberto and Ricardo went there that evening and collected the samples. After I had finished my visits I went back to the house; Max had packed up and so I loaded the car, had a swim in the pool (it was a beautiful summer's day) and we went to the Gloria plant to find that the team had finished and were ready to go. So Edilberto was left with the truck and I brought Fany, Roxana and her husband home. We first had lunch in our favourite restaurant in Mollendo where we had their fantastic *Puerto Libre* dish, which consists of *chicharones* (deep-fried fish), octopus, abalone and other shellfish, a fantastic *cebiche*, a *sarsa de mariscos* and salad. The seafood in Perú is wonderful.

Maxine decided that I needed a holiday and when she saw that KLM were advertising free holidays in Aruba, an island in the Dutch Antilles in the Caribbean, to passengers travelling between Lima and Amsterdam, I was informed that that was what we were going to do. We had planned our leave so that the children could come out for their summer holidays and we would return with them for our leave. The accommodation was in a timeshare and we were committed to attending one half-day presentation to obtain our free lodging, but what did half a day in a week mean? Maxine and I were entitled to business class while the children were doomed to steerage but I was happy to swap seats with Claire so that she could sit with her mother. The Windsor family were billeted on the eleventh floor at the Aruba Royal Resort, which of course was still under construction; although we could get breakfast in the hotel, there was no proper restaurant or bar, but that did not matter because there are many restaurants and bars in the town of Oranjestadt. It is not a large island but there is a delightful area of virgin bush and we rented a jeep and had a good look round at the wonderful windswept thorn trees, the divi divi tree, symbol of the island, and cacti and succulents: *Aloe vera* is said to have originated on the island. The wind always blows from the north-east and so the eastern beaches are useless for bathing because the wind always blows and the sea is rough but the western beaches are a delight and consequently all the hotels are along the west of the island. Baby Beach, at the far end of the island near St Nicolas Port, is a wonderful place for snorkelling and even for only a moderate swimmer there are wonderful things to see on the coral reef. The only disadvantage is that the beach is close to the port and the oil refinery, which is wonderful when it is not working. However, the sea was always crystal-clear and a deep, deep blue and the sand was soft and warm. In the second town of Aruba, St Nicolas, there is a wonderful pub – Charley's Bar – which served a good beer and a reasonably priced lunch but what made the bar was the décor, which is similar to that of Dirty Dick's in Liverpool Street, London. There is clobber everywhere, deposited by visitors, of which the strangest was an old copper diver's helmet; postcards, visitors' cards, banknotes of all denominations and currencies, straw hats, cricket bats, fishing nets, stuffed pets, I do not know what would happen if they had to clear the premises: it might be easier to burn it down and start from scratch. Over the years we have been many times to Charley's Bar where there is always a happy, holiday atmosphere and the children always insisted that we stop there. Oranjestadt has a wonderful nightlife and a great number of good restaurants and if you wanted to gamble there were plenty of casinos that served good food. The children's favourite restaurant was a little out of town in a shopping arcade, where the food was reasonable but there was always a wonderful cabaret, including limbo dancers, comedians, singers and always 'Mr Bones', the man who controlled the action. The last time we were in Aruba we found that the restaurant had gone.

We duly attended the 'Presentation' and I was press-ganged by the whole family into buying a week: "Roger, you do need a rest and you will not get one once we get to England." And for a couple of visits it was great and then the timeshare bug hit Aruba Royal Resort and before it was completed, the company went bust. Aruba, although nominally independent, was still guided by The Netherlands and after various manoeuvres the resort ended up in the clutches of an American hotel company, Divi Resorts; instead of owning our timeshare indefinitely, our ownership was reduced to thirty years, not that it mattered.

Maxine considered it to be a good buy as we usually travelled to and from Perú by KLM and the plane always stopped in Aruba. Our children also travelled to and from school by KLM; the alternatives resulted in a stop in Miami which meant they had to pass USA immigration, collect their luggage and check in again. This resulted in a great bonus for the Windsors senior. Claire and Guy were booked to return after a holiday and always we made sure to reconfirm their flight well in advance. Our friendly travel agent Maria-Angelica phoned to say that she had seen the passenger list for the children's flight and could not find their names. We phoned John Taylor in the embassy and he got on to it; he was told that they were not on the flight, although they were on the flight from Amsterdam to London. However, KLM suggested that they go to the airport and it would be sorted out there. We sent them off from Arequipa and John took them early in the morning to Lima Airport and the fun began. Finally, Guy was upgraded to business class and Claire was put with the smokers at the back. I believe that Guy swapped over with Claire once the plane stopped in Aruba and they arrived safely in Britain in time for school. I wrote a very rude letter to KLM and about three days later there was a knock on my office door and it was Aurora saying,

"There is a gentleman here from KLM in Lima and he wishes to see you."

"I wonder what he wants, show him in."

"I have come to apologise personally," said the head of KLM Perú, the real top brass. "Children should never be subjected to what they had to suffer, and so my company will upgrade you and your wife the next time you fly from Lima to Amsterdam."

"We already fly business class," I replied.

"In that case we will upgrade you to first class."

On our next leave we were duly upgraded and again Maxine had noticed that KLM were offering a promotional deal of three nights free in a hotel in

Amsterdam, and because we were travelling first class we were put into a five-star hotel in Amsterdam for our stay. Guy and Claire were livid:

"Just think what we could have done in Amsterdam for three days."

I dreaded to think.

To be certain of having a vehicle in Cajamarca it was often necessary to take the Land Rover from the laboratory north. On most occasions Edilberto would drive up and down so that it was available when I arrived, at other times I would accompany him one way and, rarely, when I felt that I had the time I would drive myself, which gave me the opportunity to examine those side valleys off the road from Chiclayo. I wish that I had had more knowledge to make a proper study of the plants. Without the children clambering to 'get on', I had the opportunity to explore some of the many archaeological sites that there are along that coastal road. Perú has about 3,000kms of Pacific coast and most of the land is a desert with almost no rainfall at all. In the high Andes there is plenty of rain coming from the Atlantic and the water finds its way to the Pacific by means of about fifty rivers. It is little wonder that what settlement there is in coastal Perú, is along the banks of the rivers. Earlier in the chapter I described how the Nazca civilisation started in the first centuries of the Christian era but that around Casma is very much older. The Sechin culture is believed to date from 1,600BC. Just outside Casma is the Cerro Sechin archaeological site, which was discovered by Peruvian archaeologists Julio C. Tello and Toribio Mejía Xesspe on July 1st, 1937. Tello believed it was the capital of an entire culture, now known as the Casma/Sechin culture or Sechin complex. Notable features include megalithic architecture with carved figures in bas-relief, which graphically dramatise human sacrifices. Like so much Peruvian archaeology, it has only been partly examined. At the site there is this huge wall which is believed to be the outer wall of a temple which seems to have been built into the hill. Carved on the wall are these fantastic creatures bearing huge clubs which you regularly see on Peruvian artefacts. There is a small museum on the site holding many of the articles found during the various excavations. The Sechins had also started to build their own Great Wall of China in adobe. Work since I left Perú has shown that there are very much older settlements in this area, some dating back to 3,500BC, making it the oldest known site of human habitation in the Americas.

What is it about deserts that stimulates the development of these human civilisations? Why do they produce such wonderful artefacts as the gold funerary mask of King Tutankhamun or the gold funerary mask of the Sechin people? Why have the Peruvians so many different cultures from the Sechin, Chavin, Nasca and Chimu up to the Incas? I am sure that there were many more that I did not visit. But Perú is a large, beautiful country with so many natural and man-made wonders and the problem for me was that I was there to work.

16

The Making of a Diplomat

It has always been important to me to try and control events rather than be a spectator and in my first term at the Dick Vet, I was elected one of the two year representatives on the Veterinary Students' Committee, the body that was responsible for student affairs. We made our money by running a dance in the college on Saturday nights and this income was sufficient to fund many different student activities from the Equine One-Day Event, the College Dramatic Society, various sporting activities, to subsidising attendance at the annual gathering of the Association of Veterinary Students of Great Britain and Ireland. I served on the committee throughout my time in college, I was treasurer in fourth year and had the honour of being elected President in my final year. One of the perks of being on the committee was the opportunity to attend the annual meeting of the International Veterinary Students Union (IVSU), which in those days held their meetings only in Europe, although students came from the United States and South America.

The first one that I attended was in Paris and it passed in a daze. On the evening of the first full day of the meeting there was a trip down the River Seine on a Bateau Mouche. I remember little of this trip as the French Government had provided the association with enough champagne to inebriate all the students in all the schools in Europe. The Paris Vet School was based in Maison Alfort, a suburb of Paris, and at the time the International Veterinary Institute was based in the school, although it later transferred to Montpellier, and this enabled people with tropical experience to address the meeting. The

French had an admirable system for their overseas staff who were given yearly contracts. They spent ten months working overseas and then had one month of leave in France followed by a month working at Maison Alfort: in this way, they kept in touch with research at home and at the same time were able to teach the students. Was it in this meeting that the seeds of the idea of working in the tropics was sown? The highlight of the conference was the evening in Versailles where we went to see the *son et lumières*. The whole party was gathered round the statue of the Sun King (Louis XIV) and a French student climbed on to the horse and conducted the mass choirs of the IVSU in a complete rendition of *'Alouette'*. It was hilarious and crowds of French people watched on and even joined in.

The following year the meeting was in Hanover and Berlin. The German students wanted to show off their new veterinary school building and the staff wanted a 'dry run' of their facilities before the World Veterinary Association meeting, which was taking place later in the year. The meeting was meticulously well organised as you would expect a German meeting to be, but things went spectacularly wrong. They had a new small animal operating theatre complete with television cameras. The students did not go into the theatre but watched on television monitors with a two-way sound system in an adjacent room. In those days the picture was only in black and white but it was my first time to see closed-circuit television and it was brilliant for bringing close-up views to a larger audience. The operation was an aural resection, opening the auditory canal of an Alsatian dog suffering from a severe infection. The operation was a great success but the dog died under the anaesthetic causing great embarrassment to the surgeons.

A trip was made to Hamburg, where most of the young male students spent the evening on the Reeperbahn watching the antics of the naked ladies, although we were early to bed because we had to get up at 4:00am the following morning to take the coach to the port of Bremerhaven to watch the trawlers arrive and the veterinary inspection of the fish landed. Unfortunately, no trawlers came in as the sea was too rough and there were no fish to inspect. The worst thing about the stay in Hanover was the *wurst*. No evening meal was complete without a German sausage, in fact most evening meals were nothing but sausage and I loathe boiled sausages.

After a visit to the beautiful mediaeval town of Celle, we were taken to Hanover Airport from where we flew to Berlin. We were billeted in several hotels in the centre of West Berlin and three of us were allocated to a room in which there was one single and one double bed; the Cambridge student grabbed the single bed and so Dai Powell, a Bristol student, and I had to share the double. Dai and I, in company with Clive Jordan, a London student who spoke fluent German, and several Dutch students spent the evening in a beer cellar where we drank beer from litre-glass *steins*. On leaving the bar we found that every one of us had stolen their drinking vessel and we assumed that the price of the glasses was factored into the price of the beer. On our return to the hotel room we found that our duvet was missing – our sleeping Cambridge student was the culprit and had hung it over the wall of the balcony; luckily it was a warm night and so we slept without the duvet. The next morning our colleague found that the duvet had blown away in the night. That afternoon, Berlin hosted a reception for the association in the town hall. Willi Brandt was mayor and he made a delightful speech of welcome. On the platform were many dignitaries including the 'Rektor' of the Berlin school and every time that the mayor referred to him he called him 'Herr Professor, Dr, Dr, Dr, Braun.' The speeches were all in English or were translated into English and after the ceremony we adjourned to a large room set out with small tables where we sat and were offered the local speciality to drink – *Berliner Wasser* – a very light lager into which is gently poured raspberry puree. It sounds awful but was, on that hot summer afternoon, absolutely delicious. The next day we visited the vet school of the Free University of Berlin whose ground bordered East Berlin with its great wall. On the far side of the wall was a command post such as you see in those old movies about German prisoner-of-war camps. The tower was of wood with four log struts leading to an observation post with a machine gun. A coupe of 'Vopos' (East German soldiers) were watching us intently and when all the male conference participants decided to have a pee against the wall (which was built on East German soil), the machine gun was trained on us, much to the amusement of the women.

In the afternoon, we had a coach tour of East Berlin with an East German veterinary student as our guide. What a dreary place was East Berlin after the excitement of the West. Rows and rows of drab concrete apartment buildings and the highlight of the tour was a visit to the Russian war cemetery! At the time, there was a constant procession of East Germans defecting to the West and we suggested to our guide that we hide him on our coach and get him to the West.

"I do not wish to leave," he replied. "I wish to stay and change things. If all the people who are dissatisfied with life here leave, then we shall never be free."

Whatever happened to him I do not know, but things have changed and Germany is again one country.

Clive Jordan and I decided that on our free morning we would visit East Berlin and see things as they were and so we presented ourselves to Checkpoint Charlie, where you could cross into East Berlin, and we arrived at a moment of high drama as two Vopos had just defected. On the corner of the West Berlin street that marked the boundary (the wall was built on East German soil) was a chemist shop outside of which, on the shopfront, was a large barometer/thermometer and these two soldiers had made a habit of sauntering together up to their side of the road seemingly to look at these instruments. On the morning in question, after looking at the instruments, they had broken open their rifles and walked into the West. The balloon went up, hooters sounded, the border was closed and within a few minutes a large black car swept up to the border and out jumped a smart Russian officer in riding breeches, but there was nothing he could do. The birds had flown. We never got into East Berlin as the border remained closed. Clive and I spent a happy hour in the museum at Checkpoint Charlie which showed the methods by which people had crossed the wall to freedom. Perhaps the strangest sight on those crazy, divided days was the Russian war memorial, for some reason standing in the British sector close to the Brandenburg Gate. The memorial was a tank. I do not remember whether it was a World War Two tank or a bronze replica, but there it stood as an affront to the Berliners who set about desecrating it. To stop this, the Russians obtained permission from the British authorities to have soldiers patrolling the tank. The locals were not too keen to see Russian soldiers who were subjected to verbal and physical abuse. Unable to defend themselves without causing an international incident the Russians were the butt of Berlin practical jokers and so the British erected a barbed wire fence round the soldiers and this was patrolled by British soldiers. To me this summed up the whole stupidity of the Cold War. The Soviet Empire survived for another thirty years but eventually collapsed, the wall was torn down and Germany was reunited.

Perhaps the third IVSU was the most enjoyable, or was it that I was accustomed to the people? I had been asked to lead the British delegation, which meant that I had to attend all the council meetings during the conference. The meeting commenced in the veterinary school in Cordoba, which I remember was a beautiful building with a great deal of marble used in the construction, but we were not long there as it was a travelling conference journeying the whole of Andalusia. I remember a night in Seville where I had to have my hair cut! I saw the great River Guadalquivir which you could walk across without getting your feet wet, so small and shrivelled were the channels, and yet in winter ships of 10,000 tons could berth in their docks. Jerez was fantastic with our tours of the various sherry growers. I remember these huge barrels signed by Nelson and the Duke of Wellington that still contained sherry from those bygone years. A glassful of the sherry is used to seed each new barrel produced. We were offered lunch by the wine grower, Sr Osborne, and we sat at one long table on the veranda and regaled ourselves with the most glorious seafood; every three feet or so there were bottles of dry, medium and Amontillado sherry. I was thinking to myself what a wonderful lunch, when Sr Osborne stood up and said:

"*Senores y señoritas, vamos al comedor para almorzar.*" ("Gentlemen and young ladies now, let us proceed to the dining room for lunch.")

We had just had the pre-lunch drinks.

I was scarcely able to eat the wonderful *paella* set before us but the Spaniards set to with a will. Our entertainment was not yet finished because immediately after lunch we adjourned to the bullring to watch the young bulls being trained for the fight and the trainee fighters learning their art. The young bulls all had lead weights on their horns to stop them causing injury, the sword was made of wood and only the cloak was real. The ring was about a quarter size and there were no picadors but the trainee toreadors put on a great display for us. Before long the show was over and then we were asked if we would care to chance our arm with the bulls. I decided that this was definitely not for me as the Dutchmen and Germans got sent sprawling. The funniest was Hans, a Utrecht student, who stood there facing the bull as it charged but at the last moment he lost his nerve, turned and fled, to receive a sharp jab from the bull up his backside, which sent him flying. The stockman rushed in and got the bull away from the fallen Dutchman, who decided to have another go, with the same result. By now Hans was fuming and decided that he had to face the bull. When the bull charged for the third time, Hans threw away his cloak and sword and grabbed the bull by the horns and with a great twist had the bull on the ground. The Spaniards booed and whistled but the students all cheered. When the tiny female Colombian delegate decided to have a go in the ring, I knew that I had to follow suit for the honour of Britain. I was scared as the bull charged but managed to pirouette out of its way. Having done this twice I considered that honour was saved and gracefully and gratefully retired.

What made this conference so special were the journeys each day when the Dutch and British commandeered the back rows of the coach; there developed a special bond between the students of the two nations. The highlight of the whole tour has to have been the visit to the gypsy caves in Granada, where we sat and ate dinner at long tables in the open air, which started about 10:00pm. What made the evening unique was that after the meal, a Spanish student climbed onto the bare wooden table and, accompanied by his guitar, recited the poem '*Granada*'. In those days, I did not speak a word of Spanish but somehow the rendition made me understand every word. That performance haunts me still. Happy memories of happy student days.

Was it my involvement in international affairs as a student that prepared me for professional life? Who knows? What I did know was that I enjoyed meeting people from different cultures which is why I loved working overseas and was really enjoying my time in Perú. I was working in the post-mortem room when Aurora told me that the ambassador wished to speak to me. We had no phone there and so I had to clean up rapidly and go into the office to take the call.

"Roger, ODA want you to go to Washington to represent them at the Pan-American Health Organisation Annual Congress. You are a lucky b— going to Washington in May with the almond in blossom. Apparently, they have nobody that they can send from London and you are the closest vet. I will get the travel department here to make all the arrangements for your journey and you can pick up the tickets on your way through."

"What do they want me to do?" I asked Keith.

"You will be Britain's official delegate to the organisation, but more than that I do not know. I have no doubt that they will send you the agenda for the meeting and if there is anything specific they want, or if they want you to vote on any specific issue, they will inform you."

Like most things veterinary, it had a low priority in London.

"How long will I be away?"

"I think that you should go on the Saturday morning to get to Washington on the Sunday: it's a three-day meeting, Tuesday Wednesday and Thursday.

You can have a free weekend at government expense and return on the Monday."

"It sounds rather a jolly jaunt, I have never been to Washington."

"May is much the best time to visit, after the cold of winter and before the steamy summer weather sets in."

Because of the odd schedules of Aeroperú I had to fly early on the Friday morning to ensure catching the Saturday flight to Miami: they only flew from Arequipa early in the morning. It was not until the García presidency was coming to an end that it was possible to fly to and from Arequipa other than in the early morning. The president, at a stroke, opened the skies to competition. This enabled me to spend the day with Aurelio Málaga in his laboratory in Chorrillos. Aurelio had worked as a consultant for PAHO and so he was able to give me the details about their Washington headquarters. Dr Málaga was acutely embarrassed as the laboratory had no money to buy adequate materials for working with the rabies virus. I could not help but think back to the days in Botswana where the laboratory had sufficient money to buy whatever disposable items we needed and how lucky we were in LABVETSUR, where we were not subject to government fiscal control.

I was driven to the airport in the ambassador's car in good time to catch the American Airlines flight to Miami. The flight from Miami was on time when it disappeared from the schedule! I had checked in and passed through immigration when we were informed that there had been a phone call to the airport saying that there was a bomb on the plane and so it had been diverted to the Pisco airbase of the Peruvian Airforce. The poor passengers were being sent back to Lima by coach about 250 miles, while the northbound passengers had to wait while the plane was searched for a bomb, which was not there. We took off six hours late, I missed my connexion to Washington and spent the night in the Miami Airport Motel, a hotel which I was to come to know and where I always enjoyed my stay. There was no direct flight to Washington on the Sunday and so I had to fly to New York and take the short hop to Washington.

Keith was quite right, Washington is a beautiful city and in May with the almond in blossom it was quite stunning. Pennsylvania Avenue with the White House dominant was a delight with the magnificent Indian and Japanese Embassies being the finest. Britain is badly let down by its embassy which is in post-Second World War grammar-school brick with the iron window frames. It is the poor relation among the embassies.

The meeting was a great introduction to international diplomacy and the meeting chamber was arranged like the United Nations, each delegation with its own name board. The United Kingdom was seated next to the United States, which gave me a great feeling of inferiority – the lone UK delegate was seated next to three American delegates and behind them were their civil service team with their files and folders to keep the delegates informed. I found the three days of negotiations tedious in the extreme, with points of order and supplementary notes. There was no doubt in my mind that this was not a meeting of scientists but a meeting of lawyers and politicians. I could understand why they were unable to find anyone in London to come. I had received no instructions from London as to what I was to do or say and during the three days of deliberations I spoke on only one topic – foot-and-mouth disease. The Americans constantly lumped Britain with Europe, and I had to keep reminding the meeting that Britain was free from the virus and that we did not vaccinate. I really became upset when the Americans showed a map of Europe with almost the whole of the continent including Britain showing as infected. My language became quite undiplomatic as I informed the meeting that people should make sure that they had their facts correct before publishing them.

I do not pride myself on my linguistic skills but in South America I have always tried to speak Spanish to the local people and I think it might be said that I speak fluent if grammatically bad Spanish. However, my ego received a real boost in Washington; after one session, I adjourned to the bar where I met up with a group of Mexican veterinarians and we were discussing foot-and-mouth disease, when one of the vets said,

"Why do you speak Spanish with a Peruvian accent?" I always assumed that I spoke with a strong English accent! He knew me as the UK delegate and did not know that I worked in Perú, until I explained. This changed the whole course of the conversation as we began a discussion on the importance of diagnostic laboratories in disease control. It was an excellent way to end a day of political mumbo jumbo, and I still treasure "Why do you speak Spanish with a Peruvian accent?"

That evening I went to the Folger Theatre based in the political heart of the capital. The previous evening I had gone to a porn cinema in one of the scruffier parts of the city. It was the first time that I had heard of porn being shown in a proper cinema and it was an interesting experience. However, when I left the cinema I began to doubt the wisdom of being in this part of the city late at night and I took refuge in the foyer until I was able to hail a cab which took me safely back to the hotel. I was going to have an evening of culture to make up for the lapse. I really went for a good laugh, at the thought of Americans trying to deliver the words of Shakespeare. The play was *Love's Labours Lost*, a play about which I knew nothing. I went to laugh, but I was gobsmacked before they were five minutes into the play: the actors could have been trained in Stratford, their accents were faultless and the acting of all was superb.

Before going to the theatre I knew nothing of Mr Folger, nor of his library in which the theatre operates. Henry Folger made his money as an executive with the Standard Oil Company of New York. All his life Folger was a Shakespeare addict, and he bought a 1685 Fourth Folio in 1889. He and his wife became avid collectors of Shakespeare's works and memorabilia. After the First World War, they started looking for a home for their books and they persuaded the US Congress to give them land next door to the Library of Congress. The classical building was completed in the early 1930s and houses the world's largest collection of Shakespearean artefacts including eighty-eight copies of the 1623 First Folio. The Elizabethan theatre in the library was not originally intended for performances but now hosts a world-class group.

The play was stunning and what made it even better was that during the interval you could stroll round the library, wine glass in hand, looking at the magnificent display of Folios and Shakespeareana. I was thrilled at having discovered the Folger Library and could not believe that I had never heard of it before.

I visited the Lincoln and Washington Memorials but for me much the best experience of my visit to Washington was going to the Arlington Cemetery where I stood at the foot of John Kennedy's grave. From my student days, he had been a hero of mine; perhaps the greatest leader of the West since Churchill. I can forgive his foibles and sexual peccadilloes because he had a vision for society that I could believe in:

"And so, my fellow Americans: ask not what your country can do for you, ask what you can do for your country."

I stood head bowed and watched the twinkle of the eternal flame and I do not know why but my thoughts turned to the poem '*The Burial of Sir John Moore at Corunna*' by C. Wolfe:

Few and short were the prayers we said
And we spoke not a word of sorrow,
But we steadfastly gazed on the face of the dead,
And we bitterly thought of the morrow.

I do not know for how long I stood in reverie, thinking what might have been had he lived. Perhaps his reputation would have suffered. Would there have been an American war in Vietnam? All I knew then was that a great man had fallen.

From Kennedy's grave I went to the Vietnam War Memorial Wall, and there I pondered on the futility of that war: the half a million Americans that gave their lives, fighting for what? Five million Vietnamese died and many years later I saw in the Hanoi War Museum the *Book of Sacrifice* in which on page after page were listed the names of those mothers who had lost seven or more children to the war. I thought, *Why do the Americans consistently back the wrong side?* Any impartial examination of the politics of Ho Chi Minh and Diėm show one to be a simple patriot who, when he could not get help from the West asked the Communists, who were only too happy to help; the other was a corrupt despot. The might of France and America was defeated and this was Ho Chi Minh's mistake: he should have allowed the Americans to think that they had won, then they would then have poured in aid to rebuild the country. As it was, Uncle Ho had to do it on his own. Many brave Americans died but dreadful acts were committed by their government including the use of napalm and Agent Orange and perhaps the worst of all was the massive bombing of Laos, which was supposedly on their side! There was much to think about at the Vietnam War Memorial.

I decided to return home via the Wagners in College Station, Texas and so when the meeting concluded I flew to Houston where Gale was waiting to drive me the hundred or so miles to his home. Gale was a Texan scientist who had been working in Plum Island, off the coast of New York, which is where the government laboratory for exotic animal diseases was located. Gale had been sent to work in Muguga, Kenya when Maxine and I were living there. Gale had been working with the United Nations project to produce a vaccine against East Coast Fever; and after he had obtained clearance from the American Embassy in Nairobi he employed Maxine as his secretary and we became great friends. Gale was an immunologist with a particular interest in diseases caused by protozoa. That evening I was taken out to dinner in the Hilton Hotel and I could not believe my eyes: there was a wall of *sillar*, that soft white volcanic rock that I thought only occurred in southern Perú.

On my tour of the veterinary school on the Saturday morning, I was saddened to see that the old building in which Smith and Kilborne in 1893 did their ground-breaking research work into the cause of Texas Fever (a malaria-like disease of cattle in which the red blood cells become parasitised by the protozoan parasite *Babesia bigemina*) had been pulled down to make way for development. Smith and Kilborne were the first to show that blood cells could be infested by protozoa and they showed that the infection was spread by ticks. I was surprised by how many British vets were working in the College Station Vet School of Texas A&M University. The professor of parasitology had been the year below me at the Dick; the professor of virology had worked on bovine respiratory viruses at the famous veterinary institute in Compton, near Newbury, and the vet who ran their wonderful stud of horses had previously been in practice in Essex. It was good to see the old faces again.

It was also good to hear the news of the Wagner daughters; the elder, Kristin, was married to a physician and living in Nebraska, quite a distance from Texas. The younger daughter Lisa was about to be married but was still living at home. Gale and Bev had decided to move once the girls had both gone to a house they were designing further out of town. We talked of the happy days in Muguga and Gale's American colleagues such as LaRue Johnson who was busy teaching camelid medicine, in which he was now a leading expert, in Colorado State Vet School. Talking old times with old friends is always fun but all too soon it was time to return to Arequipa, not an easy place to reach from Texas. I had to fly from Houston to Miami, Miami to Mexico City, Mexico City to Guayaquil via Panama City and finally to Lima and Arequipa. I am not sure that I achieved very much but at least I ensured that the Americans knew about the status of Britain with regards to foot-and-mouth disease.

Some time after my return from Washington I received a letter from Tony Irvin, the ODA veterinary adviser, asking if I would be happy to represent ODA at a meeting on the 'Provision of Animal Health Services in Developing Countries' organised by the Intermediate Technology Group, to be held in Nairobi; he wanted someone to find out what they were up to. Had I known what I was letting myself in for I am not sure I would have accepted;

however I had worked with the group in Botswana and had been impressed by their approach to development. I flew to Lima in the morning to get the night flight on Aeroperú to Rio de Janeiro. I spent the day preparing my talk in the British Council Reading Room, which was across the road from their main office. I was very surprised when a member of the staff came running in to say that I had a call from Chicago; since I knew nobody in Chicago, this was a real surprise. The man on the line was Tom Hunt who had obtained my phone number in Arequipa. When he phoned LABVETSUR he was told that I was in Lima at the British Embassy and was given their number. On phoning the embassy he was redirected to the British Council and for an hour and a half we talked; I was glad that he was paying the bill. Tom Hunt ran an animal import/export organisation which had been set up to deal in African mammals for American zoos. When the fashion had turned away from keeping animals in zoos, he had branched out into working with llamas and alpacas for American, Australian and European farmers, where there was a burgeoning trade. Tom had heard that at last Perú was going to allow the export of camelids, something for which I had been fighting for more than two years. It was crazy that Perú should ban the export of these animals when Chile was a willing seller: in fact Chile was exporting more than their entire national herd every year! All that was happening was that Peruvian camelid owners smuggled their animals into Chile from where they were sold on at massively inflated prices, with the Chilean middlemen receiving much of the money. I had sat in the office of the Peruvian Minister of Agriculture trying to explain to him that the Peruvian economy would benefit greatly were the *campesinos* allowed to export their animals directly. The minister refused to accept that Peruvian animals were being smuggled out until I showed him that Chilean animals sold to America had antibodies to foot-and-mouth disease in their blood. Chile had had no cases of foot-and-mouth disease for several years and did not vaccinate their animals. Perú had the disease and vaccinated cattle and camelids: animals with antibodies to the disease came from Perú.

At last Perú had agreed to the export of camelids and Tom Hunt wanted to be the first in on the act, and wanted my advice about setting up a quarantine station in Arequipa. I thought that his company would be good for Perú and offered all the help that we could give. After we had discussed the details I suggested that he call me again on my return.

"Where are y'all off to?" he drawled.

"I am going to Kenya for a meeting of the Intermediate Technology Group," I replied.

"Well, I'll be darned," he exclaimed. "You must go visit with my brother Don, Don lives on Mount Kenya and runs the Mount Kenya Game Ranch, alongside the Mount Kenya Hotel. Say, you must go and see him. I'll phone him this morning and arrange for you to stay with him. You'll love Don and his lovely wife, Iris: they will take great care of you."

And so it was all arranged and I was given Don's phone number in Nanyuki. And Tom arranged to call me on my return. This would add additional zest to the trip, I thought.

I passed a comfortable if sleepless night on the Aeroperú flight to Rio but was able to sleep on the flight from Rio to Cape Town on South African Airways. I had to change there for Johannesburg from which I caught the flight to Nairobi. I had not yet reached fifty years of age and so was able to handle the numerous flights and changes of time zone. I was met by the Intermediate Technology driver but could not believe where he was taking me: I had not been informed that the meeting was to be held in a nunnery! The Dimesse Sisters Convent in Karen, set in a rural suburb of Nairobi. I was even more surprised when I arrived at the convent to be told that the nuns had double-booked us and that for the weekend we had to share the facilities with a meeting of Catholic priests from round the African continent. My room for the next two nights was where the visiting priest slept when he came to take early mass; it connected directly to the chapel and I was awoken at 5:30am by the singing of the nuns. I thought the most ungodly thoughts. The food was excellent and when I finally was given a proper room it was most comfortable. The main problem was that I had many friends in Nairobi and I wanted to go out at night to see them. This presented problems as the door to the outside world was shut at 8:00pm and Alsatian dogs were released in the grounds to deter intruders. In order to get back in after hours you had to make a formal application and had to state the time you would return so that the dogs could be rounded up.

During the evening I spent with Paul Sayer and Olwen in their lovely house on the Loresho Ridge, Paul suggested that I stay the night and that he would drive me back to the convent the next morning, which seriously discombobulated the nuns and their dogs. It was lovely to see Paul again; he has always been a friend that I never saw enough. His first wife, Elma, had looked after me at the end of Maxine's long labour with our first child, but some years later she had died from ovarian cancer. Olwen lived in the adjoining property, had been a great friend of Elma's and was widowed when her banker husband was killed in a car accident while driving in the Rift Valley. Olwen, like Paul, had been born in Kenya; her father, Humphrey Slade, was a distinguished lawyer and was appointed Speaker of the House of Parliament when Kenya became independent. Paul and Olwen made a lovely couple and I had the most enjoyable evening.

The meeting itself was most refreshing and I was very interested in some of the technologies discussed. I had had contact with the organisation in Botswana where they produced windmills for pulling water out of the ground, corn grinders that worked off a bicycle, wind-up radios and torches.

It was when the meeting took to the road that the problems began I chose to visit Eastern Province to find out about the training of paravets and the work that they did. The first night was fine as we stayed in the Pig and Whistle in Meru which was still very much what it had been twenty years previously: I am not even sure that the owners had changed. I was able to luxuriate in a large cast-iron bath, even if the enamel was a little discoloured: the water was hot and the Tusker beer was cold. The following day we set off for the game park and the veterinary assistants' training school where we were to stay for the next two nights. I was very distressed to see what had happened to the veterinary services in the area; when we lived in Kenya, Geoff Smith was the provincial veterinary officer for Eastern Province, based in Embu, and his colleague Jerry Haigh was the district veterinary officer in Meru; between them they controlled what went on in the province, before Jerry left the department to set up a private practice in Nanyuki. Now there were veterinary offices in Embu, Meru and Maua, the town near the game park, manned by a total of ten vets who never left their offices because there was either no transport or no petrol to put in the vehicles. Keen young vets would soon become disillusioned about their role and the descent into idleness and lack of interest would have a spiralling effect.

We watched the paravets being trained and at least they were taught useful practical skills, but it seemed to me that with ten vets there should be no need for paravets. The training given was very similar to that offered by the Botswana Agricultural College and the end product was similar, but in Botswana there was a shortage of vets and so farmers had some access to trained help. In Kenya, they were replacing the services that were available if only there was money to get the vets out into the field. I could not help but believe that the system we were developing in Perú, where the farmers paid for their services, was the better way to go.

Accommodation in the college was primitive to say the least, four to a room with two sets of iron bunks which were decidedly uncomfortable as the bunk frame rubbed through the thin mattress. If the accommodation was bad, the food was worse, being designed for young Africans coming from their tribal villages. It was only for two nights. The second day we travelled round the villages to watch the assistants at work. Nominally they reported to the local vet but since they never came to the villages and the assistant never went to town, the interchange was minimal. It was difficult to reconcile the service that farmers received compared with what had happened in the past. I felt that the chance of controlling an outbreak of disease was minimal. Our journeys took us through the game park and we met several game wardens and I asked what had happened to the white rhino that I had worked so hard to keep free from sleeping sickness (trypanosomiasis) all those years ago. It seemed that there were still six animals in the park: three of the original six and three calves. Three adults had disappeared, their horns no doubt ending up in China. The wardens had been armed in an attempt to prevent the poachers taking them all. I suspect that they failed.

We left early the following morning to return to Nairobi in a day, and we stopped at the Isaac Walton Hotel in Embu for lunch, where I was able to have a swim and a sandwich. On return to Nairobi I phoned Don Hunt who knew all about me and he extended a warm invitation for me to visit them.

"You can take the East African Airways plane from Wilson Airport on Saturday morning and Iris will collect you at the airport in Nanyuki."

"I will try and book a flight and let you know," I said.

"Only phone me if you can't get a flight, but there is nearly always a spare seat or two." And so it was arranged.

The final meeting of the workshop was a round-up of the different groups describing their activities and overall it had been a most impressive meeting. If all the organisations that were supported by ODA performed as well, then British aid was being usefully spent. I was taken to Wilson Airport by the conference organisers and had no difficulty in getting a flight to Nanyuki in a small twin-engined plane that sat about a dozen people. The flight was smooth, the landing even and the surprise enormous when I met Iris as she had flown to meet me in her single-engine plane. Iris is a beautiful, tall, elegant German woman, who was warm and friendly and an excellent pilot as we flew the short distance up the hill to the Mount Kenya Game Ranch. They had a landing strip near their home and a lad to put the plane away in its small hangar as we drove in the Land Rover to their house, and what a house it was. A patio overlooked the swimming pool towards the peaks of Mount Kenya. Over the years that we were friends I found out the story of the Hunts. Don had made his fortune as a presenter of the American equivalent of *Blue Peter*, which had become a national programme when a young chimpanzee was brought into the show. Don had been a great friend of William Holden and Stefanie Powers and with other buyers they had formed a syndicate to buy the Mawingu Hotel and estate. Don had taken over the land and had turned it into the Mount Kenya Game Ranch, and they financed the running costs by selling acre plots to rich, mostly film star, purchasers, for them to build wonderful houses with glorious views of the mountain. The hotel became the very up-market Mount Kenya Safari Lodge, with the patrons having access to the game ranch with its hospital/orphanage. When William Holden died, land was set aside to build a wildlife foundation to teach young Kenyans about their heritage. I was given my own rondavel, which was where William Holden had stayed when he was in Nanyuki. It was a luxurious self-contained unit with a glorious sitting room with its own log fireplace and an equally comfortable bedroom.

Over lunch, which was taken on the patio, I was asked if I would mind if we all went to watch the King's Own Royal Border Regiment Beat the Retreat at the Nanyuki Club. I thought that it was a splendid idea and the Hunts had been invited to the cocktail party after the retreat. The regiment had been in the Nanyuki area for several months of training. Various units of the British Army used the facilities for tropical training and when they left they Beat the Retreat as a means of saying thank you. After a siesta and afternoon tea, we drove down to the Nanyuki Club to find the entire club furniture lined up on the cricket pitch, for the guests to watch the soldiers marching and the band playing. The big sofas and comfy armchairs were reserved for the dignitaries – the provincial and district commissioners, the general commanding the local army unit, the bishop, the mayor and of course the local member of parliament, all black. However, almost all the remaining guests were white, mostly drawn from the local farming community. We sat down on the hard chairs and promptly at 6:00pm the band marched in and saluted their distinguished guests. What struck me as amusing was that there were more Africans in the British Army band than there were Africans in the audience. It was a most impressive display and performance and for more than half an hour we were entertained by the marching and the music. The band retreated, the show was over, but for the select guests there was the cocktail party – those who had given the officers hospitality.

In those days, I drank gin and tonic and it certainly flowed. I was standing talking to a soldier when I heard this voice behind me: *Caroline Holdcroft*, I thought, and turned to the voice. Was that Caroline? She should be in South Africa and it was some years since we had been near neighbours in Gaborone. I knew that her family farmed in the Nanyuki area. I looked again, perhaps it was Caroline.

"Excuse me!" I said. "But are you Caroline?"

"No!" came the reply. "I am her sister."

I explained who I was and how I knew Caroline and we fell to talking. By a strange coincidence Caroline was in Kenya at the time but she was not in Nanyuki, but Nairobi. We arranged that Caroline would phone me at the Hunts. The remainder of the party went by in a blur and we returned to the safari lodge for dinner before a whisky nightcap in Don's cosy bar.

On Sunday, we visited the orphanage/hospital where I saw my first bongo. To preserve the species from extinction on Mount Kenya, Don had persuaded President Kenyatta to allow him to capture all the bongo on the mountain. Most were shipped to San Diego and other zoos in the United States to form part of a breeding programme. The bongo is closely related to the mountain eland, which are still relatively common, and bongo embryos were successfully implanted in mountain eland mothers. The aim was to breed a good number of bongo in captivity and then return them to the mountain. Using surrogate eland mothers would speed up the process. A few were kept in the safari park for breeding purposes and as an attraction for tourists. They also had a pigmy hippopotamus which had been a present from a visiting president. Crested cranes ran free in the orphanage. There were no predators as Don felt that the safari park was not large enough to allow the herbivores to prosper alongside lions or leopards. At a subsequent visit I did have to treat some cheetah cubs which had been brought to Iris by a farmer who found them on his land after the mother had been killed by poachers. What happened to them after they grew up, I do not know.

I was then taken for a drive by Don and perhaps the most interesting animals in the park were an albino zebra herd, but there were hartebeest, wildebeest, giraffe, Thomson and Grant gazelle, impala, bushbuck and waterbuck; later they were to acquire some white rhino. Don kept the most interesting to the last when I was taken to the William Holden Wildlife Centre, where there was a *rebaño* of llamas, shipped over by his brother Tom. The llamas served two purposes: they acted as pack animals when the student visitors to the centre trekked up into the mountain; also, the faeces from the llamas were collected and put into a digester, which provided methane for cooking and lighting when there were students. The William Holden Centre had been set up to provide free wildlife education for Kenyan young people and it operated through the Four K Clubs in the schools. The club would write and request places and they would bring the children to the centre where they were accommodated in tents that were permanently erected inside huts; this was to give the children the feeling that they were camping and they had to assist with the preparation and cooking of their food. During their stay, which might be for a weekend or three or four days in the week, the children received talks on wild animals and the bush from members of staff and guest lecturers. The students visited the orphanage and safari park and made day trips into the forest that surrounded the mountain. There was a well-stocked library at their disposal. The object was to teach the students to value their heritage and help with conservation of Kenya's wonderful wildlife.

William Holden died suddenly and unexpectedly and within days Don had received cheques to set up a memorial to him from Ronald Reagan, then president of the United States, Frank Sinatra and many others. They could not be cashed and had to be returned to the sender, while Don and Iris together with Stefanie Powers set up a Kenyan trust to allow it all to take place. It duly happened and Stefanie became the chairman of the trust and a corner of the safari park was set aside for building the centre. The money was raised and there was sufficient to invest for the running costs and people who had received so much pleasure and profit from the wildlife were able to ensure that the animals survived.

All too soon the wonderful conclusion of my trip to Kenya came to an end and I had to return to Nairobi for the flight back home. Don and Iris drove me back to Nanyuki Airport from where I had an uneventful flight back to Nairobi; the journey back home was anything but uneventful. From Nairobi to Johannesburg, to Cape Town to Rio all went to plan but the Aeroperú plane from Lima arrived in Rio with a serious problem and the return flight was cancelled. Unfortunately(?) I had to spend three days in Copacabana, at the expense of Aeroperú waiting for my flight to Lima. By a strange coincidence

I was booked into the Windsor Hotel on Copacabana Beach and it was during carnival! I decided against going into the city to view the parades as I was concerned for my personal safety but I watched it all on the television, interspersed with trips to the beach for a swim and to watch the young ladies parading along the strand. The three days passed all too quickly and soon I was on the rickety old plane making its way to Lima and so home. I had experienced a great variety of accommodation in that time from the luxury of the Hunt rondavel to the discomfort of the agricultural college bunk. I was able to report to ODA that in my opinion the Intermediate Technology Group was making a valuable contribution to Third World development.

When I was working in Dumfries and later, I carried out several consultancies in Kenya and I always tried to make a visit to the Mount Kenya Game Ranch where I was accommodated in the luxurious William Holden rondavel. One such visit occurred when Stefanie Powers was there, and it was a delight to meet this charming star; little did I know that several years later we would work together in India. On several of these visits I went prepared to give talks to the students in the William Holden Centre. I remember Stefanie telling me how thrilled she was when more than half the Kenya Cabinet had spent time in the William Holden Centre during their schooldays.

My third 'diplomatic mission' came about as the result of my own efforts. Aurora spoke perfect English but many Peruvians had great difficulty learning sufficient English to pass the TEFL English test: to gain entry for a technical course required the student to pass at level 5; 6 was required for a degree course and 7 for a master's. Many Peruvians found this a very difficult task, and some otherwise bright professionals never managed it. I constantly called to mind Marcos's comment that trying to learn English in Cajamarca was like trying to learn to swim from a book without access to a swimming pool. We even had students staying in the house with us for a fortnight and during the day Maxine would hold conversational and grammar classes with them. Some still failed. I suggested to Tony Irvin that perhaps we should train some of our students in the British-run laboratories in Asunción, Paraguay or Santa Cruz, Bolivia and in the vet schools in Chile.

"We know nothing about the quality of the teaching in Chile," said Tony. "Perhaps you had better go and find out."

And I went... At the time Chile had three veterinary schools, in Santiago, Valparaiso and Valdivia. I decided that it would be sufficient to visit two schools and so I wrote to the deans of Santiago and Valdivia who both offered a warm invitation to visit their school. Maxine and I decided to make a holiday of it and so we arranged to have three days in each city, which would give me time to look at several different departments in each faculty.

Hotels in Santiago were much more expensive than Perú, £50 a night whereas in Perú we considered £10 expensive, and so we did not stay in the centre but in a small hotel that was quiet and very friendly. The dean, Professor Hugo Gonzalez, collected me each morning and drove me the 25kms to the school, which had been built outside the city but was quickly being encircled by the booming city. Maxine spent her time visiting the capital while I looked at various departments in the veterinary school and had discussions with the staff. The departments that interested me most were clinical medicine, and pathology with its various branches of microbiology and parasitology. What has always interested me most in vet schools outside of Britain was the amount of clinical material that they received. So often the learning is from a textbook with live or dead animals being rarely seen. The Chilean schools were the exception and both stood up well in comparison to those at home, and I was very impressed with the teaching staff.

At night we went to several fantastic restaurants; whereas hotels were expensive, restaurants were cheap. The best one we found served a set meal for about £5: eat all you like. The selection of first courses was unforgettable: there were oysters, crabs, mussels, machas and about twenty different types of sausage, hams and about thirty different salads. I think we both had about four plates of the hors d'oeuvres and the main course was a choice of fresh salmon, paella, plus a mountain of meat dishes that we did not even look at. There must have been fifty different puddings and we each had two. Between us we drank a bottle of excellent Chilean white wine.

On our last night in Santiago, Professor Hugo Gonzalez invited us out to dinner and collected us from our hotel. To get to the restaurant we had to leave the car at the foot of a cliff of San Cristobal (Saint Christopher) Hill which overlooks the city and take a funicular railway to the summit: my first venture in such transport. There we had a drink and watched the sunset and the lights come on before going into the restaurant to eat.

We had to be up at the crack of dawn to get to the airport for our 8:00am flight to Valdivia. The hotel forgot to wake us and so at 6:15am we phoned to ask why we had not had the call and were informed that it was only 5:15am.

The clocks had gone back that night and we did not know. We arrived at the airport with plenty of time to spare. Standing in the queue next to us for his plane to Paraguay was Ernest Carden, a friend of some years who travelled South America for the Milk Marketing Board selling British bull semen. He, too, had not heard of the change in the clocks. We had some breakfast together and went our separate ways. Thanks to thick fog our plane could not take off and we waited for about three hours.

The reception that we received in Valdivia was even warmer and we stayed in the best hotel in town. We were met by Fernando Wittwer, a Chilean vet who had studied in Liverpool. Although of German origin he did not speak the language but did speak excellent English. We were booked into an excellent hotel – large, comfortable and quiet. Valdivia is named after Pedro Valdivia, the founder of Chile, and is about 1,000kms south of Santiago in the most beautiful countryside, with natural forests, lakes and rivers. The city boasts three rivers that unite to form the River Valdivia. It is only 15kms from the sea but until recently, when a bridge was built over one of the rivers, the only way to get there was by boat. We had hoped to boat down but it was not to be. Dr Wittwer was detailed to look after us as both he and his wife had studied in Liverpool, he in reproduction and infertility, while his wife had trained in midwifery in Liverpool Royal Infirmary.

The vet school and indeed the whole university is on an island in the River Valdivia. I thought that Santiago was good but Valdivia is in a different league! Their facilities compare very favourably with any British veterinary school, and it was almost a home from home as many of the staff had been trained in Britain, mostly in Liverpool. Those staff who had not trained in Britain had studied in Germany, Australia or the USA. As in Santiago, they were very friendly and I really enjoyed my short stay with them. The Wednesday morning was free and first we took a boat trip round the island before visiting the town centre. Maxine did a great deal of shopping, so much so that we had to buy an additional suitcase!

I remember little about the Valdivia school other than how delightful the staff were and what a pleasant place it would be to study. The dean of the school arranged for me to meet the vice chancellor of the university and explained about the German influence in the country:

"There are four universities in southern Chile and three of the vice chancellors' surnames begin with 'von'; the name of the fourth, who you will be meeting, is Braun."

Dr Braun proved to be a delightful man who was very interested to know why the British were sponsoring a veterinary project in Perú and did I think that they might assist Chile? I felt that I must pour cold water on that suggestion because Chile was a much better developed country than Perú. There was not the poverty in southern Chile. I also pointed out that General Pinochet had only just departed and that he was not popular in Britain. I mentioned how impressed I was with his veterinary school and I hoped that it might be possible for the British Government to sponsor students to study in Valdivia. It was a good meeting.

While I had been working Maxine had been shown around the city by Mrs Wittwer and had had a great time in the museum where she saw a double piano, the first she had ever seen. Fernando and his wife took us in their car to see the sea and some ancient forts that were used to defend the city against pirates such as Francis Drake. We ended up at their house where we were entertained to dinner. The following night we took them out to a restaurant where, on the Wittwers' recommendation, we had an unknown, but delicious, South Pacific fish. Maxine and I had risen early that morning to go down to the fish market on the quay and watch the boats unload their haul and then walked round the fish market on the riverbank and saw swordfish that must have weighed almost 1000lb.

Perhaps that was what we ate in the restaurant.

It had been a very interesting visit to Chile and I was able to report to ODA that both the veterinary schools I had visited were excellent places to train our Peruvian vets and laboratory technicians, and it would obviate the need to teach the people to speak English. I still believed that where possible the vets should be trained in Britain because I wanted them to feel an affinity with my country and I had learned during my travels that people who had trained in British universities, when they returned to their countries, looked upon Britain with affection and turned to Britain when they needed help. It was for this reason that I was furious when the Dick Vet, together with ODA, decided to close the Centre for Tropical Veterinary Medicine and why I fought in vain to save it.

Our visit to Chile was the last 'diplomatic' trip I made while in Perú, but not the last journey outside Perú. I had been a member of the Society for Tropical Veterinary Medicine for several years, but I had never attended one of their meetings; when I heard that their biennial conference was to be held in Puerto Rico I asked ODA to sponsor my attendance so that I could present the results of our work on the economics of parasite control in South American camelids and the benefits of veterinary laboratories to the farmer based on my experiences in Botswana and Perú. They agreed.

On the Saturday morning, I set off for Puerto Rico; they say that lightning never strikes twice: I was in Lima Airport waiting in for the American Airlines flight to Miami. We sat in the departure lounge and waited... and waited.The plane did not arrive from La Paz! Finally we were told that there was a bomb scare, not that there was a bomb on board but that one would be put on when the plane landed in Lima and yet again the plane had been diverted to Pisco. The pilot was not keen to stop at Lima on the return journey. The *Sendero Luminoso* or MRTA (Revolutionary Movement of Tupac Amaru, the old Inca leader) were up to their tricks. Thanks to the fact that the minister of transport's wife was travelling, pressure was put on the pilot and the plane finally arrived. Our hand luggage had been through the machine so many times that it was almost radioactive. There were soldiers everywhere. The flight to Miami was uneventful but dull with lousy food and worse service. They had forgotten to put the feature film on board and so we saw Jane Goodall and her chimps at least four times. I would not recommend American. The US, which was the pioneer of good service then, had the worst airlines in the world.

We were delayed at least six hours and so that night I ate prawns in the hotel dining room and went to bed. I was up late the next morning, had a huge hearty American breakfast, to avoid having lunch, then hired a car and drove to downtown Miami. Having driven along the beach for a few miles I got my guidebook out and drove off to Orchid Jungle, in the opposite direction. This is set in a little of what remains of the old Florida jungle full of live oaks, false figs, creepers, lianes, very similar to the Amazon jungle. The company was started many years ago and at the time had over 8,000 species of orchid and they were growing in the trees. It was a magnificent spectacle, beautiful flowers many with exotic scents.

From the Orchid Jungle I went to see the Coral Castle built by some nutcase Latvian who was jilted the night before his wedding. He came to the States and built this castle single-handedly: some of the coral blocks weigh up to thirty tons. He hand-made all his tools from old bits of cars; e.g. he split his coral with levers made from old leaf springs which were hammered in lines at the depth that he wanted. There are chairs and tables made from coral and the main door which weighs nine tons can be opened with your little finger. How he bored the central pivot is anyone's guess. He made a sundial that tells the date as well as time.

On Monday morning I phoned round till I found what I wanted and went to buy gas fittings for the lab. They cost $100 thereby saving the lab over $200 (we had been quoted $330) even when the cost of the car hire was included. From there I drove downtown and went to the Omni Centre where I did all the shopping that Maxine wanted: when living in Perú you have to take opportunities presented to buy goods unobtainable in the country. I purchased a copy of a new word processing package for the laboratory – Word Perfect 5.1 – from a store in Miami. The price in England was £450, the *presupuesto* in Arequipa was $750 and I paid $280 and that included tax! The lab made a fortune out of my trip. Once back to the hotel, I packed up my purchases in a large bag and left them with the hotel porter. After I had returned the car the rental company drove me to the airport and from there on to the plane for San Juan.

The Hotel Condado Beach was fairly dismal for the price ($150 or £100 in those days) per night just for the room with nothing special about it at all except that it is the coldest hotel in which I have ever stayed, the north of Scotland in winter not withstanding. Despite numerous requests to turn down the air-conditioning, we all froze. I had a constant battle with the staff: I would open my window (after I had finally forced it open with my penknife) and switch off the air-conditioning. The maid would come in and shut the window and turn the cooling up to maximum. It took several days for me to stop this. I won in the end and thereafter slept well. On the Tuesday morning, I took the bus into the old town and spent a fascinating day looking at two of the most impressive forts in the Caribbean. The Christopher Columbus guards the land and the El Morro fort was totally impregnable from the sea (not with modern Gulf weapons of course) rising almost 200 feet straight out of the water with gun emplacements at various levels. I did not realise that Puerto Rico was the most important island in Spain's defence of her South American colonies. But it controlled the shipping routes to the south. They were both redesigned and rebuilt by a couple of renegade Irishmen and this prevented them being taken by Drake among others. From there I walked to the Fortaleza or Governor's Mansion which was the original fort defending the island in the sixteenth century. I had a delicious virgin piña colada (without the rum, Puerto Rico is the home of Bacardi Rum) and an ice cream, which served for lunch.

The old town is a delight, beautiful old Spanish houses which after years of neglect are at last being restored. San Juan must be the most beautiful city of colonial Spain. The same cannot be said of new San Juan which rates with the scruffier parts of Lima!

Back to the hotel for the start of the congress. Ibrahim Kakoma, the secretary, had worked with me at Muguga after he had finished his veterinary course in Uganda: he went to the States for his PhD and thanks to Idi Amin, he stayed. In true African fashion, he did not turn up despite the meeting having been organised more than a year earlier. The meeting was excellent and it slowly dawned upon me how out of date was much of my knowledge in the immunology/molecular biology world. Ten years away from the mainstream and nothing is as it was. The developments are staggering especially in the treatment of viral diseases and in the production of vaccines.

From the time the congress started I did not leave the hotel from rising until after dinner. Usually we went off for a beer to a nice warm open-air bar. It was over such a beer that Dr Yilma (an Ethiopian vet) and I decided that we knew each other: it came about when I mentioned that I had worked in Ethiopia with Dr Fikre: he and Yilma were contemporaries at vet school. He then realised that I was the man that had done the work for them on the CBPP vaccines (he like me thought that the vaccine produced by the French was of little use). I showed that the level of viable organisms in their vaccine was close to or below the lower permissible limit and he had evidence from the field that it was not working. Dr Yilma delivered an after-dinner speech on recombinant vaccines, which was superb: some of it was way over my head but I understood enough to know that this was the way forward and that Dr Yilma was right up there in the engine room. Ethiopians only have one name, in his case, Yilma, but to simplify life they often use their father's name, in his case, Tilahun.

My talks being more of a practical rather than a scientific nature were not given until towards the end of the meeting, but were both well received. I think that the audiences were pleased to listen to something uncomplicated by graphs and diagrams. Many were interested in the plight of the *campesinos* and I received many offers of help. The meeting had been worthwhile, I had met some old friends and made a few new ones. The return journey to Lima was adequate, at least we had a movie even if the food was awful. I arrived in Lima at midnight and for the second time in a fortnight had to be up at

278

6:00am the next morning for my flight to Arequipa. Of course we sat around at the airport for three hours before the plane took off, but it was good to be home. My visits to Kenya, Chile and a Caribbean island had been an additional bonus to my stay in Perú.

17

Meetings of Minds

The powers that be decided that it would be a good idea if the British veterinary projects in Latin America all met together: there was almost a straight line of projects across the centre of South America from Porto Alegre in southern Brazil, via Asunción in central Paraguay and Santa Cruz in eastern Bolivia to Arequipa in southern Perú It was decided that the first such meeting would take place in Asunción and that all British personnel, each with a counterpart, would attend (Plate 57). The concept was excellent and the meeting proved to be invaluable in co-ordinating British veterinary projects across South America. The first, held in the Chaco Hotel in Asunción was organised by Dr Carole Mullen and her counterpart Dra Stela Maciel. Tony Irvin came from London to chair the meeting. Denis Gosden and his counterpart Srta Lita Araujo, Dra Milagro Terán and me accompanied by Maxine flew from Arequipa to Santa Cruz where we changed planes for Asunción. We were met by Carole Mullen and taken to the hotel where the conference was to be held.

After a wash and brush-up we all went on the town: Maxine and I were able to take the team to the shopping centre, where we bought 'Rolex', 'Gucci' and 'Cartier' watches, 'Dior' perfume and, other fake goods on the street. We bought a watch of a different 'make' for each child and the cost of our purchases was a little over $15. The boys' watches did not last long but Guy enjoyed parading his 'Rolex' watch to his classmates. Claire's 'Cartier' watch lasted for several years until she progressed to a properly branded watch. Paraguay is the South American centre for contraband and fake goods. I well remember when we stopped in Puerto Stroessner (now renamed Puerto del Este) when we were living in Salta, Argentina and travelled to see the Iguazú Falls, stopping in the frontier town, and being totally overwhelmed by the duty-free whisky: in shop after shop there were cases of whisky lining the walls from floor to ceiling, almost every variety known to the Scots and probably a few more fake varieties. A poor man wanting to look big could order the model, year and colour of the Mercedes that he wanted and within a week it would be delivered to his door; the problem was that the car could not be taken to Argentina, Bolivia or Brazil, because that was from where it had been stolen.

We mostly assembled over breakfast as we were all staying in the same hotel but Tony Irvin officially opened the gathering in the hotel's meeting room. There was no official translator but each person spoke in the language in which he or she was most comfortable. The British team working in the Veterinary Research Institute in Porto Alegre, the southernmost province of Brazil, included Andrew Coe, and David Radley, who had been at college with me and with whom I had worked in Kenya; his Brazilian colleague, the director of the institute, Dr Paulo Reckziegel spoke excellent English but the other Brazilians spoke in Portuguese, whereas those Brits working in Paraguay, Bolivia and Perú along with our counterparts spoke in Spanish but somehow it all worked as there was always someone to translate for Tony. There were frequent stops when Portuguese was being spoken, but the Brazilians spoke slowly enough for the Spanish speakers to be able to follow what they were saying, especially as great use was made of the whiteboard. The leader of each delegation spoke about the role of their project, its aim and achievements, its strengths and weaknesses, where we could offer help and what aid we required. The Bolivian project had been going for the longest time, having been started by the Food and Agriculture Organisation of the United Nations before being taken over by ODA. But to me it suffered from the same problem as the old project in Cajamarca: it was not there for all, but only for those who joined up for the service. A strength of the Santa Cruz project was that it was linked to Reading University's Veterinary Epidemiology and Economics Unit, which was then the centre for the development of the embryonic computer systems that would revolutionise record keeping, epidemiology and economics. Andrew James who had been so much help to our project in Argentina was now leading the Reading computer team and was a regular visitor to Santa Cruz and they were using the new computer program Panacea for all their disease recording. LABVETSUR came much later to this program and in fact it never properly caught on in Perú but then our problems were different. Santa Cruz were working closely with a small number of herds, whereas we were less interested in individual herd problems than the overall health of 10,000 dairy farms. Santa Cruz had less than 500 herds but with up to 200 cows per herd, whereas our average herd size was around ten: different solutions are needed for different problems. But that was the great advantage of this type of meeting.

The first day of the meeting was a hard slog but great fun and bonds of friendship began to develop which could only be to the good of animal health on the continent. Dinner was even more fun as the wine flowed and the tongues loosened. After that first day, talks and seminars were restricted to the morning and the afternoons were given over to visiting LIDIAV, the diagnostic and research laboratory where Carole was a senior scientist. The teams were able to see the laboratory at work and to compare equipment, techniques, types of work and problems.

On the final night a semi-formal dinner was organised in a local nightclub famed for its cabaret and after the steaks, we were treated to Paraguayan music and dancing which included much playing of harps and guitars and flowing and twirling skirts (Plate 59). We were fascinated by the famous hat and bottle dances (Plate 58). It was a wonderful end to a great meeting and a taster for the tourist delights of the following day. Carole had done a great job: for those people able to remain in Paraguay, Carole had hired a bus to take us to Iguazú. We set off early on the Saturday morning and had a stop in a village on the road to buy the wonderful handmade Ñandutí lace. The most attractive sight on the drive across the waist of Paraguay to Puerto del Este was the horse-drawn farm carts with their massive wheels almost six feet in diameter carrying produce or people at a spanking trot. We stopped at Itaupú to visit the massive new hydroelectric power station on the Paraná River. Puerto del Este had only changed in name, it was still the one-street wall of whisky. This time the crossing into Brazil was painless, unlike our previous crossing from Paraguay to Brazil when we were living in Argentina, and before long we were peering over the bridge at the top of the Iguazú Falls. I have seen many large waterfalls but to me this is the most majestic of them all and the river was in good spate (Plate

60). We did not have time to cross to the Argentine side of the river and walk to the magnificent *Garganta del Diabo* (Devil's Throat) where the water pours down from three sides and when it mixes, outpours a fountain of steam – one of the seven natural wonders of the world.

For two nights in a row we ate dinner in a nightclub, this time a Brazilian one, and we were entertained by a cabaret that had great overtones of Carnival: lots of loud music and semi-naked beauties but all good fun. We spent Sunday morning at the falls again and then set off on the long drive back, but the conversation hummed as my Peruvian colleagues were busy recounting what they had done in the past week. On Monday, the team returned to Arequipa but Maxine and I flew off to Miami – the start of our home leave. Lineas Aéras Paraguaya, one of the oldest airlines on the continent, flew us uncomfortably but safely to Miami and what made the flight for Maxine was that just before the plane touched down, the hostesses walked down the aisle handing out a red rose to each female passenger.

It had been a very valuable meeting and as a result we were able to send members of the LABVETSUR team to Asunción and Santa Cruz for the specialist training that we could not offer them. I believed that Tony Irvin had gone away with a very good impression of the seriousness with which all had approached the meeting, as it became a regular feature on the calendar.

The second meeting was held in the LIDIVET laboratory in Santa Cruz, the largest of any of the laboratories in the ODA network, and the longest established. This meeting was organised by Jim McGrane. Santa Cruz is a modern city with its wealth firmly based in the oil industry. For many years the pale-skinned people of the east (the result of interbreeding between the *conquistadores* and the jungle Indians) have been trying to separate the rich lowlands from the dark-skinned Indian people on the altiplano. The city has the feel of a run-down Hollywood movie set, with low, single-storey buildings and a great deal of dust with horses and riders a common sight. The central plaza has many trees and it is there that for the only time in my life I saw sloths, hanging up in the trees; had Maxine not pointed them out I would have passed them by.

John Claxton, Fernando Alverado, Daniel Gandarillas, Denis Gosden, Maxine and I drove down to Tacna and crossed the border to Arica Airport to take the direct flight to Santa Cruz; that from Arequipa had ceased the previous year (Plate 61). Unlike the Brits, the Peruvians required visas for Chile in advance, which we obtained from the consulate in Arequipa. On arrival we were met by Anna McGrane, the wife of the British team leader Jim, and we were whisked off to the Hotel Urbana, a delightful motel a little way from the city centre (Plate 62). It proved to be an excellent place to stay, the rooms were comfortable and the grounds extensive with many trees and flowering shrubs and a large, crystal-clear pool. The staff were friendly and attentive. Following the social success of the Asunción meeting, more people had brought their wives: Carol came with David Radley and so an old tennis pairing was renewed as Carol and Maxine had played together in the Muguga Club team, fifteen or more years previously.

We remembered the story from those years, how the Radleys and other veterinary friends, the Schermbruckers, had been on a game-viewing safari in Samburu Game Park. They visited Buffalo Springs and took advantage of the swimming pool produced by the British Army during the Mau Mau era. Passing through Buffalo Springs is an underground tributary of the Uaso Nyeru River: the soldiers had blasted a hole through the rock which made a beautiful natural swimming pool about twenty yards in diameter in clear, cool water. The Radleys and Schermbruckers senior left the children playing at a nearby stream and went for a swim, which was interrupted by loud screaming; on exiting the pool the Radleys found their son in the grip of a large crocodile. With the parents holding the boy and the Schermbruckers holding the crocodile a battle ensued, trying to free young Christopher and not injure him. It was not until Ann Schermbrucker ran to the car and brought a panga (a long Kenyan agricultural knife used for a variety of tasks) and started hacking at the throat of the animal that it released its hold on the boy and they were able to wrestle him free. Into the car and Dave drove off to the park lodge at breakneck speed to alert the flying doctor, who within an hour had flown in and the boy was on his way to the Kenyatta Hospital in Nairobi. Christopher had had a miraculous escape, one crocodile tooth narrowly missed a kidney while another tooth almost but not quite reached the inguinal artery. There was great concern among the expatriate staff of Muguga as crocodiles do not eat their kill fresh but store it underwater for it to rot; consequently the teeth are home to a great variety of bacteria and the lad developed all sorts of infections and for days was on the danger list but he pulled through and then the parents had to deal with the psychological problems, but they too, were overcome and Christopher made a complete recovery and became a fine athlete, playing hockey for Malawi, a later workplace for David.

Crocodiles were much in the news at that time and another of our colleagues, Duncan Brown, who at the time of the meeting had just been appointed as the ODA veterinary adviser, had a battle with a crocodile on the same river a week later. He was camping by the Uaso Nyeru River, when early one morning, a young child was paddling on the bank when a crocodile reared out of the water and took the child by the head and swam off. The mother screamed and Duncan rushed to the bank, flung himself on the back of the crocodile and plunged his fingers into the eye sockets of the beast, which opened its mouth releasing the child, which was plucked from the water, none the worse for his ordeal: apparently the teeth had not broken the skin on the boy's head. Whenever we met after an interval, the topic of crocodiles came up and the health of the boy discussed.

Unlike Paraguay, the meeting in Santa Cruz was held in the conference room of the laboratory rather than a hotel. Duncan Brown and Tony Irvin came from ODA in London: Duncan was taking over as ODA veterinary adviser from Tony who was going back to work in Africa. It was Duncan who opened the meeting, and the format was the same as in Asunción, with the project leaders updating the meeting with their progress. Several workshops were given by Reading staff mostly on different aspects of their Panacea computer program, showing how it could be used for the analysis of disease patterns. The more I learnt of Panacea the more I realised that this was a program for use in a veterinary practice rather than in a diagnostic laboratory. I discussed with John whether it could be used in the *postas*, but we came to no conclusion. Tours of LIDIVET were undertaken and we were able to linger in those sections that interested us most (Plate 63). A visit to a major dairy farm was made and the Peruvians were delighted when we were asked to inspect some alpacas (Plate 64). On the Friday night, the McGranes introduced us to central Santa Cruz, which is when the youth of the neighbourhood all meet up, and the streets are lined by Toyota pickup trucks with the young men eyeing the talent flaunting their charms in the streets.

Most countries in South America can produce excellent beef and the ranches round Santa Cruz were no exception. Whereas Paraguay had its Indian culture and Perú its Andean folk music and dancing, Santa Cruz appeared to be completely in thrall to the Americans, and country and western, and rock and roll seemed to have taken over from local music. The conference ended on Saturday with a barbecue in LIDIVET and we dined on steak and sausages and drank Bolivian beer and Argentine wine; what was so delightful was the way that the teams mingled: strong bonds of friendship had grown up between people of the various countries, which could only be good for international co-operation.

There were problems on the return visit as the Peruvians only had single-entry visas and so were not allowed on the plane in Santa Cruz bound for Arica. They had to reschedule their flight to La Paz, take a bus round Lake Titicaca to Puno, and fly from there to Arequipa.

The next ODA meeting was scheduled for LABVETSUR but it was not to be. The date of the meeting was only a few weeks before my leaving Perú and there was a new kid on the block, as ODA had started a project in Merida on the Yucután Peninsula in Mexico. ODA decided that it would be simpler for the Mexican team to integrate with the other projects if they hosted the meeting, and so I was never able to show to the other projects what we had achieved. I believe that was the real reason why the meeting was moved: ODA did not want people questioning why they had sacked the manager of a very successful project.

It suited me to go to Mexico as it was a country I had never visited and one which should be a powerhouse among Latin American countries; sadly it has always been damaged by corruption and today it is being destroyed by drugs. Maxine was busy packing for our move and did not want to come to Mexico. The team flew from Lima to Mexico City where we had to spend a day and a half before our onward flight to Merida. The first evening we spent walking in the centre of the city where there is a huge bare plaza with the magnificent cathedral at one end. We went into the cathedral, where I learnt the true origin of Montezuma's Revenge: not an affliction of the intestines but the collapse of a cathedral. Everywhere inside the building were acroprops of various sizes and heights, supporting the collapsing stones. In order to build the cathedral, the *conquistadores* had pulled down an Aztec pyramid; all was well until the middle of the twentieth century when the city was running short of water and so the underground supplies were pumped out. As a result, the earth sank and the foundations of the cathedral went with it, subjecting the building to massive structural change. The cost of saving the building ran into many hundreds of millions of dollars. At the time of our visit the cathedral was on the road to recovery but it would be many years before the work would be completed. When we left the cathedral, it was amusing to see groups of Andean musicians busking in the plaza.

As our time was limited we were only able to visit one site of interest and everyone that we spoke to said that it had to be the Anthropology Museum and they were not wrong: it is a wonderful, modern museum built round three sides of a large grass rectangle. The exhibits, which are beautifully displayed, come from all epochs of Mexican history and pre-history and all are clearly described, with an English translation. We were lucky enough to experience a group of Totonac people perform their spectacular *voladores* rite – 'flying' from a 20m-high totem pole. The museum is set at the edge of a forest and in a clearing about 100m in front of the museum's entrance is this high totem pole. Four men climb up the pole and sit on a small shelf at the top and they wind ropes carefully round the pole. They each attach themselves to a rope and then crouch, seemingly in prayer, one each side of the platform, all facing inwards. At a signal from the leader they throw themselves backwards off the platform and they circle the totem pole as the ropes unwind; it was the most incredible spectacle, these gyrating men seemingly flying safely to the ground. This is the one abiding memory of my only visit to Mexico City. Around the airport there appear to be white pyramids projecting above the landscape: these are snow-capped volcanoes. On the Sunday evening we left the heights of Mexico City for the Yucután Peninsula and the old city of Merida.

I have little recollection of the meeting other than it was chaired by Dra Lindsay Bell and that it was hosted by Nick Honhold and his very hospitable wife. There was a talk on the geology of the Yucután Peninsula, which is a solid limestone slab and so very permeable to water; nowhere is the soil more than a couple of feet deep and so grass and flowering plants grow, but it cannot be used for crop growing. However, one result of this is that Yucután has a massive bee population and so the two main products exported are milk and honey. The ODA project was set up to increase the productivity of the dairy herd.

What I do remember clearly is the afternoon trip to Chichen Itza to visit the Maya ruins. This is to the Mayan culture what Machu Picchu is to the Incas, the best-preserved city of that people. These were fascinating and again there were pyramids: I climbed the main one, El Castillo, which gave a remarkable view of the site; it was only when I started to descend that I realised how steep it was and I had an attack of vertigo and the only way down was on my backside. Archaeologists have identified thirteen ball courts for playing the Mesoamerican ballgame but that in Chichen Itza, the Great Ball Court, about 150 metres from the Castillo, is by far the most impressive. According to the guidebook it is the largest and best preserved ball court in ancient Mesoamerica. Measuring 168m x 70m, it is like a giant fives court. The parallel platforms flanking the main playing area are each 95m. The walls of these platforms stand 8m. High up in the centre of each of these walls are carved stone rings showing intertwined serpents. This was a really brutal game and carved in the walls are sculpted panels of teams of ball players: in one panel, one of the players has been decapitated; the wound emits streams of blood in the form of a wriggling snake. As I stood there thinking about the games that had been played on this bloody court I wondered how the game had actually been played and as I type this I feel that J K Rowling has to have visited this site, which could have given her the idea for quidditch. At one end of the Great Ball Court is the North Temple, also known as the Temple of the Bearded Man (*Templo del Hombre Barbado*). It never ceases to amaze me how religion and bloodshed so often go together. Having had a wonderful tour of this enormous site we were whisked away for dinner before returning in the dark for a thrilling son et lumière telling the Chichen Itza story, and then a very late return to our hotel.

The meeting ended with a buffet supper at the Honholds' house, a wonderful evening of friendship and shared experience. Such meetings are of great value in South America where there is so much suspicion and hostility between nations, who are all essentially the same people. ODA are to be praised for having the wisdom to start and support these meetings. This meeting also gave me the opportunity to say goodbye to the many friends that I had met through my work with LABVETSUR.

18

Home, Music and Visitors

One of the highlights of the second holiday that Ma had in Perú was the joint party to celebrate all the birthdays. Maxine's birthday, her fiftieth, was in November, followed at the end of the same month by Guy who was about to be seventeen and Ma, seventy-six; Richard, turning twenty-one, and Claire, turning sixteen, were both born in December. The party was for them all and Maxine made a huge chocolate cake and instead of candles she put the numbers 1, 8 and 0. The guests were of all ages, although the majority were friends of the children, and they were all asked to guess the significance of the numbers. Only Marisol, a dear friend of Claire, worked out that it was the sum total of the ages of the birthday people. The children had a great number of delightful friends who loved coming to Avenida Lima because they were assured of a warm welcome and a cooling swim.

Unlike our pool in Argentina, the swimming pool in Arequipa was easy to maintain as it had its own built-in filtration system and a professionally made 'hoover' for cleaning dirt off the bottom. One problem was that the neighbours above us kept ducks and we frequently found them swimming and crapping in the pool. It was only after we threatened that, instead of returning their ducks we would eat them, that the invasions ceased. Winter nights in Arequipa at 8,500 feet above sea level could be very cold, although we never had frosts; on one Christmas Eve the city received a powdering of snow. The cold nights meant that the pool lost a great deal of heat and so it was not possible to swim in winter, unless you were very brave, until we heard about the insulating pool cover – the giant pale blue bubble wrap. Unfortunately, it was not available in Perú; however, on a trip through Miami (the capital city of Latin America, where the shopkeepers all speak Spanish rather than English) I found a shop that dealt exclusively with home swimming pools; they stocked the covers of the right size, and were very happy to ship one to Arequipa at a reasonable price. The bubble wrap cover was of course rectangular and our pool was kidney-shaped but with her sewing scissors, Maxine soon had it cut to shape. Thereafter we could swim all year round. In fact, in summer we found that the water got too hot for comfortable swimming unless we removed the cover first thing in the morning, before the sun had got into its stride (Plate 65).

Christmas was coming but there was to be no service in the church as there was no vicar. Alan Winstanley had just been promoted to be the Bishop of Perú and had gone to Lima and no replacement had been found, and his curate had already arranged his leave when news of the promotion came through. We decided that we wanted a carol service and with Alan's permission we organised one in the music room at home and invited the Arequipa congregation as well as Lewis and Christina. Maxine played the piano, Guy played his trumpet, Claire her viola while a few guitars were played and I read a lesson or two. It was a happy time and at the conclusion, tea and shortbread biscuits were served. The boys had been asked to spread some icing on the biscuits, but instead they went to town and decorated them with some very rude designs! However, the congregation did not seem to mind. Ma, the children and the Vaughans ensured that it was a Happy Christmas. Marzipan was totally unobtainable in Perú and you could not get almonds in Arequipa and so clever Maxine made marzipan by grinding up peanuts in oil and adding almond essence brought out from England.

Many years living away from supermarkets had taught Maxine to be very practical: she had always been a first-class knitter and seamstress and so she was able to make curtains and cushions as well as children's clothes. Improvising in the kitchen became second nature to Maxine and so during the great inflation when there were so many shortages she was able to turn her hand to almost anything. There was the great bread shortage: luckily Ron Sykes was able to help out with the official equipment and so 'animal feed stuff' on the packing list would turn out to be wholemeal flour, ideal for making bread. I love pickled fish but such dishes did not exist in Perú but there was a small river fish – *pejerey (Pamatomus saltatriz)* – that you could buy fresh in the market. Maxine persuaded the fishmonger to fillet them and turned them into the most delicious rollmops. The whole family love curry and when we lived in Kenya I acquired a wonderful recipe which is in regular use to this day. No curry is complete without lime pickle, which of course was not available in Perú, and so Maxine set to and made it, although where she obtained the recipe I do not know (there was no Internet in those days). However, the end result was superb, much better than that commercially available in Britain. Why do we not make it in Britain? It needs to be cured outside in the sun for thirty days and in Scotland you are lucky if you get thirty minutes.

And then there was cheese. Perú produces about 200 different varieties of cheese, but with the exception of the one made in Cajamarca (courtesy of the British project), they all taste the same; that is they have no taste. With all the milk remaining after we had tested it, Maxine decided that she would have a go at making cheese. At first it was just a lactic starter but later we obtained rennet and the proper cheddar culture. Maxine has 'fond' memories of her arms up to her elbows in the milk as it was heated up on the cooker. We purloined cheese moulds from LAIVE, and were given the protective wax from the same source. Once the primary fermentation was complete the proto cheeses were wrapped in cheesecloth and hung to allow the water/whey to drain off; they were then put into moulds and the remaining fluid was squeezed out of them by large cement blocks and they were matured in a small, dark, cool cupboard under the stairs for several months and the resulting cheese was... ambrosia. Strong and sharp, just as we liked it, it made a great treat after the rubbish we had had to eat before.

My parents had a long and happy life together, although not without its difficulties. They were married for more than sixty years. My father was the third child of three and was eight years younger than his sister Ethel and twelve years younger than Eva and he always felt that he was unwanted. I am sure that this was the reason why he was so passive and seemingly unemotional. He came from a long line of bootmakers and his father was the first to break with the tradition but continued to deal in leather and he was determined that Stanley would continue in the family business. Stanley was an able student and was offered a scholarship to study at the Sir John Cass Institute but his father refused him permission to go: was this the reason that he was so keen that his children should be well educated? I think so.

He and my mother had been childhood sweethearts and were married when she was twenty and he twenty-two and with the exception of the war years they were never apart. They were never wealthy and both worked into their seventies but despite this there was always a welcome for a visitor. I made this the theme of my talk at my parents' golden wedding party: "Silver and gold have I none, but such as I have give I thee" (Acts of the Apostles, Chapter 3).

Stanley Windsor marries Amelia Brown, 1928

Anyone who ever knew my parents would comment on their warmth and hospitality, and they made sacrifices so that Mary, Margaret and I could receive a good education. Not for them the foreign travel that was becoming popular; holidays were in Britain, either with family or friends or in rural bed and breakfast lodgings. We had all left school before my parents set foot in Europe and that was to go to Lyons where Mary was starting her career as a teacher.

Maxine and I were able to give them the holiday of a lifetime when they visited us in Kenya and we showed them the game parks and the wonderful Indian Ocean. We had been trying to persuade them to come out to Perú, but without success as my father was suffering from cataracts in both eyes making him almost blind, and my mother was concerned with an undiagnosed abdominal problem. My father's first cataract operation was a success but he remained unable to see as he had severe macular degeneration in that eye, which they had been unable to diagnose until the cataract had been removed. Cataract surgery was a different story in those days as you spent three days lying on your back, trying not to move. The second operation restored my father's vision and he was no longer blind.

I was in the shower early one morning when the phone rang. When I came out of the shower, Maxine made me sit on the end of the bed as she informed me that Margaret had phoned to say that my mother had died. Maxine had not gone home on the death of her father as she had two sisters to look after her mother. I also had two sisters, but I had no brother and I was always very close to my father; without fail, I wrote to him every week. We decided that I should go home. Maxine phoned Keith at the embassy and he agreed that the embassy would make all the arrangements for me to fly home, and the following day I was on my way. I was very glad that I went because I found my father in a terrible state. Dear Margaret had done everything: got the death certificate, arranged matters with the funeral directors, booked the crematorium and notified all the family and friends. Like me, Mary did not live in England and had to organise her family before leaving Paris.

My father was grief-stricken and helpless: he just sat and said nothing, did nothing, he could barely greet me on my arrival. It had all happened so suddenly. They had spent the whole day in the outpatients' department at Whipps Cross Hospital waiting for my mother to be seen. Late in the afternoon she saw a doctor who did nothing but take a blood sample. They travelled home on the bus as my father no longer drove. Mother had cooked the dinner and they had watched television and turned in at their usual time. My mother had a severe attack of diarrhoea in the night and my father had made her comfortable and they had returned to sleep. When my father awoke my mother had passed away. Although they did not know the cause of death, there was no need for a post-mortem examination as mother had been under medical care when she died. Margaret was asked whether or not the family wanted the examination and she, quite rightly, said that we did not, as it would not help mother, and would protract the problems for my father as the funeral would have been delayed.

There was a big turnout for the funeral and I was touched that so many of my friends made the effort to attend; all three of my children came from school to be with Granddad and help him through this ordeal. We decided to hold the wake at home as we thought that father would be more able to cope in familiar surroundings; he was still in a daze. Mary and Margaret prepared a mountain of sandwiches, canapés and gallons of tea, while I was responsible for wine and spirits. The party was warm and friendly. It was January and there was an interesting end to the wake when the Christmas cake made by mother was cut up and distributed to the mourners. It was somehow a fitting tribute to this hospitable woman that the last memory of her would be the delicious cake she had made.

The family thought that father would not live long after mother, but we were mistaken. He had received a message from her that she wanted him to live and this man who had been waited on hand and foot for sixty years took up cooking for himself, he even purchased a microwave oven. I came to the conclusion that mother knew that my blind father could not look after himself and so she kept herself alive to care for him. With his sight restored he could be self-sufficient and so she stopped fighting and allowed herself to die. Selfless to the very end. Slowly my father came out of his shock. Margaret, who lived within a couple of miles, would keep a close eye on his progress and I was able to return to Perú safe in the knowledge that she would make sure he was looked after. Dear, dear Margaret, from the moment her husband Mike retired she wanted to leave the vicinity of Woodford in Essex and return to where we had been evacuated in Dorset, but she refused to move while father needed her. I had father's promise that he would come out to Perú as soon as the immediate formalities were completed. And so I was able to leave Buckhurst Hill knowing that before long I would see him again.

Within a few weeks he was in Perú as he flew out with the children and was met at Lima Airport and taken home to the residency by the Haskells. Keith's father was more or less the same age as mine and they cared for him and put them on the plane to Arequipa the next morning. Like me, my father loved the sun and as soon as he had had a cup of coffee, he had his shorts on and was out in the garden with my copy of the weekly *Guardian* to read and doze until I returned for lunch. He had a wonderful time in Arequipa as all the women in LABVETSUR made a fuss of him and all Claire's girlfriends came round to visit him (Plate 68). Father was ten years older than Maxine's mother when she first visited, much more fragile, and so the sightseeing was restricted to the environs of Arequipa and to day trips to the coast and the sierra (Plate 69). Despite his poor sight he loved to watch the hummingbirds as they lined up for the feeder. We had been told that there were these birds in

Arequipa and that if you fed them they would come; we purchased a feeder which we attached by rubber suckers to a window on the garden side of the kitchen, and all that was required to attract them was a little sugar water coloured with cochineal. Within a month we had attracted five different species of hummingbird and all seemed able to hover in almost any position as they sipped the 'nectar'. Like me, my father was happy to sit and watch the antics of these beautiful creatures for as long as they continued to feed.

I took him down to the coast to see the magnificent Pacific breakers crash on to the rocks and watch the vast bird life do battle with the waves to pluck fish from the ocean. Much as I loved him, he infuriated me with his lack of response to all the new things that he was seeing. The majestic Andes, the beautiful *vicuña*, the ancient Colca churches, the Arequipa *casonas*, the intricate carving on the *sillar* facades of the churches, all were greeted with a nod of the head and the quietly spoken "Most interesting". My father had collected cacti for as long as I could remember, but seeing them in their native habitat aroused his interest but not his enthusiasm, although he was happy to walk in the bush and try to identify some of the plants. He may have shown little emotion but he saw and remembered everything and on our return to live in Britain he was always pleased to talk about his happy time in Perú. He was not impressed with cock-fighting when I took him to the Nazi stronghold in La Joya; I suspect he did not enjoy being reminded of the one time in his life when he was separated from his beloved Cissie.

By this time the young men of LABVETSUR had a *fulbito* (five-a-side football) team which was regularly thrashed by the team from the La Joya *posta*. The laboratory and the *posta* combined forces to play a proper eleven-a-side football match against a La Joya irrigation team. Father was invited to get the match under way by taking the first kick, which he did with such gusto that he almost fell over backwards and it was lucky I was there to escort him from the pitch to safety (Plate 70). He may not have shown great emotion but he was a good guest, unfailingly polite, undemanding, grateful for everything and always willing to fall in with whatever had been planned for him to do. It was only towards the end of his life that I found out that as a child he felt unwanted and this, of course, explained his lack of an emotional response and his quiet attitude towards life. It also explained the great love for his children and why he lived his life through them. The Peruvians loved him because he was a good listener, so quiet but he would try and assist them to speak English. It was during his visit to Perú that I realised from whom I had got my stoicism. Working in the Third World you have to get accustomed to hard knocks. In Kenya and Botswana we referred to it as the ABF (African buggeration factor) which had to be taken into account when planning anything. You get to a state in which you expect things to go wrong and so are not put out when they actually do go wrong and are thrilled when things go right. My father had a clever turn of phrase and frequently came out with sharp comments; perhaps the best was when he and I were in the usual scruffy Peruvian taxi, slipping in and out of the traffic. After one very smart manoeuvre, father turned to me and said: "When driving in Perú, you are either quick or you're dead."

He was a lovely man and I loved him dearly; I think that in the end his children and grandchildren gave him the love that had been so lacking in his early life. When he died just after the new millennium I think that he died a happy man. I know that he was happy to go:

"Roger, if they could give me a new body I would be all right but I am fair worn out…"

He is now reunited with his beloved Cissie.

Maxine had become a power in the music life of Arequipa and had made many friends among the local and expatriate communities: Jorst Emmel, a Peruvian of German origin and a good pianist, decided that he needed lessons from the English *maestra*. Jorst's wife, Mirtha, ran a wonderful little cottage industry making alpaca knitwear and soon the family were decked out with sweaters, scarves and gloves! Maxine loved accompanying string players, and she met a splendid German water engineer and amateur violinist, Hans Nelting, who was trying to improve the water supply to the city. After our Argentine experience of hepatitis and para-typhoid, we boiled and filtered all the water that we drank; buying bottled water had not yet become the fashion and anyway it was not available in Perú. Hans and Daggie, who was a fine cellist, were to become good friends and Maxine found Hans and Daggie to be sympathetic musicians after the Peruvians. They believed in practice and getting to the soul of the music rather than just playing it from beginning to end. It infuriated Maxine how the local people would consider it good to get from start to finish without a mistake, rather than 'feel' what the music was trying to say. She found it refreshing to play with musicians who had the same view.

Maxine believed in discipline in music above all and she considered that playing the piano was not 'practising'. She always commenced with exercises to warm up the fingers and then scales and arpeggios. Pieces had to be played hands separately and then together. Once you had the notes under control it was time to put in the interpretation. Her list of pupils had grown and she was now in great demand. Her most rewarding pupils were the daughters of a well-known alimentary tract surgeon, Dr Oscar Lópera. Pilar and Alexandra both became professional musicians and it is wonderful to read in concert programmes the curriculum vitae of Pilar who always refers to having been taught by the British pianist Maxine Windsor LRSM. Maxine's discipline and enthusiasm obviously rubbed off on the girls. Pilar's first concert was a real baptism of fire: she was playing Beethoven's first piano concerto with the Arequipa Symphony Orchestra. She was sitting at the grand piano in the '*Cultural*' concert hall in one of the great *casonas* as the orchestra played the introduction. She was about to start playing when the first shock of the earthquake hit the hall. The orchestra stopped, a second shock hit and the audience were preparing to evacuate the building, which is the normal procedure for an earthquake, when Gachi, who ran ICPNA, stepped to the front of the audience and suggested that we wait to see if there would be a third shock. There was not. The tension in the audience slowly dispersed when it was realised that the problems were over for the time being and that the concerto was about to start again. The conductor took to the rostrum raised his baton and we were underway for the second time. Considering what had happened, Pilar gave a very composed performance and Maxine was proud of her. Perhaps that was what cemented their relationship and Maxine remains in contact with her and her sister to this day. Pilar is now the conductor of the Arequipa Symphony Orchestra.

In an attempt to help Marcos pass the English test so that we could send him to Britain for training, he came and stayed with us in Arequipa for a fortnight and each day Maxine would instruct him in the language and give him tests and exercises and of an evening I would give him a talk on a veterinary subject and then give him a written test to see how much he had understood. During his stay Maxine gave a concert and Marcos heard her play and decided that she had to give a concert in Cajamarca. During my next visit to the city he took me to the church of Belén (the church in the old madhouse) which was one of the oldest buildings in Cajamarca and possessed a splendid grand piano. It was enormous, seating between 700 and 800 people.

"We will never fill this," I said.

"No, but that does not matter, we will get enough people to make a good audience, and we will make much money for the orphan children charity."

And so Maxine agreed to give a concert. As Marcos had predicted there was a good audience of about 400 and the charity did well (Plate 37). As always when Maxine performs I try to sit in the front row, which in Belén Church was about twenty feet from the piano. During one particularly quiet passage there was a loud splash as a large dose of bird faeces hit the floor almost equidistant between us. Maxine carried on as if nothing had happened; it was only after the concert we found out that the church (as do many churches in Perú) had a resident owl who was obviously unused to there being many people in the building at that time of night. Apparently it is a sign of good luck to have a resident owl in a church; it was good luck for the children's charity. The concert was well received and the playing much appreciated. The evening ended with dinner in the Cajamarques with Marcos and his fiancée, Bety, Enrique and a few music lovers. All three of our children had some musical talent but practising the piano did not appeal to Richard. Claire followed her mother in developing a great love for the piano; she also tried her hand at the viola and the charango (an instrument that inspired her when we lived in Argentina). Guy started with the piano but wanted something more striking and found the trumpet was just to his liking.

The Greek-sounding Socrates was the horn player in the orchestra, but he also played the trumpet and as a quid pro quo for Maxine accompanying his horn playing, he gave Guy some lessons on the trumpet (Plate 71). Guy was learning to play the instrument at school and was making great strides. His trumpet teacher, Mr Steve Foster, also ran the big band and they played great music. The secret of the band's success was that Mr Foster knew how to select the music that the band was able to play well, and he really enthused the young musicians to give of their best. They made a great sound. They did so well that they were invited to perform in the private schools of Zimbabwe. Guy went and he had a wonderful time. There were groupies everywhere; they played at schools in Harare and Bulawayo and were mobbed wherever they went. Guy loved the whole ambience and the enthusiasm that they engendered. Perhaps there was something of a showman in him and he was taking after his father in enjoying the limelight. Dad still has the pith helmet that he brought him back from the 'Dark Continent'.

We were lucky that our children were turning out so well balanced.

Richard, having astounded the masters at Oundle by performing among the top ten at O level, proceeded to good A levels and a place at Edinburgh University where he read for a degree in biology and later on for a doctorate in London. Guy had had a brush with the authorities at school when he was found to be brewing beer in his study and he was sent down for a week. We thought this rather a strange punishment for a boy who lived 10,000 miles away, but he went to stay with his granny for the week and I think he had a rather enjoyable holiday. The irony of the whole episode was that it was my father who had given him the kit for making the beer. My father was quite a dab hand at brewing and produced a very drinkable pint. His attempts at winemaking were not so successful and perhaps the less said the better. It transpired that the school had taken the matter of brewing more seriously than we thought and the headmaster was considering expulsion; however, Guy's housemaster at Chapman's, Rod Smith, was solid in Guy's defence, pointing out that Guy was a valuable member of the house and such a minor misdemeanour should not blight an otherwise bright academic future. Oakham School was going through a rough time itself; the wife of Claire's housemaster Dr Wheway suffered a massive brain haemorrhage when Claire was in the fifth form and a senior member of the house and she did a wonderful job of rallying the girls in the house to cope with the loss. In the sixth form she moved into Round House where the housemaster was Dr Tyler and for her A levels she was studying English, Spanish and History. In her final year at school she was the head of house when Dr Tyler died from a heart attack and again Claire had to rally the troops as well as study for her exams. The school recognised her efforts with a special prize at speech day. Guy had a close friend at school, James Weight, whose father taught at the school, and his younger sister dropped dead in Oakham and so both my children were acquainted with grief at a young age and both proved to be towers of strength to their friends. James and Guy remain friends to this day and James was the best man at Guy's wedding. To their mother's delight, both of my younger children were musical, Guy with his trumpet and Claire with piano and viola, although she preferred the former.

We were hearing of the wonderful British musicians coming to perform in Lima but not including Arequipa on their itinerary. When compared to the American or French, Arequipa was poorly served by British culture. We had had many visitors from the British Council to Avenida Lima, and after the British Council took over responsibility for administering the LABVETSUR project from the embassy, we had even more. But it was not until Andrew Moore its director came to stay that Maxine broached the subject of the British Council sending its artistes to Arequipa. Andrew was not keen on the idea because there was no representative in the city to handle the administration and he was not happy about the additional cost of accommodation: the travel budget came from London but accommodation costs were his. We pointed out that we had a large house that was sparsely occupied for most of the year and that we would be delighted to look after the musicians. A venue would need to be found because it would not be appropriate for performances to be in the American Cultural Institute: people might get the wrong idea! Discussions with Eduardo Bedoya led to the suggestion that the dining room in the old Santa Catalina Convent could be used. This was an L-shaped room but a dais could be erected in the angle so that the audience could sit and see and hear in both wings. The acoustics were reported to be good. The Banco del Sur agreed to undertake the publicity and the ticketing and Andrew agreed that future artistes would come to Arequipa.

Our very first guests were the Endellion Quartet of Andrew Watkinson (violin), Ralph de Souza (violin), Garfield Jackson (viola) and David Waterman (cello) (Plate 66). I collected them from the airport together with Sra Lia Montes de Oca from the British Council, who came to look after them, and I brought them home. Poor Ralph was suffering from Montezuma's Revenge, but so loved his food, particularly the Peruvian food, that he never allowed his stomach enough rest to recover.

Maxine organised a dinner party for them the evening they arrived, inviting Hans and Daggie Nelting (her trio players), her star pupil, Pilar, together with Reggie and Elizabeth Roberts. When the guests arrived the group were still practising in the hall and so the guests had to come into the house through the kitchen! It was a good evening and a great deal of wine was drunk and the excellent meal ended with port and a superb Stilton given to me by Bob Low, the number two in the embassy.

During dinner the quartet were asked why the group was called the 'Endellion Quartet'. David was the first to answer and he told us that the group had first met at a music festival at St Endellion on the North Cornish coast and that when they formed the quartet they had decided to use this name, dropping the Saint. Ralph (whose father was Goan, and mother Chinese; he was brought up in Bombay but has a very educated English accent) butted in:

"That is not the true story! When the group first performed we did not have a name and so our individual names were used. The concert was sponsored by an Armenian carpet dealer from Greek Street called Amdelliam but when the programme was printed the name was Endellion and in memory of our first concert we chose that name."

The leader of the quartet, Andrew, countered (and I thought we were watching *Call My Bluff*), "Ralph is speaking rubbish. The quartet is named after the famous Greek musician who first wrote music in four-part harmony; what is more natural than to name a group who play in four-part harmony after such a man?"

"Not so!" said Garfield. "The real origin of the name is a French architectural fitting. At the corner of two walls architects often fitted an *en de lyon* as a strengthening device. In some chateaux this was embellished and used as a musicians' gallery for small groups to play."

My recounting of this episode does not do justice to the original telling. The whole table was in stitches. By now all the guests realised that this was an in-joke for the quartet, who had probably got fed up with answering the question "How did you get your name?"

We took the quartet to El Gato Vitoreño for lunch the next day and poor Ralph was unable to resist the seafood and he was still having problems when they left Arequipa. The hall in the house was a perfect place for them to rehearse and while they were there our house reverberated with music.

Their concert was delightful and greatly enjoyed by a packed audience. They played quartets by Haydn, Britten and Beethoven, and the piece I best remember was the Britten with which the quartet ended the first half. The piece finishes with the longest, quietest cello note that I have ever heard; how David kept that note going without a shake I do not know. They had been fun guests to entertain and they were superb musicians. The evening was rounded off with dinner in the Arequipa Club. The next time that we saw them was in Troutbeck Bridge in Cumbria and we drove 150 miles from Edinburgh to see them perform. I was in the queue waiting to buy drinks during the interval when I overheard the man in front of me say:

"He's a scruffy bugger that second violinist, but he plays like an angel." We had dinner with them after the concert and then drove the eighty miles home to Dumfries. They are that good.

Hot on their heels came the Barbican Trio, the origin of whose name was much easier to understand: all three had met while students at the Royal College of Music which is in London's rebuilt Barbican Centre. Feeding the trio was more problematic as we had one Orthodox Jew, one vegan and only one who ate a normal English diet. There were to be no repeat visits to El Gato Vitoreño. Sophie Barber, the violinist, was the vegan; she was a small, slender, short-haired brunette with a skin problem. She never stopped eating: I explained to her that if you live on an equine diet then you must eat like a horse. I felt certain that her skin problems were caused by her diet and we argued the toss long and hard. She was a vegan not out of conviction but as a protest. She was totally opposed to the modern methods of animal husbandry as she felt them to be cruel. She did not like the removal of dairy calves from their mothers only a few days after birth; she did not approve of the way the cows were housed in winter, and in many ways I sympathised with her as I too do not approve of the way in which farming is moving, where the comfort of the cowman is more important than the comfort of the cow. And she ate and ate. But she was an excellent, elegant violinist who played with a great deal of style. Rebecca Holt ate whatever Maxine put in front of her; she was bigger than Sophie in all ways and she had longer brown hair. She had great command of the piano from the softest to the loudest. Robert Max, the founder of the group, became a long-term friend of the family, and was a well-built young man with a mop of frizzy hair, which over the years has been tamed. He had had further training at the Juilliard School in New York and was a fine, sensitive cellist (Plate 67). It was not possible to move the piano and so the trio had to rehearse in the music room which with its low ceiling made it hard for the trio to get the balance right. They had to rehearse in the convent and a grand piano magically appeared. It was lucky we knew Arequipeños with connexions. The first half of the concert started with a Haydn Trio, which was followed by the Beethoven Variations on the Tailor Kakadu theme and the first half finished with the Fantasy Trio by Ireland. The second half consisted of the magnificent *Trio No. 2 in C Minor* by Mendelssohn. A wonderful, varied concert that was greatly enjoyed by all the large audience. However, we felt that we could not take the trio to the Arequipa Club because of the dietary restrictions and so we had a small party at home where the artistes could relax and meet a few local people.

'Itchy Fingers' were the next British Council artistes to perform in Arequipa but for some reason the quartet were accommodated in a hotel. The saxophone combo did not stay very long and performed the evening they arrived and were off the next day as they were playing the following evening in Arica in Chile. We almost had a disaster on our hands because they arrived in Arequipa without their saxophones. When the plane landed in Arequipa the airline staff were unable to open the door to the luggage compartment of the Boeing 727 and so none of the luggage was offloaded and the plane flew on to Tacna. On its return, the ground crew managed to open the door and unload the luggage and so at 6:00pm the musicians received their suitcases and their instruments and the driver from the Banco del Sur and I rushed them to the *Turistas* Hotel for a quick wash and change and then off to the 'Cultural' to see where they were performing, and to have a quick rehearsal before the concert began. By now the Banco del Sur were in charge of all local arrangements and had decided to change the venue because of the make-up of the group, and they considered that the music was not of the type to be performed in a monastery, particularly when one of the items to be played was called 'The Devil's Pulpit'. I went home for a quick change before taking Maxine back to the concert hall. I have to admit that the saxophone is not my favourite instrument and I was viewing the evening with some trepidation. I need not have worried, as they played the complete family of the instrument from the soprano to the contrabass saxophone and their programme was so varied that it was a really enjoyable evening. Their leader, Mike Mowat, wrote much of the music played by the group and as they played without music, the group were able to move about on the stage, adding to the interest. Maxine had prepared a chilli con carne and so we ended the evening at home with the musicians and local friends.

The next band to play were more a small orchestra than a group. They were the 'Wind Soloists of the Chamber Orchestra of Europe' and there were a dozen of them. On this occasion I did not even have to meet them: as there were so many the bank hired a large minibus to take them round town. Because of the size of the group the Banco del Sur decided that a larger auditorium was needed and so the hall of the University of San Agustin was used: this university is said to be the second oldest university in the Americas, second only to San Marcos in Lima. It was refounded in 1828 when the main building was erected. Like all grand buildings it was built in *sillar* and the ceiling of the concert hall was surfaced with small tiles of the stone. Is there something about music that gets the earth moving? As with the concert of Pilar so with the wind soloists: no sooner had they started playing, than the earth trembled as a small earthquake hit the city. A couple of tiles from the ceiling detached themselves and fell to the floor; luckily it was over the gangway and nobody was injured. It stopped before the audience vacated the building and thereafter the concert was uninterrupted. We did not have to host them after the concert as Reggie Roberts, the British Consul, held a dinner party in the Arequipa Club. I believe that there were two flutes, two oboes, two clarinets, two bassoons, two basset horns and two French horns, and they obviously enjoyed playing together and it was fascinating to watch the interchange of looks and gestures as they were performing. I sat next to a clarinettist at dinner and he lived in Fairlop Road, Leytonstone, which was the road adjacent to Fillebrook Road, where I was born and lived for the greater part of my childhood. Sadly my birthplace has been demolished to make way for the M11 motorway. Maxine sat next to Douglas Boyd who went on to become one of the world's leading oboists.

About this time we received a strange letter from the embassy instructing us that we had to post an armed guard at our gate for twenty-four hours a day and that the money to pay for this would be paid by London. The letter did not come from the ambassador, but from the administration section; nevertheless, it was Keith that I phoned.

"What on earth is going on?"

"We have received instructions from London, that because of the recent spate of murders of foreigners by the *Sendero Luminoso*, we all have to have armed protection."

"But I do not want armed protection; if we post a guard at our gate we will stand out like a sore thumb. You have only to drive down Avenida Bolognesi and you can see where all the senior military live by the guards at their gate. If we put a guard on our gate, then everyone will know that there is someone different living there. I would rather merge with the crowd, I feel much safer like that."

"Could you drop me a line to that effect and then if your throat is cut my back is covered. I think that you are right and so I will back you if ODA make a fuss."

We did not have a guard, and lived safely ever after.

The bell rang one morning and Flora answered it and was given a letter; it was from the Mayor of Yanahuara, Roger Caceres, the son of the city's mayor, Luis Caceres. We were informed that he wished to brighten up his suburb and all householders were required to paint the walls that fronted the street. I thought that it was a leg-pull and tossed it onto the bin. A fortnight later we received another letter, which noted,

'You have not painted your external wall and are to do so immediately.'

I sat down and wrote a letter to the mayor pointing out that one should not paint brick walls; that you built your wall with 'facing' bricks so that it always looked nice. Poor Maxine had to hand-deliver this letter to the town hall because we had been instructed to paint the wall within forty-eight hours. As with most things in Perú, it took an age before she found the person who could receive such a letter. And then the blow fell as a few days later we received a third letter informing us that since we had not painted our wall as instructed we were fined $200,000! This had gone far enough: I wrote to the mayor stating that as we were only tenants it was not us to whom he should be writing but to the owner; I did not give her name. We heard no more.

A phone call from Marjorie Michell in April 1989 informed us that the Interplast team were coming to Arequipa and Marjorie wanted to know if we could help with accommodation. Interplast is a group of medical professionals, plastic surgeons, anaesthetists and nurses, that travel to countries in the Third World where they carry out reconstructive surgery on the poor children with genetic defects such as cleft palate, hare lips, or adults with disfiguring burn problems. These dedicated professionals give up their holidays to work unpaid in a foreign land. They receive flights to and from their host country and are provided with free board and lodging during their stay. Maxine agreed to take up to four as we always enjoyed meeting people from different countries. In the end we only had to host two – Robin Young and Brita Sattvoll, both nurses from California. These poor women did not know what hit them and they were working for up to fifteen hours a day. We hardly saw them as they left the house at seven in the morning and did not return often until ten at night. They finished so late that they came home, ate a meal left in the oven for them and then collapsed into bed. They saw nothing of the city and little more than the inside of an operating theatre. Even on their last day when all the hosts were invited to a dinner in the Old Mill in Sabandia, they worked until 6:30pm. It was an excellent party for the helpers which went on late and we did not get to bed until 2:00am.

The following year we were asked to host three, Marilyn Ropey and Corky Buckley, both theatre nurses from California, and John Persing, a surgeon from Virginia. I met them at the airport and took them home and after a wash and a cup of tea I took them on a tour of Arequipa: I did not intend that they should go home without having seen our beautiful city. I need not have worried as their programme was much better organised and they returned to our house most evenings in time to join us for dinner. The visit in 1991 was equally well organised and we had three theatre nurses to stay, Joginder Sikand, Merrill Reynolds, and Betty Colbeck; all worked together in California. At the end of each visit by the Interplast team there was a great dinner party at the mill which went on into the early hours. As a result of these visits many children were able to live useful and productive lives and we had met many delightful and caring professionals.

Our children had adjusted well to living in Arequipa and in a Spanish culture and they had made many friends that they had found for themselves. Arequipa was a safe place to live in and we allowed the children great freedom. Richard and Guy were more than able to look after Claire and so they went to nightclubs for dancing, to cafés and the cinema and they usually walked there and back or occasionally took a taxi. They were wise enough to avoid the market at night and they never had any trouble. Elections were in the air and there was great excitement at the thought that finally they would get rid of Alan García as president. Mario Vargas Llosa, the internationally renowned author, was put forward by the right-wing coalition FREDEMO, and his main opponent was the head of La Molina, the prestigious agricultural university in Lima, Dr Alberto Fujimori, whose parents were Japanese. The children took after their parents and were of the right-wing persuasion and persuaded their friends to join them in supporting Dr Vargas Llosa, who at the time was living in London, but came out to Perú to meet the people.

As an Arequipeño he started his campaign in the city and ended it there, and of course a visit to FONGALSUR was a 'must' as they had such a great influence over the farming community in the department. José Miguel Rivas, the then president of FONGALSUR, brought him to the laboratory to meet the staff and he was happy to pose for pictures with them and generally endeared himself to all (Plate 72).

He ended his campaign with a great rally in the Plaza de Armas in Arequipa on the Friday before the election. Stands were built to accommodate all the people expected to come; the town band was there playing away. People mounted the massive scaffolding dais and gave long speeches about what a great president he would be; armies of supporters marched in under various banners and two of our three children together with all their friends marched in with the youth wing and finally to deafening applause the man himself entered the plaza, mounted the dais and gave a towering speech about what he planned to do as president and we were sent home to prepare for victory. No electioneering is allowed on the day before the election and there was an eerie quiet in the city that Saturday as elections in Perú are always held on a Sunday. Voting in Perú is compulsory, as I think it should be in Britain, and people who do not vote are heavily fined. The results came out and our man had narrowly won, but without an overall majority and so there would be a second ballot. Vargas Llosa versus Fujimori, and the latter won easily. The reason was not difficult to understand Fujimori was pure Japanese and so had facial features like the Indian people and the *mestizos* who make up the majority of the population. They had never had a president of their own before and so whatever their political persuasion, they voted for him. Like most Peruvian presidents, he started well and many of his economic reforms put Perú back on the right track, and he destroyed the *Sendero Luminoso*. Once they had captured Abimael Guzman, the head of the organisation, it died. However, he changed the constitution enabling him to serve a third term and the corruption started, followed by kidnapping and murders. He fled to Japan from where he tried to resign his presidency, which was not accepted by the Congress and he was impeached and deposed. On a visit to Chile he was captured and extradited to Perú where he was put on trial and he now languishes in jail. It was a sad end for a man who had done so much good. 'Absolute power corrupts absolutely.'

19

All Good Things Must Come to an End

I do not know why my relationship with the bureaucrats of ODA was never good: it had started badly with the interview in London and from then on, I was constantly battling with them for money, not to pay running costs but to fund expansion of the laboratory services. Every veterinary or livestock adviser that had visited the project had been impressed with what we were achieving and what we were planning to do. We had established a laboratory service that was more than paying its way, it was funding the local costs of our visits to the sierra to work with the camelids of the *campesinos*. Apart from the incinerator, I had to fight for every piece of equipment that we needed. It was all so strange, because when I suggested that we recruit two Peruvian vets with a view to training my successor, ODA immediately agreed to pay their costs for the first two years. Whenever we needed a consultancy, be it Jim Carroll for mastitis, Dr Roger Connan for parasite control or Dr Laborde from Uraguay for teaching us about testing milking machine equipment, then I received wonderful support. When I asked for scholarships to train staff in Britain or in South America, London did all the negotiations with the institutes and bent over backwards to assist the scholars.

But getting money for equipment was like prising a rope from the fist of a drowning man. Of all the jobs that I had done, this was the one with the greatest potential for being a long-term success. The laboratory in Gaborone, Botswana, had to continue efficiently because the export of meat to Europe depended upon a good functioning laboratory and so the Government of

Botswana was happy to pay all running costs; but LABVETSUR would live or die depending upon its own efforts. I had two good men and a good woman who could take over from me. All three were being trained or were about to be trained in Britain: Dra Milagro was already in Edinburgh at the Centre for Tropical Veterinary Medicine studying pathology, Dr Luis Olivera was lined up to go to Liverpool Veterinary School to study parasitology with Professor Clarkson, and Dr Fernando Fernandez would eventually study in the Ayr campus of the Scottish Agricultural College where he would be trained in avian diseases. I hoped to see them all back and working in the laboratory before I made my choice of who should succeed me, so that I could work in tandem with them taking the lead before I departed. Such was not to be.

In addition to the scientists visiting the project, ODA sent a succession of bureaucrats to Arequipa to see how I was administering the project. They were mostly pleasant, well educated, and we enjoyed accommodating them at home. At the end of their stay they would often take us out to dinner at La Choperia where we would introduce them to the delights of Peruvian cuisine: their *aguadito de mariscos* was sublime. There was one major exception to the rule: a youngish man who stayed for a couple of nights and on the second evening he arrived at the house definitely the worse for drink. He had an appointment with Reggie Roberts in his office the following morning. At the time that he should have been at his meeting he was still in the house and Maxine suggested that he had best get moving and he made to leave when Maxine stopped him: he was wearing a T-shirt and tackies: "You cannot go to meet the British Consul dressed like that: Sr Roberts will be wearing a suit and tie, and you as a representative of the British Government should give him the same courtesy."

He left a few moments later wearing a jacket and tie and proper shoes.

We enjoyed entertaining British visitors in the house. Much as we loved the Peruvians it was a delight to have people from home to stay and to speak English. Consequently, our home was always open to visitors and rarely did the embassy or British Council staff or people from London stay in a hotel in Arequipa; instead they were entertained in 'Hotel Windsor', and this led to my undoing. Jim Maund had replaced the Brighton Queen in charge of the South American department and was visiting all his projects. He had recently joined ODA from 'Save the Children' or some such non-governmental organisation and I should have been suspicious when he declined our invitation to stay: he regularly ate with us and we had a cocktail party in his honour. He was horrified to see an aid worker living in a decent house with a swimming pool, when we should have been living in a shack like the people with whom we were working; try as Reggie did to point out to him that as the project manager, I had to deal with decision makers in the city who would not be comfortable visiting me in a shack but felt quite at home sitting in our sitting room drinking a pisco sour.

He showed little interest in the work of LABVETSUR when he paid his cursory visit to the laboratory. By now, Lucho was no longer president of FONGALSUR but had passed the reins to Miguel Rivas who as the owner of a stable of *caballos de paso* was keen for the laboratory to succeed. On the return from my next visit to Cajamarca I was staying with the Haskells and when the driver who collected me at the airport dropped me at the residency Toni greeted me warmly and said that Keith was waiting for me at the pool with a gin and tonic.

"Come and sit down, Roger, have a gin, and tell me how was the trip to the north and how are Enrique and Marcos getting on?"

"LABRENOR is getting on very well, thanks to your efforts, and yes I will have a gin."

Keith poured me a large gin.

"They have started work on the *Brucella* eradication scheme and the money is beginning to come in. The farming community have really decided that they want the laboratory to succeed and are rallying round."

"To change the subject, Roger, I had a telex from London today saying that they are not going to renew your contract."

There was a long silence, during which I was too gobsmacked to reply.

"I shall fight it, of course, but I do not hold out much hope; once these bastards have made a decision it would be too great a loss of face to go back on it. What did you do to upset him?"

"Had it been Maund's predecessor, I could understand it, because I have been battling with him for five years, but Maund I hardly know as he has only been in office for a few months and I have not yet had a chance to cross swords with him. The only thing that I can think of is that he did not approve of my lifestyle, living in a a decent house with a garden and a swimming pool. Having worked only for NGOs before I think that he believes that aid workers ought to live as and with the poor."

"It seems a pretty poor excuse for sacking someone, particularly when they have done a good job which has given the Arequipeños a great impression of Britain and the British."

"I am particularly sad because this is the first time that I have really had the opportunity to put my ideas into play. This is the first job I have had where no local wanted my position: the Peruvians are sensible enough to know that at present they cannot run the laboratory. When they want my job, it will be time to go. I have three good vets all vying to take over from me and my plan was to make the choice and hand over the laboratory but remain as an assistant vet for a year to help them stand up to the Peruvian bureaucrats who will be jealous of their success."

"Well, I can try with that story but I do not think that it will work. What will you do?"

"Richard is at Edinburgh University and Guy and Claire will be off my educational hands in the summer and so I will no longer be working for school fees, and I am still young enough at fifty-two to offer an employer a decent amount of time."

"Had you been planning to stay here until you retired?"

"Not really: I thought a couple of years to choose the new boss and then just one year of hand-holding. That would take me to fifty-five and much less employable and so perhaps leaving with the job undone might be to my advantage, if not to LABVETSUR."

"But what will happen to LABVETSUR?"

"It depends upon whom they select to replace me. The way in which I have set up the laboratory is that basically all vets do the same work, equally sharing the clinical work and the administration. The only work that I do that is not done by the others is attending the board and looking after the finances. A self-financing laboratory cannot afford to have a non-working vet, and so, when you ask for a replacement for me make sure you get a keen young pathologist and not a pen-pusher."

"Hold on, I haven't lost you yet! We will take that step when and if it comes."

And on that happy note we joined Toni and so to dinner.

As I expected, Keith's efforts hit a brick wall. He wrote and explained why he felt I should stay to complete the task and he quoted the chaos that had happened to the ODA project in Cajamarca with their regular change in leadership. He received a very complimentary letter from Maund saying what a wonderful job I had done but that ODA felt that having done all the basic work establishing the laboratory, what was needed now was someone with a financial background to finish the job for ODA, and close the project, while leaving a flourishing laboratory under Peruvian leadership. Once I knew who was to replace me I realised that Maund had already found my replacement before firing me. I suggested to Keith that he should write back pointing out that I had led the laboratory through a period of inflation that had peaked at an annual rate of 3,800% and that it had needed someone who knew about finance to keep the laboratory afloat in those turbulent times. But the die had been cast and Clive Woodham had been selected to replace me. This sealed the doom of LABVETSUR. Clive was laboratory-trained and an old friend of mine but for the past ten years he had been working for the Development Bank for Latin America in Mexico, mostly in the office looking at, rather than working in, projects. He was responsible for setting up several veterinary laboratories in Central America but as a facilitator rather than the laboratory director. I do not know whether Clive was offered the job to make up for their having improperly sacked him almost twenty years previously. Did ODA have a corporate memory that went back that far? An excellent man in many ways, he was not going to enthuse his successor with the desire to get his hands dirty: so important in Latin America. The most that Maund was prepared to offer Keith was a visit from their latest veterinary adviser, Dra Lindsay Bell.

She arrived on the first flight on a Monday and was met at the airport by John who took her to the hotel and later brought her to the laboratory. Like Jim Maund she had refused my invitation to stay at Hotel Windsor and like Maund she stayed in the *Turistas* Hotel in Selva Alegre. I had never met her and had no idea what to expect. She was a small woman with short blonde hair, very smartly dressed in a well-pressed skirt and a beautifully tailored blazer. Our first meeting was not auspicious. She was tired, having arrived from Miami at midnight and left her hotel at 5:00 in the morning for the flight to Arequipa. She looked it: I do not know how old she was but I put her in her late thirties. She was obviously under great strain as this was her first visit since she took up the post, and for her it was a real baptism of fire. She met John, Alastair and me in my office and then was taken on a conducted tour of the laboratory by three of the professional staff. After which we had a one-to-one meeting, when I asked what she was here for! I pointed out to her that I had had enough of instant experts coming to Arequipa and writing reports that were full of rubbish. I quoted from several reports and pointed out the crass errors that they had made. I decided to go down with all guns blazing! Aurora brought us a coffee and I waited for the onslaught that never came. She spoke to me more in sorrow than anger:

"Why have you antagonised the people in London? You had a sinecure here in Arequipa that could have kept you in a job until you retired."

"The problems were not of my making," I said. "All that I have done has been to try and establish a functioning, self-financing diagnostic laboratory, and I have succeeded. Despite all the financial problems of Perú, we have pulled it off. This action of ODA may well destroy all that I have built. Changing the helmsman in a yacht race is never a good idea, especially when you are in the lead. I had hoped to stay here and see my successor safely at the helm before I left. When you get back to London, you can tell them that I have salvaged the project that they destroyed and you closed down in Cajamarca as well as having built a wonderful team of Peruvians here in Arequipa, and now ODA are in the process of destroying that as well."

"Please do not get so worked up, I can see that you are upset."

"I am not bothered about me: it is probably in my interests to go now rather than in three or four years' time. I am arrogant enough to know that I will have no trouble in getting another job to see me through to retirement. No, I am worried about my staff: many of them have been with me through thick and thin; I want to ensure that they are left with the systems they deserve, so that if they follow the plan then LABVETSUR will continue to be a success. That they have a long-term future is my main concern."

"You obviously care for your staff, which is why LABVETSUR has been so successful; it is just a pity that you did not put as much effort in to making friends in London."

"I am afraid that I have always thought that the bureaucrats were there to ensure the well-being of those at the coalface. When I was working in Kenya on secondment from the Ministry of Agriculture to ODA, we had this wonderful personnel officer called Gladys Wilmshurst who looked upon us as her children and she did everything in her power to make sure that our project got everything it needed. I have always thought that that was how bureaucrats should behave. I think that Hamlet has got it right when he talks about 'the law's delay' and 'the insolence of office'. They should be there to assist us to get things done rather than operate as if every penny spent comes from their own pockets."

"I can see why you are not popular in London. But what I really want to see is what you are doing with that electronic counter that you would not lend me when I was working in LIDIVET!" (LIDIVET was in Santa Cruz, Bolivia.) But there was a smile on her lips.

I asked Percy to tell her what we were doing for mastitis control and then again sat her down in my office with the senior Peruvian staff. I was not required to translate as Lindsay spoke much better Spanish than me: her mother was from Central America where her father had been a British diplomat, she was bilingual and had studied veterinary medicine in Spain.

John took her to the hotel for lunch since she did not wish to join him. At three he took her to Reggie's office but was made by her to sit outside. That evening he took her to Lucho's house and again was sent away while she spoke to him. The next morning, John and I took her down to La Joya where she again took off the Peruvian vets for a chat away from us. However, she did look marginally better and was seen to smile: this latter definitely improved her looks, which were severe at the best of times. We drove back to Arequipa for lunch with Lucho to find that he was ill in bed; we offered to feed her but again she declined. That afternoon she had a session with the staff where she told them what was happening and then would not allow them to speak. The next move was to visit Gilberto Paz, who had taken over from Miguel Rivas as president of FONGALSUR, and again John was kept out: Gilberto told me afterwards that he was most surprised that one of his men was not there to advise him. After that meeting she then came to see me and asked me again why I had upset London. I told her that I had tried to do the task set me by London, but I felt that my first duty was to the Peruvians to set up for them a service that we all thought necessary. To do this I had had to disagree with London. She also told me that there was precious little chance of any further help for Cajamarca, to which I replied, "Then why was I asked to go up there, giving up weeks of my time, and spending thousands of pounds in travel costs? And to what purpose has the ambassador devoted his time and energy giving LABRENOR a future? Above all why have we wasted the time of the Cajamarquinos, and given them false hopes?"

Lindsay declined when I offered to take her to the Arequipa Club for dinner on her last night: when I had suggested to Maxine that we invite her home to dinner, her reply was:

"We are *not* entertaining *that* woman." Maxine unfairly held my sacking against Lindsay and would not let me invite her home to dinner: she was always a much stronger upholder of my rights than me!

On the Wednesday morning, Dra Bell went off to Lima escorted to the airport by Alastair. That night she dined with Keith and Toni. When I spoke to Keith the following morning he told me that he thought she was "either very tired, drunk or mentally deranged." He had never met such an aggressive woman in his life; she seemed determined to get her retaliation in first (his words)! She started off by telling him that she was a South American (her mother was Spanish and she was brought up in the diplomatic service) and it was essential that LABVETSUR had a Peruvian vet immediately. Keith told her that I had been training three Peruvians, two of whom were currently in Britain studying to take over from me and would still be when my contract came to an end. He also pointed out to her that she was in Perú as the representative of the British Government and not as a South American vet! Then she told him that she had closed Cajamarca, and could see no reason why it should be reopened. He suggested to her that if her mind was closed then there was no point in her going to Cajamarca. He was furious with her, and as he was about to travel to Britain because the new president, Fujimori, was opening an ecology meeting in Kew, he would have an opportunity for discussions with ODA before she would return to Britain. Despite Keith's efforts, the battle was lost.

It was time to think of packing up and preparing for the move, but it was a time for celebration in Arequipa: they were about to hold a party for the 450th anniversary of the founding of the city and Maxine was invited to play in the anniversary concert. This was to be a two-piano recital with Arequipa's leading pianist Hugo Cueto and the concert was to be in the Teátro Municipal which was normally used as a cinema. Technically, Hugo was a fine pianist but it drove Maxine mad trying to make him feel the music: it was enough for him to get from beginning to the end of a piece without playing too many wrong notes.

She would return from a rehearsal tearing out her hair. She was worried about pushing too hard because he was a delightful man and she did not want to upset him, but she felt that it was her reputation at stake. The Teátro Municipal had its own grand piano but the second one had to be brought to the theatre from the town hall. This was a Steinway grand dating from the early 1920s and it had a history. Apparently on arrival at the port of

Matarani as it was being unloaded the cradle slipped and the piano was unceremoniously dumped in the sea. The dockers managed to salvage the piano and it was shipped up to Arequipa and the story goes that when they opened the lid there were dead fish inside the body. This was obviously an unlucky piano because during the move to the theatre, the piano, which was carried by four men the three blocks, was again dropped; this time the pedals were damaged and so a rapid repair job was needed to be carried out in time for a final rehearsal on the stage. The inside of the piano was filthy and Maxine refused to play it until a vacuum cleaner had been used (Plates 73 and 74).

The concert was a great success playing to a full house of more than 700 people. They performed works by Brahms, Schubert, Handel, Mozart, Poulenc, and finished with one of my favourite piano pieces, 'Scaramouche' by Milhaud, in which there is a race at the end to see which pianist will finish first! It brought the audience to their feet. When the applause died down Maxine and Hugo were presented with large bouquets of flowers and then the *Alcalde*, Sr Luis Cáceres Velasquez, came on to the stage 'to say a few words', which lasted almost as long as the concert, at the end of which he presented Maxine and Hugo each with the city's *Diploma de Honor* (the equivalent of our 'Freedom of the City'), not just for their performance that night but for their service to music in the city over the past few years. The evening concluded, as did many such evenings, with a group of us going to the Arequipa Club for dinner.

We were having breakfast one morning when the phone rang and Maxine answered and called out, "Roger, it is Keith wanting to speak to you."

"Yes, Mr Ambassador?" I said. "What can I do for you so early in the morning?"

"I am calling you at home because this is a highly confidential matter. Promise me that you will not mention this conversation to anyone."

"May I tell Maxine?"

"Yes, but it must go no further; you must not mention it to the children. If you were to be offered an MBE [Member of the Order of the British Empire], would you accept it?"

I was stunned, and for a moment was too shaken to speak.

"Are you there?" came Keith's voice.

"Yeeees," I stammered, "but I do not know what to say. I am thrilled; of course I would accept."

"Good, I had to ask you, but this is not an offer, you understand; although I have never known anyone who replied in the affirmative not to get it. Many, many congratulations and may I say that it is well deserved; you have done a great job for Britain and I hope that this will go some way to make up for ODA not renewing your contract."

"I still cannot believe it, and yes it much more than makes up for the disappointment of not being allowed to complete the job I came to do."

"You will not hear anything until the Queen's Birthday Honours List comes out in early June. But please remember, not a word to anyone."

"Thank you again," I said and I sincerely meant it as I was sure that Keith had been responsible for setting the wheels in motion.

The city was alive with events to mark this important anniversary and perhaps the most singular was a fashion show which was to be held in a local secondary school hall. The clothes to be shown were alpaca garments made by Mirtha and leather jackets and waistcoats made by her friend. Maxine was approached by Mirtha who asked her if our children would act as models. Maxine laughed and said that there was no chance that our children would agree, but she undertook to ask them. She first asked Richard and was staggered when he said that he would do it if the other two agreed. If big brother would do it, then the two younger ones were game and a greatly surprised Maxine phoned Mirtha and gave her the good news. There were just a couple of rehearsals before the big night when the children met the other models including Marité de Taboada and her brother Ramíro who were visiting from Montreal; they were Arequipeños but their parents were separated and their mother had taken them and the rest of the children to live in Canada; they were in town visiting their father.

The fashion show was a wow; Guy was enchanted that *all* the regional winners in the Miss Perú Beauty Contest would be sitting in the front two rows. As almost all things Peruvian, it started half an hour late by the time all the audience were in and the performers ready to go. The music started, the compère made the initial announcements and then Marité paraded down the catwalk with great aplomb in a leather skirt and contrasting leather jacket (Plate 75 and 76). Guy had been enhancing his confidence with a liberal quantity of Cerveza Arequipeña and each time that he entered it was with a great swagger and he got perilously close to the end of the catwalk in his efforts to show off his manly charms to the assembled beauties; on more than one occasion I thought that he might fall in their laps. With hands on his lapels, he was the chimney sweep in *Mary Poppins* to a T. Even Claire, who at the time was experiencing teenage shyness, acquitted herself very well and strutted with the best of them. I was very proud of the way my children handled the whole evening, they could have been doing it all their lives. The fashion show went like clockwork: Mirtha was delighted with the way the evening had gone and felt that our children had performed wonderfully well. It had been a great coup for her to have had foreign models showing off the clothes.

This fashion show had a great impact on the Windsor family: Richard was very taken with Marité, a beautiful and educated young woman, and soon made plans to see her again, and they spent a couple of evenings together (without a chaperone!) before Richard returned to Edinburgh and Marité to Canada. This was not the end of the affair as they maintained contact: Richard made several visits to Canada and Marité spent a term in Edinburgh before Richard completed his degree. They were married in 1994 while he was working for his doctorate in Mill Hill and they have two delightful daughters, but that is to get ahead of the story.

There was a wonderful firework display to mark the actual anniversary and I have never seen such a show of pyrotechnics; tableaux that would never be seen in Britain. The actual fireworks were set off from the Puente

Grau and we had a wonderful view from Avenida Ejercito. The Peruvians are great at making what they call *castillos*, towers of bamboo, thirty or more feet high, frightfully dangerous, and once lit, the display moves from level to level and they make wonderful patterns and designs.

The most incredible one that I ever saw was not during the anniversary display but during a religious procession celebrating *El Señor de los Milagros* (Lord of the Miracles). Throughout the month of October, the believers go to church and make a specific request, and as a sign of their piety they wear the purple robe for the rest of the month: for women it is like a cassock tied at the waist with a white rope, for men it is just a purple shirt. It dates back to colonial times when a black slave painted the image on the walls of a run-down property. In spite of earthquakes and attempts to erase it, this miraculous image has remained intact. Thousands of believers dressed in purple outfits sing and pray to accompany the image of the crucified Christ in procession. In honour of Black Christ, bullfighting takes place at Plaza de Acho in Lima, which brings together the most prestigious bullfighters of Spain and the Americas. To mark the end of the month there is a procession around Arequipa. The statue of Christ is taken from the Saint Augustin Church and carried on a cart pulled by many men in their purple shirts. The procession is led by a band and at each church the procession stops, prayers are said, a hymn is sung and the *castillo* ignited. The one that sticks in my mind made a picture of the coat of arms of *El Señor de los Milagros*.

The Peruvians do not go much for rockets, preferring their *castillos*, and the one that concluded the anniversary display was a waterfall of white fire running down from the bridge and the words 'AREQUIPA 450' appeared in red (red and white being the colours of the Peruvian flag). The town band played the Arequipa anthem and the display was at an end.

Right to the end there was a battle with the bureaucrats; my allowance to take our possessions back to Britain by sea was seven cubic metres. Tony Flanagan came up from Mollendo and looked at our stuff and said that what we had amounted to between five and six cubic metres. However, to send that to Britain as loose freight would cost at least seven thousand pounds.

"Take my advice and book half a container, then you put in what you want and it will not get mixed up with other people's stuff. Half a container will cost you about three thousand pounds and then there will be the cost of packing the breakables and the lorry to bring the stuff to us, say another five or six hundred pounds."

It was the house rental all over again:

"You are entitled to seven cubic meters, not twelve and a half."

In desperation I phoned Keith and explained the situation and said I would be delighted to get the Flanagans to put the two quotations in writing, but he thought that that would not be necessary as it made sense to save the government money.

When the packers arrived, although they did the glass and china, I packed all our paintings and there were ninety-two! It was sad to see the piano manhandled onto the back of an open lorry but I was certain that Tony and Mike would make sure that the container would be carefully packed. And so it was.

I was inundated with letters from all over Perú and from various institutions. Perhaps the one that gave me the most pleasure was the one I received from Ing Rodriguez, the owner of Leche Gloria, the man who had ensured that our project was successful.

Dr. Roger Windsor
LABVETSUR
Arequipa

Dear Dr. Windsor:

It is with great regret that I have heard of your imminent return to England.

As I am shortly travelling abroad, I will be unable to be present at the luncheon to be given in your honour on Saturday. However, I felt I must write and thank you personally for your optimum collaboration, and your unstinting efforts to help the cattle farmers here in the south of Peru. I am sure your knowledge and guidance has helped them to reduce and in some cases to erradicate the diseases and illnesses suffered by their animals. You can be immensely proud of the enterprise which you are leaving behind, and which I am sure will carry on with the task which you began.

I would like to offer you my very best wishes for your future professional success, and trust that we will see you again in Arequipa, perhaps in the not too distant future.

Yours very sincerely,

Jorge Rodriguez R.
Presidente Ejecutivo

Then began the round of parties: Marjorie Michell had a lunch party for us with her two widowed sisters, son Tony, and Michi Searle. All was well until the main course, which was *diamante*, a delightful Pacific fish of the salmon family. Maxine had eaten half when she asked to be excused from the table and went to the lavatory where she was violently sick; when she returned to the dining room she was deadly white and obviously in some discomfort. We had to make our excuses and I took her home where she went straight to bed and remained until the following day when she woke feeling perfectly well. This was the start of her salmon allergy which plagued her for several years.

Before our luggage went we had a party in the house for all our friends including all the staff of LABVETSUR, and the friends of our children. I wanted it to be a Peruvian party and so I hired a *folklorico* group to play Andean music, and they played in the hall while the guests moved from hall to sitting room, kitchen and garden, and there was a buffet laid out in the dining room and for the last time Kuki did the catering.

Lucho, who was both annoyed and saddened by my departure, arranged with the alcalde for me to be awarded *La Diploma de Honor con medalla de oro*. The ambassador and his wife were to be the special guests of the city. Keith and Toni stayed with us, almost the last guests to stay with us in Arequipa, and Keith had arranged through Reggie for a party for a hundred guests at the Arequipa Club.

The day started with the meeting in the principal auditorium of the town hall: the laboratory was closed for the morning as the whole staff were invited (Plates 77 to 81). I felt that the honour was as much for them as a personal honour to me. Without their hard work, sacrifice and determination to succeed we might well have gone under during the financial crisis. Once the audience was seated the stage party trouped in and sat at a long table under the painting of '*The Founding of the City on August 15, 1540 by García Manuel de Carbajal at the Villa Hermosa de Nuestra Señora de la Asunción*'. Lucho, Keith, the *alcalde*, I and several other dignitaries of the city stood for the national anthems of Britain (this time the correct one) and Perú and the *Himno Nacional* de Arequipa. Lucho as the promoter was asked to state why I deserved the award, Keith then had to say a few words about British aid to Arequipa and the *alcalde* said how grateful he was to the British Government for their help and how valuable the project had been for the development of agriculture in the region and that it was thanks to the efforts of Dr Windsor that Arequipa now had a flourishing veterinary service;

321

as a thank you to me for my services he would now give me my *Diploma de Honor* and put the gold medal around my neck. The audience applauded and then it was my turn to speak. I thanked the mayor and the city for the honour that they had done me. I thanked the people of Perú and those of Arequipa in particular for the kindness and friendship that I had been shown during my six years in the country. I said what a privilege and pleasure it had been to work in such a wonderful country and then I was able to pay tribute to the staff of LABVETSUR. I wanted the staff of the laboratory to understand that it was thanks to their hard work that I had received the honour, and that I was receiving it on their behalf. It was quite an emotional moment.

A great number of us then adjourned to the Gato Vitoreño for lunch. Lucho was horrified that I should take the ambassador to a café where you sat at formica-topped tables and ate from plastic plates. I explained that Keith, like me, was more interested in the quality of the food than the ambience.

It was time to put our feet up and have a siesta to prepare for the party in the evening. For this party, only the English community, the senior laboratory staff and our friends were invited. It was a bittersweet evening for us, saying goodbye to people that we had grown to love over our time in the country. The conversation flowed along with the pisco sour, wine and beer and the club laid on wonderful food for the occasion: an excellent finger buffet. After we had eaten, Keith and I went to the head of the staircase from where Keith was able to speak to the people. Keith had cleverly organised with the mayor that my Peruvian honour and the farewell party for me were on the day before the Queen's Birthday and so at the end of his very kind speech he was able to announce that I had been awarded the MBE in the Queen's Birthday Honours List. As we were drinking our whisky before going to bed that night I was able to say to Keith what Dr Málaga had said to me a few months previously: "This has been the proudest day of my life."

We had sent our sea freight off to Matarani. Maxine and Guadalupe had cleaned the house and we had given away all those things that we were not going to take back to Britain. We packed our suitcases and ended our time in Arequipa as we had begun in *La Posada del Puente* taking our breakfasts in the open air, in the sun by the side of the beautiful Rio Chili. We had had a wonderful six years, perhaps the most enjoyable of my life; we had a wonderful marriage where Maxine and I were both partners and friends, we had three delightful children all bright and happy and performing well in their educational institutions.

Newspaper advertisement for farewell lunch

My only sadness was for my friends in LABVETSUR; I knew that I had not completed my task and that my successor would not finish the job in the way I intended and I feared for the long-term future of the staff at the mercy of Peruvian jealousies. I felt that I was deserting a team that had given me their total loyalty and dedication, but there was nothing more that I could do. Would they be able to weather the storm and bring the ship LABVETSUR into a safe harbour with a long-term future? Only time would tell.

I was entertained to farewell lunches round the regions (Plate 82), and at each one I was presented with a silver plate bearing an inscription. Perhaps the most impressive was the one given by LABVETSUR where an advertisement was placed in all the local papers inviting people to come. Maxine and I ate the delicious local cuisine and then sat through the interminable speeches as one after another of the lunchers extolled my virtues. After a while the embarrassment wore off and I sat there and let my mind wander over the interesting experiences I had had at that particular venue. Perhaps the most amusing of the lunches was at Santa Rita where the Lozada brothers had their farms. I cannot recall the venue but there were about fifty people, mostly men, seated at long trestle tables on a covered patio adjoining the garden of a private house. The lunch was eaten, the fruit consumed and we were supping our Cerveza Arequipeña when Lucho rose to talk. The moment he opened his mouth, a caged parrot hanging from a tree in the garden gave forth, and drowned poor Lucho, who had to give up and sit down. Brother Enrique rose and spoke: silence from the parrot, who sat and listened as one after the other of the participants said their piece. And then Lucho tried to present me with the silver platter; all was well until he spoke, when again the parrot gave forth at such volume that Lucho had to give the plate to brother Daniel to make the presentation. What Lucho had done to the bird I do not know but it certainly had a grievance against him and only him. Our departure from Arequipa was marked by so many lunches that it became hard to tell them apart, but in my final week I remember taking the staff of LABVETSUR and the La Joya *posta* for a lunch in a new *picantería* and after the lunch Héctor Begazo presented me with a goat skin *pergamino* on which was painted the coat of arms of Arequipa, the volcano Misti, the Puente Grau, the *posta* in La Joya, and LABVETSUR; there was an inscription thanking me for my services and signed by them all. This brought it all home to me and there were tears in my eyes as I thanked them all for being with me through the bad times and the good times.

In one of his final acts as president, Alan García had deregulated air travel, which made it possible for new airlines to start up and suddenly it was possible to fly from Lima to Arequipa at any time from seven in the morning to nine o'clock at night. We decided to fly from Arequipa to Lima on the midday flight on the Sunday and what a party was held in the airport: to this day I do not know who organised it but there was champagne for all and canapés, and someone had brought a portable cassette player and Andean music drowned out the airport sound system so that they switched it off! All the laboratory and project staff were there, Reggie and Evelyn Roberts, Alfredo and Connie Roberts, Marjorie Michell, and sisters Claire and Beryl, and son Tony (Michael had already relocated to Lima), Michi Searle, Lucho and Roxana Lozada, David and Sonia Hallenbeck and their three boys, the Lopera family, Hans and Dagi, Hugo Cueto and his wife and other members of the musical fraternity, Rev Simon and Clare Brignall, many of the children's friends and so many more that I cannot name. We danced and chatted and hugged and embraced and drank and laughed and cried. We said our fond farewells and we knew there would be many that we would never meet again. As we strapped ourselves into our seats for take-off I was overtaken by sadness, and sat there in silence alone with my thoughts. We spoke little on the flight but cheered up at the sight of Keith and Toni. As we knew few people in the city we spent only a few days in

Lima before flying on to Miami, where we had a couple of days' break before going home.

On the plane from Miami to London I turned to Maxine and said, "Where next?"

In the weeks before our departure I had replied to several advertisements for jobs, in particular I had applied for a job with Save the Children as regional director for East Africa and with Oxfam for a similar managerial post in Africa. There was no Internet in those days and so faxes had to be sent to Britain with details of my *curriculum vitae* and each faxed page cost £1 to send; by then my CV ran to more than forty pages when I included a list of my publications. Neither Save the Children nor Oxfam gave me the courtesy of a reply and it was only when I phoned them for information that I informed that the jobs had gone elsewhere. I now never give to Save the Children or to Oxfam.

I knew that Maxine wanted to stay in Britain, and as there was no longer a need to earn school fees I could take a job anywhere. We had only been home a few days when my copy of the *Veterinary Record* arrived and in the 'Appointments Vacant' column there was an advertisement for the post of veterinary investigation officer to run the Dumfries VI Centre. I had to work in Scotland because the English service was run by the Ministry of Agriculture, and although I had been promoted to the rank of VIO I had resigned from MAFF in Botswana and so I could only join them as a foot soldier, which after my Botswana and Peruvian experiences I was not prepared to do. And so I applied for the post in Dumfries and we waited.

Although I had left ODA, my battles had still not finished. I was owed a gratuity of £8,000 which had not been paid. Then the bombshell landed: ODA would be withholding £6,000 to pay for the 'damage' we had done to the house in Arequipa. Our landlady in Arequipa, Kuki Lozada, had carefully remained away from Arequipa during the time that we were leaving and so Alastair Grieve from LABVETSUR and Christine Banham from the British Council did the handover and agreed to all Kuki's baseless demands. The litany of the destruction we had wreaked on her house and garden had to be seen to be believed. Stupidly I had not procured her agreement in writing to the changes we had made to the bedrooms and she swore blind that it had been done without her knowledge. Had I been there I would never have paid her until the changes had been reversed. Maxine was incensed.

"What a cow… We got rid of all those grotty rooms which were plastered with cuttings from glossy magazines: we brought expensive wallpaper from Britain to liven up the bedrooms and we filled the garden with flowering plants, and she says we damaged her house. What a cow."

There was nothing I could say to that. Instead I wrote letter after letter to ODA and was bashing my head against a brick wall. In desperation I threatened to refer the matter to my solicitors and that did the trick. The amount that I would be required to pay was reduced to £1,500. I accepted. A lawyer might well have cost more and although it irked me at the thought of paying that woman for having improved her house, it got the matter settled but I was desperately disappointed that Alastair had let me down so badly; of Christine Banham, the less said the better.

Maxine, Claire and I visited the town of Dumfries and both agreed that they could live there, and so I went for my interview for the job with a light heart. The only person on the SAC interview panel that I did not know was the chairman and I left the meeting with the feeling that I had done my best and that it was in the lap of the gods. I was offered the post and accepted it. We were off to live in Scotland.

When Richard was informed of my new job he replied in his usual pithy but rude way,

"So you are staying in the Third World!"

Epilogue

No sooner had I left Perú than the British Council in Lima enticed Aurora to leave the project and work for them. This I felt was treachery on the part of the council, to poach a member of staff from the project that they were managing just when the laboratory was to get a new leader. Aurora understood my system of management and for almost six years she had been the fixer in the laboratory who knew what to do and when. I do not reproach Aurora for leaving, as I believe that she felt her loyalty was to me, having given her the opportunity to develop her career, and I was leaving. Almost every South American I have ever met had the desire to go and live in the capital city. When we lived in Salta, north-west Argentina, more than 1,000 miles from the capital, many of the farm owners lived in Buenos Aires and visited the farm once or twice a year; the manager lived in Salta and only the farm workers lived on the farm. I could never understand this hold that the nation's capital had on their citizens, and particularly Perú; I could not believe that anyone would want to leave the beautiful city of Arequipa with its wonderful climate to live in Lima with its cold mists and massive slums, but it was the great magnet, and Aurora went, never to return.

It is thirty years since the start of the LABVETSUR project and twenty since ODA withdrew funding. FONGALSUR no longer exists, the laboratory continues to function with a much reduced staff and Leche Gloria has gone from strength to strength and now has factories in Arequipa where it has taken over the FONGALSUR campus, the PROLACSUR plant in Majes which had gone into administration, and in Lima and Cajamarca. It has taken over Casa Grande which will ensure that this once great sugar producing estate will return to profitability. It is interesting to note that two Arequipeño companies, Gloria and Michell, are now both major national businesses.

From the moment I heard that ODA had appointed Clive Woodham to take over the laboratory, I knew that the project would not achieve its long-term objectives that I had set. To succeed, the laboratory required a boss that could carry out his or her fair share of the routine work, which meant dividing much of the administrative burden amongst all the veterinary staff. After ten years working as an administrator in the American Development Bank, Clive converted the job of *gerente* into that of an administrator and my work was undone. At the end of his first contract, ODA closed the project.

Milagro had gone off to Edinburgh to study for a masters degree in tropical veterinary medicine; in the middle of her course she was delivered of twin boys, and returned to Perú. With the twins weaned and in the care of her parents, she returned to Edinburgh to complete her degree. Luis Olivera went to study parasitology with Prof. Clarkson at Liverpool but he could not acclimatise to living on the rural Wirral and transferred to the masters course in Edinburgh, which he successfully completed; he did not remain long with LABVETSUR but took a job with Leche Gloria. Fernando Fernandez studied for a masters degree in poultry science at the Scottish Agricultural College in Auchencruive, Ayr, and his wife and daughter came with him. On the successful completion of his course, he returned to Arequipa.

All three of these candidates, selected to be the first Peruvian *gerente*, successfully completed their studies in Britain; all three were passed over for the post by Clive and he appointed Rosa Perales. Lita Araujo had also returned triumphant from the Royal Veterinary College in London, but she, Percy, Roxana, and several others were fired. They took their case to the court, won, and were reinstated. Lita only worked for a few weeks before she found a new job in Leche Gloria and started working there in May 1995. It was not long before Percy left to set up his own *posta* based in the city but specialising in mastitis control. Fernando, seeing the way things were going, obtained a job in the new veterinary faculty in Arequipa and as Luis Olivera had already gone, neither of the people selected and trained to run the laboratory remained. ODA must accept that they were responsible for this disaster: the two members of staff, whose salaries they had paid and who had been selected as candidates for running the laboratory, had both been trained at the expense of the British taxpayer but were no longer in the employ of LABVETSUR.

Despite all these problems, LABVETSUR managed to function efficiently, weathering the loss of the financial input from Britain, and they were doing so well that they aroused the jealousy of FONGALSUR, who were going though a bad time under the presidency of Ing Sardón, so much so that he instructed the gate keeper not to allow the entry of vehicles proceeding to the laboratory. Staff at the laboratory went to see Reggie Roberts, still British Consul, and asked him to help resolve the problems. Through his American contacts Reggie found an American aid agency to sponsor a consultancy and I was asked in 1997 to undertake a short-term consultancy to help resolve the problems, or as Reggie said to me, "knock a few heads together."

I was met at Lima Airport by Aurora and taken to her home in Surco where I met her husband Alberto and her two delightful children, Daniela and Jesús, and we went to a *picantería* for lunch where I had my favourite *cebiche mixto:* what a delight. Aurora and Alberto had stayed with us in Dumfries when she was sent by the council for training in Britain. It was lovely to see her again and the time passed too quickly before she had to take me back to the airport. I was met at Arequipa by Reggie and Evelyn, Lucho and Roxana and by Sr Salazar bearing his tape measure and notebook. I had previously told Aurora that I wanted her father to make me a blazer and a tuxedo and he measured me on the spot. I was taken to La Posada del Puente, where I was to lodge during my short time in Arequipa, and had a pleasant drink with the Lozadas and the Roberts.

The consultancy started the next morning with a meeting in Reggie's office where he explained to me what had been going on in FONGALSUR: how they were experiencing financial difficulties and the battle with the laboratory was a smokescreen to divert attention away from the problems in the organisation. Reggie had organised meetings for me with the board of FONGALSUR that afternoon, and with the board of LABVETSUR later in the week. Edilberto would be at my disposal with the LABVETSUR Land Rover to take me to meetings with the organisations controlling the various irrigations, and PROLACSUR; he then took me to lunch in the Arequipa Club where I was able to bring my membership up to date by paying the subscriptions of a *socio ausente* for the years I had been away. I needed to do this as I wanted to give a party in the club to meet all our old friends, as there would not be time to meet them all individually during my short, busy stay in the city.

And then it was off to LABVETSUR to see my old colleagues and friends. Little had changed, the shed on the roof was still there; nothing had been done about the planned extension and I thought to myself, *It will not happen now*, and it did not. Roxana, Milagro, Fernando (F) and Fernando (FAP) were still there but Lita, Luis and Percy had gone. The new *gerente*, Dr Jorge Manrique, who had been brought in from where and by whom I do not know, was a pleasant man but he preferred the office to the laboratory or the farm and so was a financial drain on the laboratory.

I had discussed my tactics for the FONGALSUR board meeting with Reggie and so after the usual exchange of pleasantries I started with a potted history of the laboratory:

"Ing Luis Lozada Casapia, your distinguished former president, persuaded the British Ambassador, John Shakespeare, to talk the British Government into setting up a veterinary project in Arequipa – *not* under the direct control of the Peruvian Government but under a board headed by you – FONGALSUR. This was the first such project in Latin America. You nursed this fledgling project to life, providing the building, finance to convert it into a working laboratory, equipment to get it working, staff salaries until the laboratory was able take over their payment, a bookkeeper within your finance department, and publicity to make the project known. And what a great publicist Lucho was for you.

"LABVETSUR is your creation, and its success has brought great credit on the mother organisation not only in the south but throughout the whole nation. Because of this I cannot understand why you are trying to destroy what you have made. I have come to see you, because I also have given six years of my life into building up this self-financing laboratory for you, and all the *ganaderos* in the south: I do not want to see all my work, worry, indeed part of my life, destroyed."

When I sat down there was not a dry eye in the house. I was thankful that my Spanish was still up to the task. There was much back-tracking and comments that actions had been misunderstood and one after the other the board members stood up and reaffirmed their commitment to the success of LABVETSUR. Ing Sardón brought the meeting to a close with the statement that we should drink a toast to the continuing success of LABVETSUR and FONGALSUR, and in came the piscos and the pink and yellow biscuits. Some things never change!

On my return to La Posada del Puente there was Sr Salazar sitting in the reception waiting for me so that he could fit the blazer and the tuxedo. I tried on both garments and they fitted perfectly. But he muttered and tutted and made marks with his tailors' chalk. Once finished we sat in the bar and had a quiet drink and I told him how sad I was that Aurora had gone to work in Lima. He agreed with me and said how sad were he and his wife with their only child so far away.

"But she is happily married with two lovely children and so we are content." And with that the small, quiet gentleman climbed the stairs to the Avenida Bolognesi and took a taxi home.

The rest of the week passed in a flash, but the real point of my visit had been achieved: FONGALSUR and LABVETSUR were once again on an even keel. The highlights of the visit were being elected an honorary member of the *Colegio Medico Veterinario de Arequipa* and being given the 'Freedom of the Irrigation of Majes' by AUTODEMA, the controlling authority. Somewhere I managed to squeeze in a lunch with Edilberto in El Gato Vitoreño in Vitor where, of course, I had the *frito mixto de mariscos*. Again, on my return, Sr Salazar was waiting for me, this time with the finished articles, both beautifully made. A small, neat man and an impeccable craftsman, it was little surprising that he had produced such an efficient, hard-working, capable daughter.

The party in the Arequipa Club on the Friday night was a delight. While we had been living in Dumfries, Richard had married the Arequipeña girl he had met at the fashion show and this was the first opportunity for me to meet her mother, Alicia Nuñez Borja, and brother Manolo, as well as a meeting of many old friends in a relaxed and convivial environment. Marjorie Michell was there with her sister Beryl; sadly sister Claire had died, and Michael and Tony had by then gone to Lima. The Lozadas, Lucho, Enrique and Daniel, were there with their wives; Reggie and Evelyn and Reggie's brother Alfredo with his wife Connie; Eduardo Bedoya and Gachi, the Hallenbecks, and the Emmels were also there and the Flanagan brothers came up from Mollendo. It was a most enjoyable evening if tinged with sadness because I knew that I would probably never see many of these people again.

All too soon I was back in Lima for a couple of days to write up my report, which I did in the offices of the British Council, although by then Aurora had gone to work for the American Embassy. Although the bishop Alan Winstanley and his wife had returned to Britain, the missionary Penny de Marcés arranged transport for me to go out to her church in the *pueblo joven* Via Salvado as I had brought gifts for them from St John's Church in Dumfries. The mission station was a most inspiring place with a school and facilities for young people. My job was done and all too soon I was on the plane back to Scotland.

When the British Government stopped funding the LABVETSUR project it was decided that the *postas* should become separate legal entities with their own boards of control although LABVETSUR would have a seat on the board. Héctor Begazo ran the *posta* until he went off to Argentina and Brazil for training and during his absence Hugo Zea took over. On Héctor's return, Hugo was not keen to relinquish the post and so Héctor went to work in the laboratory; however, it was not long before he was headhunted by a poultry consortium. He remained working with the poultry industry and for the past sixteen years has been technical adviser to poultry farms throughout South America.

Mismanagement, that perennial vice in developing countries, was the cause of the demise of the *posta* in La Joya. Social security contributions and tax payments were not made and when the authorities started to close in, it was decided to close the *posta*: Hugo went to work in La Yarada and the other vets remained in La Joya working for themselves. The building used by the *posta* had been lent by the irrigation authorities and with the flat built by FONGALSUR was returned to them.

There was a similar tale of woe in the *posta* in La Yarada. Taxes and social security payments were not paid; Dr Linares continues working there in his own private practice.

LABRENOR has seen good times and bad times since the end of the British aid project, and in 2016 its income was sufficient to employ two veterinarians, one laboratory technician and a cleaner. It was also able to pay its bills, service its vehicle, and purchase new equipment and reagents. Dr Elmer Alvarez Contreras informed me that 2016 had been a difficult year for the laboratory as several non-governmental organisations had closed their operations in Cajamarca which reduced the number of submissions to the laboratory. He hopes that the future will show an upturn in the work so that LABRENOR will not have to close after more than forty-four years of service to the farming community.

Contacts in Lima informed me that FONGALSUR was undone by two presidents; during their periods in office they accumulated a debt of 60,000 new soles (the currency that replaced the inti, about £15,000) for cattle vaccines from a state entity. After not being paid for two years this entity seized FONGALSUR's land and put it up for auction. At the auction Leche

Gloria paid 500,000 soles for the terrain which seven years previously had been valued at 2,000,000 soles. Leche Gloria wanted the land as their factory was beside FONGALSUR. Undoubtedly the black hand of corruption by the state employees, and possibly that of the two presidents, played its part. Lucho was devastated at the loss of the organisation he had so brilliantly nurtured, but neither he nor anybody else could do anything about it. Leche Gloria bought the whole estate to extend their factory and as the laboratory was in the way it was demolished and replaced by a smaller modern building on the further extremity of the site, where it works with a greatly reduced intake of specimens and fewer staff members. There is no doubt in my mind that ODA and in particular the South American Department staff were responsible for their project not achieving what it could and should have done.

God works in a mysterious way
Yet not so strange as ODA. (Anon)

The laboratory continues with routine examinations of samples from sick animals; work in the surveillance of brucellosis continues, but the Milk Ring Test is no longer the official test for the infection; it has been replaced by the ELISA test. Staff continue travelling to the different milk plants in Arequipa, Moquegua and Tacna, to collect the samples for the ELISA test. Work has expanded in quality control of water and food for human and animal consumption. For the past three years LABVETSUR has been working to obtain ISO 17025 accreditation which gives an international seal of approval for their work. It is hoped that such accreditation will be received before the end of 2018. Claudia Choque is now the chief laboratory technician and LABVETSUR continues to train *practicantes*. She informed me that the daily meeting still takes place when the staff meet to discuss all outstanding cases. I was wondering how to conclude the Epilogue when I received an email from Claudia which said:

'Today LABVETSUR is thirty years old! After all this time I can tell you that your dream still goes on!'

Glossary Of Spanish Terms

Please note that in Spanish 'ch' is a letter

aguadito	thin soup broth (basic ingredients: coriander and chicken)
alcalde	mayor
Alliance Française	French equivalent of the British Council
altiplano	high plain on the Andes – over 3500m
ambulantes	street traders
Asociacíon Cultural Peruano Norte Americano (ICPNA)	US equivalent of the British Council
azucar	sugar
barrio obrero	working class suburb
bastante por hoy	enough for today
caballo de paso	a 'pacing' horse similar to US quarter horse
camarones	freshwater crayfish
camote	sweet potato
campesinos	country people
campiña de Arequipa	irrigated countryside round the city
Casillero del Diablo	Pigeon hole of the Devil (Chilean wine)
casona	mansion
castillos	'castles', bamboo towers for fireworks
cebiche mixto	a dish of raw fish and shellfish 'cooked' in lime juice
cebolla	onion
ceja de selva	eyebrow of the jungle (1500–2500m)
Cerro de Arena	Hill of Sand
Cerveza Arequipeña	the local Arequipa beer
Colegio Medico Veterinario	College of Veterinary Medicine

Comité de Administración	company board
conchitas a la parmesana	queen scallops in a parmesan sauce
conquistadores	Spanish colonial soldiers
convenio	legal agreement
corvina	Pacific equivalent of cod
costa	coast also a geographic region
cria	young camelid (like calf or lamb)
Cultural	ICPNA
cuy chactado	deep-fried guinea pig
chicharrones de pollo	a skewer of marinated deep fried chicken
chifa	Chinese restaurant (also used for a dish consisting of rice with egg)
choclo	sliced maize cob
chop	local beer (from maize) hence *choperia*
choza	peasant house
chuño	Andean freeze-dried potato
chupe	thick soup
chupe de camarones	freshwater crayfish thick soup
Diploma de Honor *con medalla de oro*	Diploma of Honour with a gold medal (Peruvian equivalent of 'Freedom of the City')
dulce	sweetmeats, pudding
estancia	large farm
fiebre de alpaca	alpaca fever - a disease of young alpacas
flauta, tambor y *caña*	recorder, drum and pan-pipes
folklorico	folklore – applied to music or art
FONGALSUR	
Fondo de Fomento para el Desarrollo de la Ganaderia Lechera de Arequipa	Fund for the Development of Dairy Farming in Arequipa
frito mixto de mariscos	fried mixed shellfish
fronton	ball game, a cross between fives and squash
gambas	prawns
ganaderos	cattlemen
gato	cat, also used for men with blue eyes
Gato Vitoreño	the Cat from Vitor – thought to refer to the owner of the restaurant
gerente	managing director – CEO
Himno Nacional	National Anthem

huevos de toro	bull's testicles
huevos revueltos con jamón	scrambled eggs with ham
Iglesia de la Compañía	the church of the Jesuit Order
ingeniero	title of person with an engineering qualification from a university
Laboratorio Regional de Sanidad Animal del Sur del Perú	LABVETSUR
leche de tigre	'tiger's milk', spiced lime juice used to 'cook' fish
lenguado	Pacific equivalent to Dover sole
machas a la criolla	Peruvian shellfish in a local sauce
medialunas	croissants
mermelada	jam
mestizo	mixed race
monte	literally mountain, but used for mountain pasture
municipalidad	town hall
narco-traficante	drug-dealer
(el) Niño	warm current that negates the effects of Humboldt Current
orina	urine
padrino	godfather
paella	a dish of rice with seafood and meat
papas picantes	spicy potatoes
parrillada	barbecue
pasa montañas	antiterrorist soldiers, refers to type of hat the terrorists and soldiers used, it covers head with holes for eyes, mouth and nose.
pasta básica	impure extract of cocaine
picantería	café/restaurant serving local food
platanos fritos	fried plantains
porongo	milk churn
posta de medicina veterinaria	a veterinary practice
practicantes	students doing practical work for their degree
Prefect	the president's representative in a department
pueblos jóvenes	slum towns: literally new towns
rebaño	herd when applied to camelids

rescate (Cuarto de)	the gold room in Cajamarca
rocoto relleno	stuffed chilli pepper
Salchichería Alemana	German seller of sausages - butcher
sarsa de mariscos	mixed shellfish in a spicy sauce
selva	Jungle/forest
Sendero Luminoso	Shining Path – a terrorist organisation
Señora Perú	"Mrs Peru" winner of competition for married women
sierra	mountain
sillar	white volcanic rock, used for building
socio ausente	absent member
sombrero	broad-brimmed hat
soroche	mountain (altitude) sickness
superintendente del campo	head of field services
tesis	thesis
tina	large receptacle for milk
toque de queda	curfew
triciclo	bicycle with a vending barrow in front
uvas de Italia	grapes from Italy – a variety of vine

Index